Mathematics for Chemists

MATHEMATICS FOR CHEMISTS

D. M. Hirst

Department of Molecular Sciences, University of Warwick, Coventry

M
MACMILLAN
EDUCATION

First published 1976
Reprinted 1978, 1981, 1983 (with corrections), 1985, 1987

Published by
MACMILLAN EDUCATION LTD
Houndmills, Basingstoke, Hampshire RG21 2XS
and London
Companies and representatives
throughout the world

Printed in Hong Kong

ISBN 0-333-18172-7

Contents

Preface

A sound knowledge of the elementary aspects of many areas of mathematics is indispensible to the study of the quantitative aspects of chemistry. This book presents the mathematics required for the study of chemistry to honours degree level in British universities and polytechnics. The material presented should also be suitable for chemistry majors and first-year graduate students in North American universities. It has evolved from a course of lectures given over the past ten years to first-year students in Molecular and Biological Sciences at the University of Warwick.

Students of chemistry have, in general, a more limited mathematical background than physics or engineering students. This book does not assume that the student has followed an A-level or other post-O-level course in mathematics. Therefore the calculus is developed from first principles. The approach is descriptive rather than formal in that the emphasis is on the application of mathematical techniques rather than on the proving of theorems. Some results are quoted without proof where the derivation is more confusing than illuminating.

Wherever possible, mathematical techniques and ideas have been illustrated with chemical examples. It has often been necessary to present applications without explaining the underlying theory; for a full explanation the reader should consult texts on physical or quantum chemistry such as those included in the bibliography.

The material presented here should prepare the student for the study of quantum mechanics and group theory. A chapter on group theory has not been included because it was felt that the topic could not be adequately covered in one chapter and because many excellent texts on group theory in chemistry are available.

Numerical and statistical methods are becoming increasingly important in the analysis of experimental data. Introductory chapters on these topics have been included to give the student some background before he consults more complete treatments of these subjects.

Several problems, indicated by '(U.W.)', have appeared in University of Warwick examinations. The copyright for these problems is vested in the University of Warwick and the author is grateful for permission to reproduce them here.

The author is grateful to Dr S. P. Liebmann who read much of the manuscript and to Mr M. S. Hunt and Professor P. J. Harrison for reading chapters 13 and 14, respectively.

March 1975 D. M. Hirst

Preface

[illegible]

A sound [illegible] elementary aspects of many areas of mathematics is indispensable to the study of [illegible] aspects of chemistry. [illegible] the material [illegible]

[illegible]

Several problems [illegible] have appeared in [illegible]

The author [illegible] the manuscript and [illegible]

March 1975 [illegible]

1

Review of Basic Material—Functions, Inequalities

1.1 FUNCTIONS

The concept of a function is probably familiar to you, but since this is fundamental to the material to be presented in this book, it is important that we review the definition.

When we say that *y is a function of x*, we mean that if we take some particular value of x, say x_1, we can find a corresponding value y_1 of y. Thus a function is a rule for associating a number y_1 with each number x_1.

$$x_1 \to y_1 \tag{1.1}$$

For example, if

$$y = 2x^2 + x + 1 \tag{1.2}$$

then for x = 1, y = 4 and for x = 2, y = 11. This relation gives us a method for associating a value y with each value of x.

x is the *independent variable* because we select a value of x and then associate with it a value of y, the *dependent variable*. In general, we write y = f(x), which means 'y is a function of x' or y = y(x). x is sometimes called the *argument*.

We use a function whenever we express some physical phenomenon in a quantitative manner. For example, when a substance A decays by first-order kinetics, the concentration a at time t is given by

$$a = a_0 e^{-kt} \tag{1.3}$$

where a_0 is the initial concentration and k is a constant.

1.1.1 Graphical representation of functions

A convenient representation of a function is a *graph*, in which we conventionally have right-angled *cartesian co-ordinates* labelled the x-axis (horizontal) and the y-axis (vertical). The x-axis is sometimes called the *abscissa* and the y-axis the *ordinate*. The axes intersect at the origin O. Values of y, y_i are calculated for a series of values of x, x_i and each

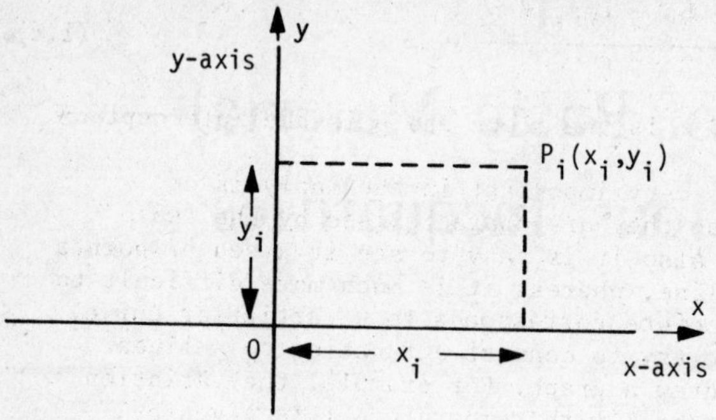

Figure 1.1

pair of values is represented by a point P_i on the graph (figure 1.1). x_i and y_i are known as the *co-ordinates* of the point P_i and are usually written as (x_i, y_i). The points P_i are then joined up to give a smooth curve. Clearly, the more points we plot, the more accurate will be the representation of the function.

1.1.2 Types of function

(i) The linear function

The simplest type of function is the linear function

$$y = mx + b \tag{1.4}$$

whose graph is a straight line (figure 1.2). The *intercept* on the y-axis is the value of y when x is equal to zero and is equal to b. Another important concept is the *slope* of a line. If we take two points on the line with co-ordinates (x_1, y_1) and (x_2, y_2), the slope of the line is defined by

$$\text{slope} = \frac{y_2 - y_1}{x_2 - x_1} \tag{1.5}$$

and is, in fact, equal to the tangent of the angle θ between the line and the x-axis. It clearly doesn't matter where the points (x_1, y_1) and (x_2, y_2) are on the line. The slope of the straight line $y = mx + b$ is given by

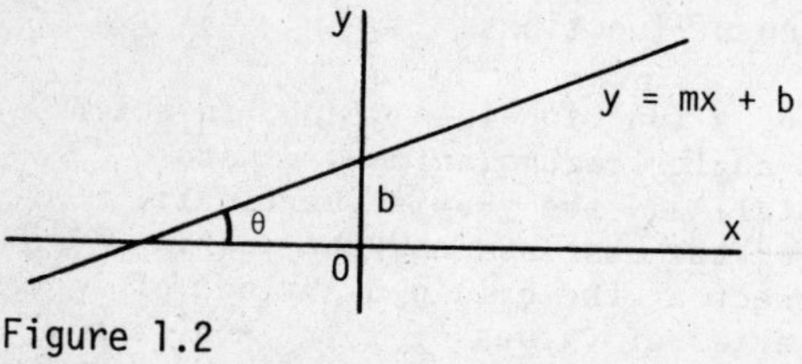

Figure 1.2

$$\text{slope} = \frac{(mx_2 + b) - (mx_1 + b)}{x_2 - x_1} = m \qquad (1.6)$$

Thus for $y = mx + b$, m is the slope and b is the intercept on the y-axis.

Linear graphs are very important in the analysis of chemical data because they are characterised by the two parameters b and m. Also it is easy to see if a set of points lies on a straight line, whereas it is much more difficult to decide if a set of points corresponds to a particular curve. Wherever possible we try to convert a function to a linear form if we wish to draw a graph. For example, the variation of equilibrium constant K with temperature T is given by

$$\ln K = -\frac{\Delta H^{\circ}}{RT} + C \qquad (1.7)$$

provided that ΔH°, the heat of reaction, is independent of T. R is the gas constant and C is a constant. Plotting K against T would give a curve that would be difficult to analyse. However, if we plot the logarithm of K, $\ln K$, against $1/T$, we get a straight line of slope $\Delta H^{\circ}/R$ from which ΔH° can be obtained.

(ii) Quadratic function

A *quadratic function* has the general form

$$y = ax^2 + bx + c \qquad (1.8)$$

and its graph is a *parabola* (figure 1.3). We shall define the slope of a curve in the next chapter. If there are real values of x for which $ax^2 + bx + c = 0$, the curve will intersect the x-axis at the values of x given by the formula

$$x = \frac{-b \pm \sqrt{(b^2 - 4ac)}}{2a} \qquad (1.9)$$

(iii) Single-valued functions

In the two examples above, there is only one value of y_1 for each value of x_1 and we say that the functions are *single valued*. This concept is important in quantum mechanics because wavefunctions are required to be single valued.

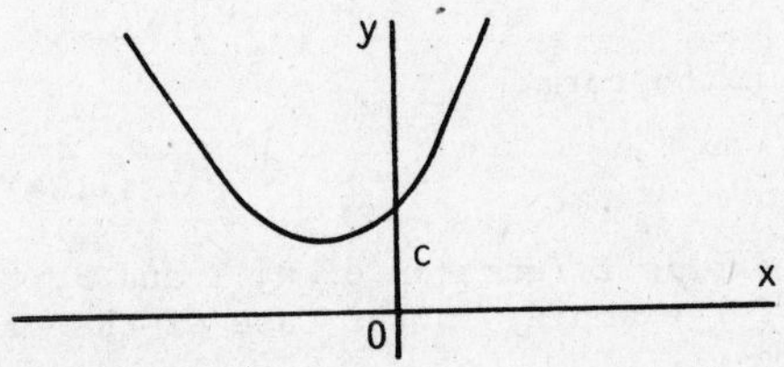

Figure 1.3

(iv) Many-valued functions

If we can associate several values of y with one value of x, then the function is *many valued*. An example of this is $y^2 = x$ for which there are two values of y, $+\sqrt{x_1}$ and $-\sqrt{x_1}$ for each value of x_1.

(v) Regions for which a function is undefined

So far we have assumed that the independent variable x can take any value. However, if we consider $y^2 = x_1$, we see that x can only have positive values or be zero. For the function

$$y = \frac{x}{\sqrt{(x^2 - 16)}} \qquad (1.10)$$

x is restricted to being larger than 4 or smaller than -4, as otherwise we would have the square root of a negative number. We must also exclude $x = \pm 4$ for which y is infinite. If a function is only defined for a certain range of values of x, this should be specified; for example

$$y = \frac{x}{\sqrt{(x^2 - 16)}} \qquad x < -4 \text{ or } > 4 \qquad (1.11)$$

(vi) Functions of many variables

In chemistry a quantity frequently depends on two or more variables. For example, the pressure P of a gas depends on the volume V, the temperature T and the number of moles n. For an ideal gas

$$P = \frac{nRT}{V} \qquad (1.12)$$

where R is the gas constant. In order to define P, we need values of V, T and n.

(vii) A polynomial

A function such as

$$f(x) = a_0 + a_1 x + a_2 x^2 + \ldots + a_n x^n = \sum_{i=0}^{n} a_i x^i \qquad (1.13)$$

is known as a *polynomial of degree n*. Such a function is defined for all values of x and is finite if x is finite.

(viii) Implicit functions

We can rewrite equation 1.12 in the form

$$V = \frac{nRT}{P} \qquad (1.14)$$

that is, we can write V as an *explicit function* of n, T and P. We cannot always do this, as, for example, in the case of the van der Waals equation of state

$$\left(P + \frac{n^2 a}{V^2}\right)(V - nb) = nRT \tag{1.15}$$

If, in this case, we wish to regard V as a function of P, T and n, then V is an *implicit function* of these variables.

(ix) Even and odd functions

A useful classification of functions is into even and odd functions. An *even function* of x is one that remains unchanged when the sign of x is reversed; that is

$$f(-x) = f(x) \tag{1.16}$$

whereas an *odd function* changes sign

$$f(-x) = -f(x) \tag{1.17}$$

Examples of even functions are $y = x^2$, $y = \cos x$ (see section 1.1.3) and these functions are symmetrical about the y-axis (figure 1.4a). $y = x$ and $y = \sin x$ are odd functions and are not symmetrical about the y-axis (figure 1.4b).

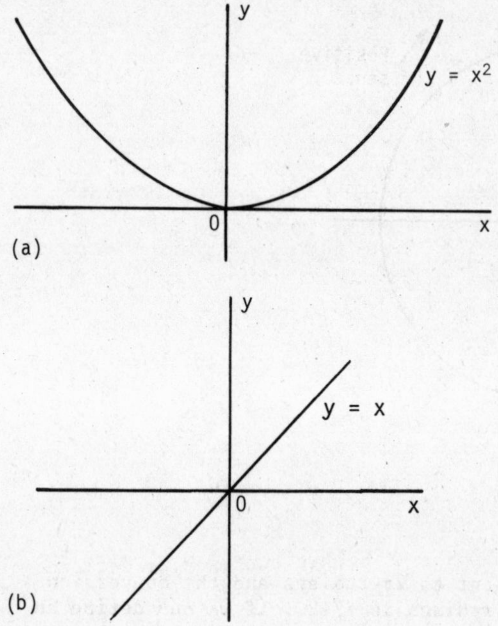

Figure 1.4

(x) Transcendental functions

Certain functions such as trigonometric, exponential and logarithmic functions cannot be expressed *exactly* in terms of algebraic functions. They are called *transcendental functions*. We discuss them in more detail in the following sections.

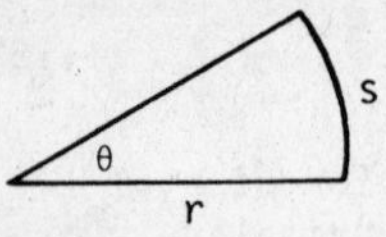

Figure 1.5

1.1.3 Trigonometric functions

We shall review briefly some basic ideas about trigonometric functions. We shall use the *radian* as a measure of angle. If an angle θ subtends a length of arc s of radius r, the angle θ in radians is given by (figure 1.5)

$$\theta = \frac{s}{r} \qquad (1.18)$$

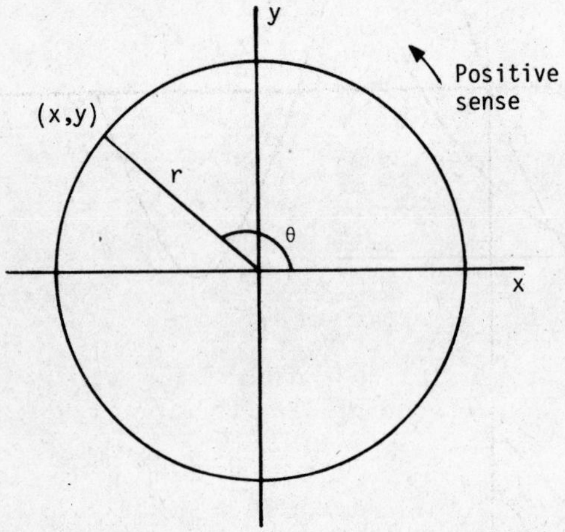

Figure 1.6

Clearly 360° is equivalent to 2π radians and the conversion factor from degrees to radians is π/180. If we can define an angle in a positive sense as in figure 1.6, the three basic trigonometric functions, sine (sin), cosine (cos) and tangent (tan) are defined by

$$\sin\theta = \frac{y}{r}; \qquad \cos\theta = \frac{x}{r}; \qquad \tan\theta = \frac{y}{x} \qquad (1.19)$$

These functions will have different signs in different

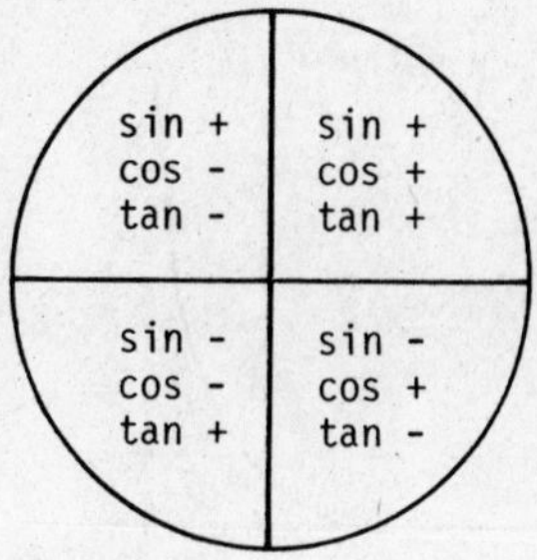

Figure 1.7

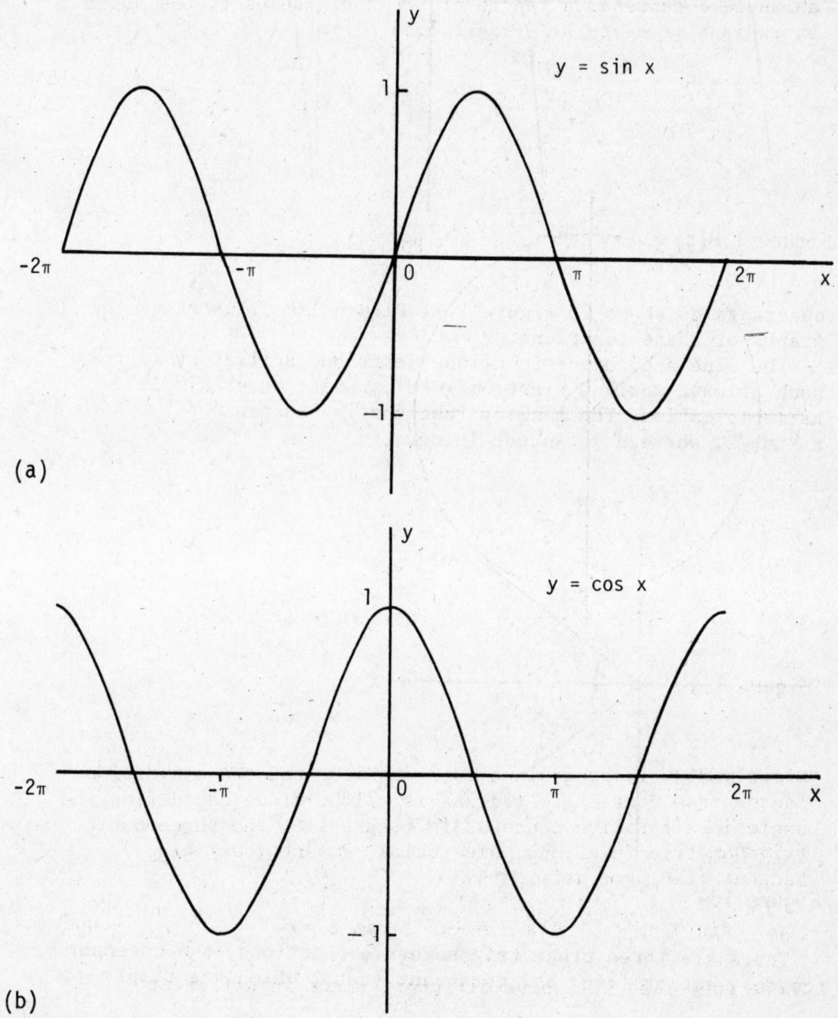

Figure 1.8

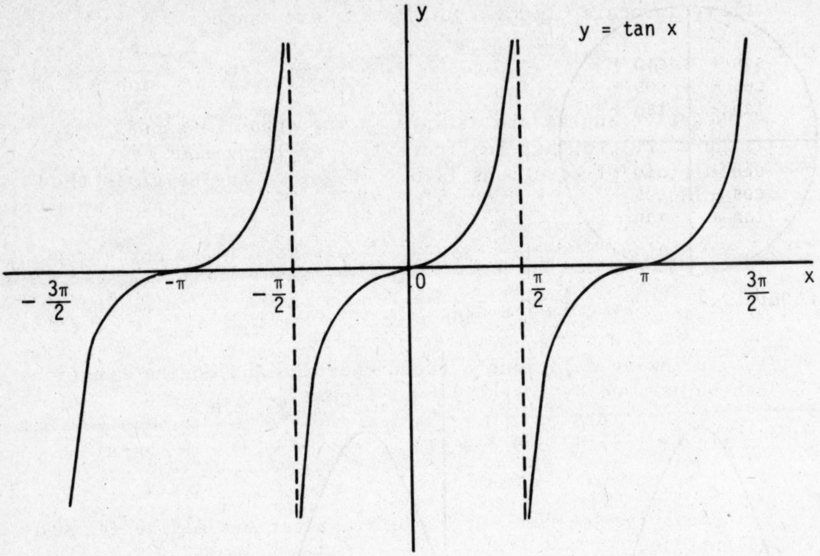

Figure 1.8(c)

quadrants as shown in figure 1.7. Figure 1.8 illustrates the graphs of these functions.

The sine and cosine functions describe oscillatory systems such as wave motion, electromagnetic radiation or simple harmonic motion. The tangent function is undefined for $x = n\pi/2$, where n is an odd integer.

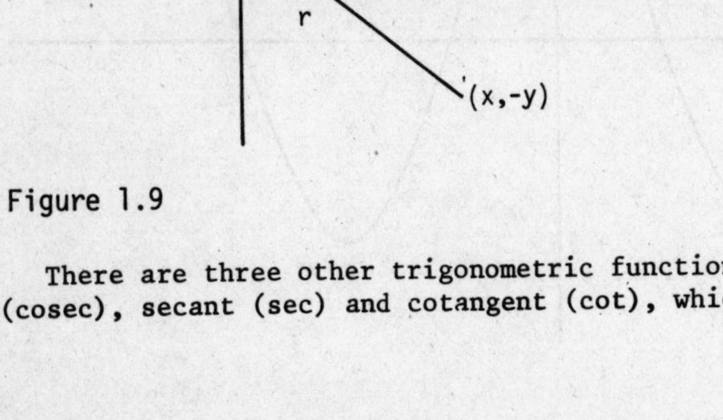

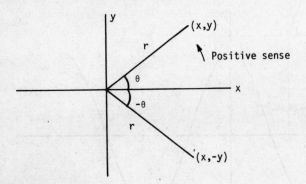

Figure 1.9

There are three other trigonometric functions, the cosecant (cosec), secant (sec) and cotangent (cot), which are simply the reciprocals of the sine, cosine and tangent

$$\sec\theta = \frac{1}{\cos\theta}; \quad \operatorname{cosec}\theta = \frac{1}{\sin\theta}; \quad \cot\theta = \frac{1}{\tan\theta} \tag{1.20}$$

Negative angles are defined in the opposite sense (figure 1.9) to that in figure 1.6. Applying the definitions of equations 1.19 to negative angles gives the relations

$$\sin(-\theta) = \left(\frac{-y}{r}\right) = -\sin\theta; \quad \cos(-\theta) = \left(\frac{x}{r}\right) = \cos\theta$$

$$\tan(-\theta) = \left(\frac{-y}{x}\right) = -\tan\theta \tag{1.21}$$

The following relations between the sine and cosine functions can be derived by inspection of figure 1.10

$$\sin\left(\theta + \frac{\pi}{2}\right) = \frac{x'}{r} = \cos\theta; \quad \cos\left(\theta + \frac{\pi}{2}\right) = -\frac{y'}{r} = -\sin\theta \tag{1.22}$$

Relationships between trigonometric functions may be derived as follows.

(i) From equations 1.19 it is obvious that

$$\tan\theta = \frac{\sin\theta}{\cos\theta} \tag{1.23}$$

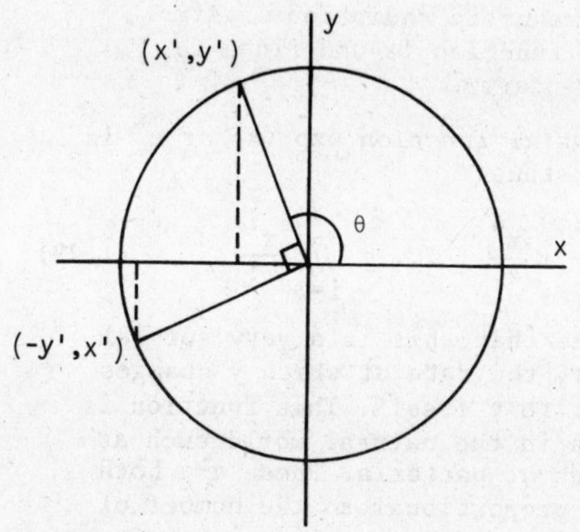

Figure 1.10

(ii) In figure 1.6, $x^2 + y^2 = r^2$, so

$$\cos^2\theta + \sin^2\theta = \frac{x^2}{r^2} + \frac{y^2}{r^2} = 1$$

that is

$$\cos^2\theta + \sin^2\theta = 1 \tag{1.24}$$

(iii) Two alternative forms of equation 1.24 are

$$\cot^2\theta = \operatorname{cosec}^2\theta - 1; \qquad \tan^2\theta = \sec^2\theta - 1 \tag{1.25}$$

(iv) The following formulae can be derived

$$\left.\begin{aligned} \sin(A + B) &= \sin A \cos B + \sin B \cos A \\ \sin(A - B) &= \sin A \cos B - \sin B \cos A \\ \cos(A + B) &= \cos A \cos B - \sin A \sin B \\ \cos(A - B) &= \cos A \cos B + \sin A \sin B \end{aligned}\right\} \tag{1.26}$$

(v) Equations 1.26 lead to the multiple angle formulae

$$\left.\begin{aligned} \sin 2A &= 2 \sin A \cos A \\ \cos 2A &= \cos^2 A - \sin^2 A = 1 - 2\sin^2 A = 2\cos^2 A - 1 \\ \sin 3A &= 3 \sin A - 4 \sin^3 A; \\ \cos 3A &= 4 \cos^3 A - 3 \cos A \end{aligned}\right\} \tag{1.27}$$

(vi) By taking linear combinations of equations 1.26, we obtain

$$\left.\begin{aligned} \sin A \cos B &= 1/2[\sin(A + B) + \sin(A - B)] \\ \cos A \cos B &= 1/2[\cos(A + B) + \cos(A - B)] \\ \sin A \sin B &= 1/2[\cos(A - B) - \cos(A + B)] \end{aligned}\right\} \tag{1.28}$$

1.1.4 The exponential function

One way of defining the *exponential function* exp (x) or e^x is in terms of an infinite series; thus

$$\exp(x) = 1 + \frac{x}{1!} + \frac{x^2}{2!} + \frac{x^3}{3!} + \frac{x^4}{4!} + \ldots = \sum_{i=0}^{\infty} \frac{x^i}{i!} \tag{1.29}$$

In the next chapter we shall see that this is a very special function in that for y = exp(x), the rate at which y changes as x changes is, in fact, equal to y itself. This function is used to describe many phenomena in the natural world such as radioactive decay and the growth of bacteria. These are both processes that occur at a rate proportional to the number of particles present at any one time. Another application is to the dependence of the distribution of particles among energy levels on temperature. If we have a total of N particles, the number N_i in a level having energy E_i at temperature T is given by the Boltzmann distribution

$$\frac{N_i}{N} = \frac{\exp(-E_i/kT)}{\sum_i \exp(-E_i/kT)} \tag{1.30}$$

where k is the Boltzmann constant.

The argument of the exponential function can be any function f(x)

$$\exp(f(x)) = 1 + \frac{f(x)}{1!} + \frac{[f(x)]^2}{2!} + \frac{[f(x)]^3}{3!} + \ldots \quad (1.31)$$

Writing the exponential as e^x implies that we are raising a number e to some power x. e is given by

$$e^1 = 1 + \frac{1}{1!} + \frac{1}{2!} + \frac{1}{3!} + \frac{1}{4!} + \ldots = 2.71828 \ldots \quad (1.32)$$

This is a valid way of thinking about the exponential, since it does obey all the usual rules for exponents; for example

$$e^{x_1}e^{x_2} = e^{x_1+x_2}$$

$$e^{-x} = \frac{1}{e^x} \quad (1.33)$$

Figure 1.11 shows graphs of e^x and e^{-x}.

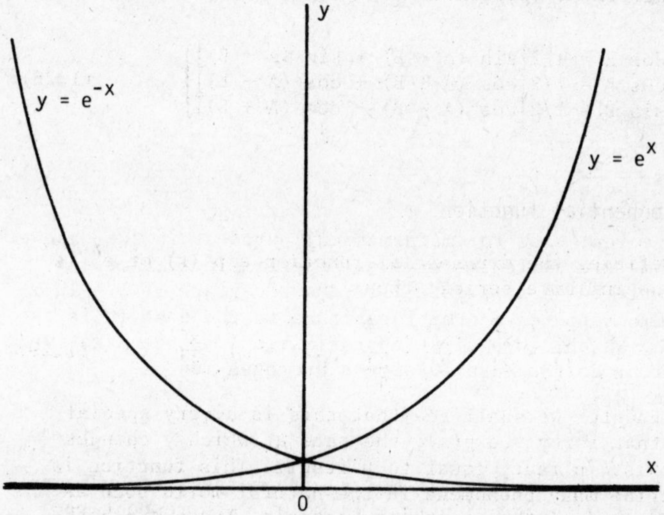

Figure 1.11

1.1.5 The logarithmic function

You are almost certainly familiar with the use of logarithms for calculations. These are *common logarithms* to the *base 10*. The logarithm to the base 10 of x, $\log_{10}x$, is the power to which we have to raise 10 in order to obtain x

$$x = 10^{\log_{10}x} \qquad (1.34)$$

The subscript 10 indicates that we are using logarithms to the base 10. The basic properties of logarithms, as applied in calculations, are given by the following relations

$$\left.\begin{aligned} \log(xy) &= \log x + \log y \\ \log(x/y) &= \log x - \log y \\ \log(x^n) &= n \log x \end{aligned}\right\} \qquad (1.35)$$

Base 10 is the most convenient for calculations but logarithms can be taken to any base. Let us define a function that is the logarithm of x to the base a

$$y = \log_a x$$

that is

$$x = a^{\log_a x} \qquad (1.36)$$

It is quite easy to change from one base to another. Suppose we require the logarithm of x to the base b, $\log_b x$, defined by $x = b^{\log_b x}$. Taking logarithms to the base a gives

$$\log_a x = \log_a \left[b^{\log_b x}\right] = (\log_b x)(\log_a b)$$

Therefore

$$\log_b x = \frac{\log_a x}{\log_a b} \qquad (1.37)$$

The most convenient base for mathematical purposes is the base e. Such logarithms are called *natural* or *naperian logarithms* and are usually written *ln x*. Figure 1.12 shows a graph of y = ln x.

A very common application of logarithms to the base 10 is the concept of pH, which, to a first approximation, is the negative of the logarithm to the base 10 of the hydrogen ion concentration $[H^+]$

$$pH = -\log_{10}[H^+] \qquad (1.38)$$

On this basis a solution that is molar with respect to hydrogen ions has a pH of 0, a solution that is molar with respect to hydroxyl ions has a pH of 14 and a neutral solution has a pH of 7.

1.1.6 Hyperbolic functions

From the exponential function we can construct a new type of function, the *hyperbolic functions*. The basic ones are the hyperbolic cosine (cosh x) and the hyperbolic sine (sinh x), which are defined as follows

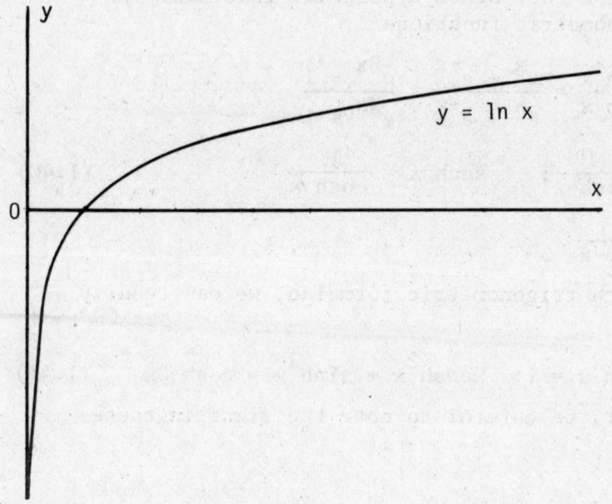

Figure 1.12

$$\left.\begin{aligned}\cosh x &= 1/2(e^x + e^{-x})\\ \sinh x &= 1/2(e^x - e^{-x})\end{aligned}\right\} \qquad (1.39)$$

and are shown graphically in figure 1.13.

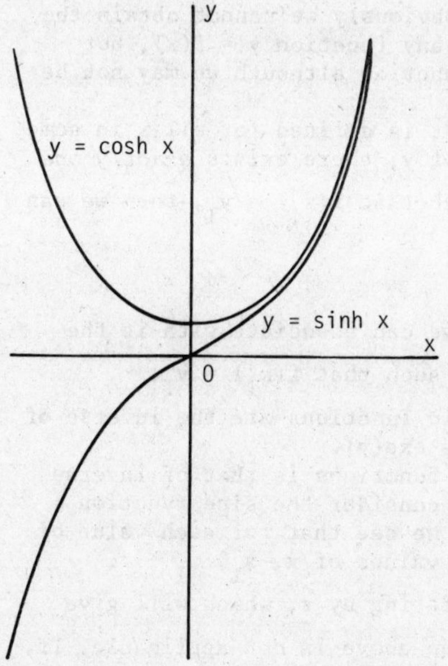

Figure 1.13

We can also define four other hyperbolic functions by analogy with trigonometric functions

$$\tanh x = \frac{\sinh x}{\cosh x} = \frac{e^x - e^{-x}}{e^x + e^{-x}} = \frac{e^{2x} - 1}{e^{2x} + 1}$$

$$\operatorname{cosech} x = \frac{1}{\sinh x}; \qquad \operatorname{sech} x = \frac{1}{\cosh x} \tag{1.40}$$

$$\coth x = \frac{1}{\tanh x}$$

Also by analogy with trigonometric formulae, we can readily show that

$$\cosh^2 x - \sinh^2 x = 1; \qquad \cosh^2 x + \sinh^2 x = \cosh 2x \tag{1.41}$$

You should, however, be careful to note the signs in these expressions.

1.1.7 Inverse functions

If we have a very simple function such as

$$y = 4x - 3$$

we can easily rearrange it to write

$$x = \frac{y + 3}{4} \tag{1.42}$$

We call x the *inverse function*. Obviously we cannot obtain the inverse function in this way for any function $y = f(x)$, but often we can define an inverse function although we may not be able to write it down explicitly.

Let $y = f(x)$ be a function that is defined for all x in some interval. If, for some value y_1 of y, there exists *exactly one* value x_1 of x in the interval such that $f(x_1) = y_1$, then we can define an inverse function

$$x = g(y)$$

by the rule: given a number y_1, we can associate with it the unique number x_1 in the interval such that $f(x_1) = y_1$.

The exponential and logarithmic functions are the inverse of each other. If $y = \ln x$, then $x = \exp(y)$.

An important class of inverse functions is that of inverse trigonometric functions. When we consider the sine function $y = \sin x$, we hit a snag because we see that for each value of y there is an infinite number of values of x, x_1, $x_1 + \pi$, $x_1 + 2\pi$, $x_1 + 3\pi$, etc., each differing by π, which will give that value of y and the definition above is not applicable. If, however, we limit ourselves to the interval $-\pi/2 \leqslant x \leqslant \pi/2$, we get the *principal value of x* and the definition is now applicable, because for each value y_1 of y there is just *one*

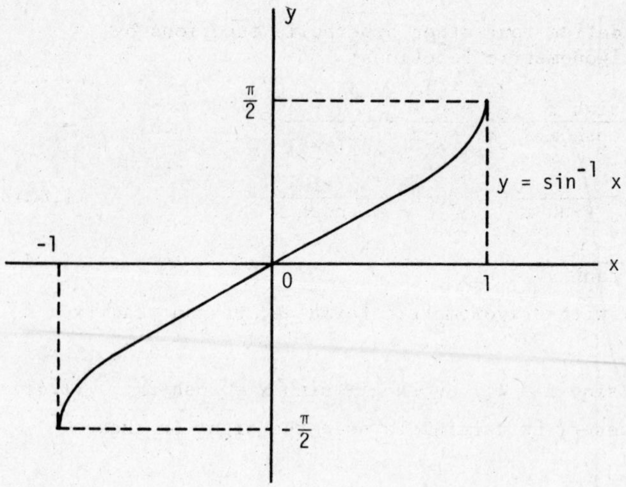

Figure 1.14

value x_1 of x in the interval. We define the *inverse sine function* or *arcsine function* $x = \sin^{-1} y$ or $x = \arcsin y$, where x is the angle whose sine is y with the restriction that x lies in the interval between $-\pi/2$ and $\pi/2$. The graph of $\sin^{-1} x$ is given in figure 1.14. Clearly x must lie in the range $-1 \leqslant x \leqslant 1$. The *inverse cosine* or *arccosine function* is defined by

$$\cos^{-1} x \; (\arccos x) = \frac{\pi}{2} - \sin^{-1} x \tag{1.43}$$

and is thus limited to the range of values $0 \leqslant \cos^{-1} x \leqslant \pi$, with x again restricted to the interval $-1 \leqslant x \leqslant 1$.

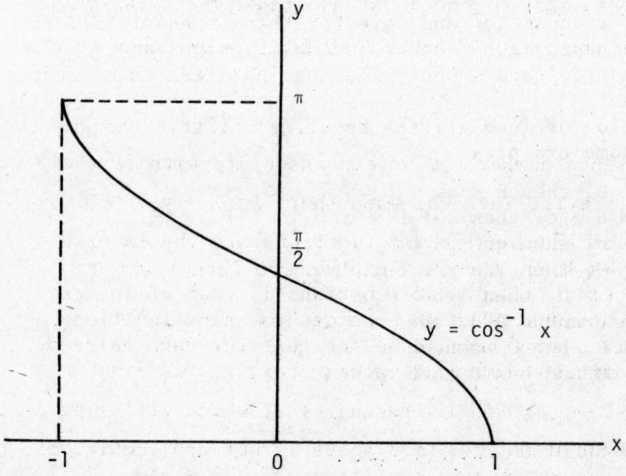

Figure 1.15

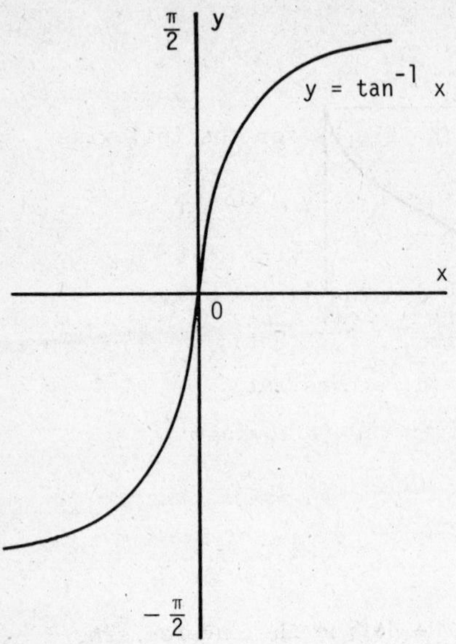

Figure 1.16

Figure 1.15 shows the graph of $\cos^{-1}x$. We can similarly define an *inverse tangent* or *arctangent function*, $y = \tan^{-1}x$ (arctan x), where y is restricted to the range of values $-\pi/2 < y < \pi/2$. (Note that we have to exclude $y = \pm\pi/2$ because $\tan(\pm\pi/2)$ is undefined.) Figure 1.16 illustrates the graph of $\tan^{-1}x$.

1.2 INEQUALITIES

In chapter 1 we have used the signs < and > to mean 'less than' and 'greater than,' respectively, and the signs $\leqslant$ and $\geqslant$ to mean 'less than or equal to' and 'greater than or equal to'. These are examples of *inequalities*. Other inequality signs are $\neq$ meaning 'not equal to' and $\nless$ and $\ngtr$ meaning 'not less than' and 'not greater than'.

The manipulation of inequalities requires a little thought at first. We give some examples

(a) If $a > b$, then $b < a$.
(b) If $a - b > c$, then $a > b + c$.
(c) If $a > b$, then $-a < -b$.
(d) If $a > 0$, then $1/a > 0$ but if $a < 0$ then $1/a < 0$.
(e) If $a > b > 0$, then $1/b > 1/a > 0$.
(f) If $a > b$ and $c \geqslant d$, then $a + c > b + d$.
(g) If $a < 0$, $b > 0$ then $ab < 0$.
(h) If $a < 0$ and $b < 0$ then $ab > 0$.

1.3 PROBLEMS FOR SOLUTION

1. What are the slopes of the straight lines passing through the following pairs of points?

(i) (−5, 1) and (3, −2);
(ii) (3, 2) and (11, −1);
(iii) (4, 2) and (8, 5).

2. How would you draw straight-line graphs for the following functions?

(i) $y = x^2$;
(ii) $y = x^{1/2}$;
(iii) $x = a \exp(-kt)$ (a, k constant);
(iv) $\ln k = \ln k_0 + Au^{1/2}$ (k_0, A constant);
(v) $\ln y = \ln a + b \ln x$ (a, b constant).

3. Find the values of x that satisfy the following quadratic equations:

(i) $2x^2 - 3x - 4 = 0$;
(ii) $3x^2 + 4x - 9 = 0$;
(iii) $x^2 + 3x + 5 = 0$.

4. For what ranges of x are the following functions defined?

(i) $y = \dfrac{x - 3}{3x^2 - 1}$;
(ii) $y = \surd[(x - 1)(x - 3)]$;
(iii) $y = \dfrac{x + 2}{(x - 1)(x + 3)(x - 2)}$;

5. Classify the following as even or odd functions:

(i) $x^3 + 6x$;
(ii) $\tan x$;
(iii) $x \sin x$;
(iv) $x^2 + 2 \cos x$;
(v) $\sin^{-1} x$.

6. Without using tables find values for:

$\sin(\pi/4)$; $\cos(\pi/4)$; $\tan(\pi/4)$; $\sin(\pi/3)$; $\cos(\pi/3)$; $\tan(\pi/3)$.

7. Derive equations 1.27 from equations 1.26.

8. Derive equations 1.28 from equations 1.26.

9. Express the following in terms of sums of trigonometric functions:

(i) $\sin 3A \cos 3A$;
(ii) $\sin 2A \sin 7A$;
(iii) $\cos 4A \cos 5A$.

10. The product $\cos(2\pi\nu_k t)\ \cos(2\pi\nu t)$, where ν_k and ν are frequencies, arises in the theory of Raman spectroscopy. Express the product as a sum of two cosines.

11. A standing wave is the sum of two waves

$$\psi_1(x,t) = a_0 \cos\left[2\pi\left(\frac{x}{\lambda} - \nu t\right)\right]$$

and

$$\psi_2(x,t) = a_0 \cos\left[2\pi\left(\frac{x}{\lambda} + \nu t\right)\right]$$

travelling in opposite directions. Express the sum as a product of a cosine function of x and a cosine function of t.

12. Evaluate: exp (2.5); exp (-2); exp (3.7); exp (-10).

13. Without using tables write down: $\log_{10} 100$; $\log_{10} 10^{-6}$; $\log_{10} \sqrt{10}$; $\log_2 16$; $\log_2 0.5$; $\log_2 0.125$; $\log_2 64$.

14. Work out: $\log_3 2$; $\log_5 10$; $\log_2 7$.

15. What is the conversion factor for converting logarithms to the base e to logarithms to the base 10?

16. Evaluate: $\sin^{-1}(0.5)$; $\sin^{-1}(0.8660)$; $\tan^{-1}(1)$; $\cos^{-1}(0.3)$; $\cos^{-1}(-0.3)$; $\sin^{-1}(-0.7)$.

2

Differential Calculus

Chemistry is concerned with change, so we shall need to develop methods to treat rates of change in a quantitative manner. The differential calculus enables us to do this but first we need to discuss the concept of a limit.

2.1 LIMITS

The idea of a limit is fundamental to calculus, and we shall therefore consider it at some length. We shall start with what may appear to be a trivial example. Let us evaluate $y = x^2$ for a series of values of x close to 3 *but not* equal to 3.

x	2.9	2.95	2.99	2.999	3.001	3.01	3.05	3.1
y	8.41	8.70	8.94	8.994	9.006	9.06	9.30	9.61

We can see from these figures that as x approaches 3, x^2 approaches 9 and that we guess that we can always find a value of x that will make x^2 as close to 9 as we please. We say that as x approaches 3, x^2 tends to the limit 9 and write this formally as

$$\lim_{x \to 3} x^2 = 9 \tag{2.1}$$

A less trivial example is the function

$$y = \frac{x^2 - 1}{x - 1} \tag{2.2}$$

in the region of x = 1. When x = 1, y = 0/0, which is undefined. However, we can calculate y for a series of values getting closer to 1.

x	0.9	0.95	0.99	0.995	0.999	1.001	1.005	1.01	1.1
y	1.9	1.95	1.99	1.995	1.999	2.001	2.005	2.01	2.1

Inspection of these figures indicates that as x approaches 1, y approaches 2, and we may say that although f(x) is undefined when x = 1, a limit does exist

$$\lim_{x \to 1} \frac{x^2 - 1}{x - 1} = 2 \tag{2.3}$$

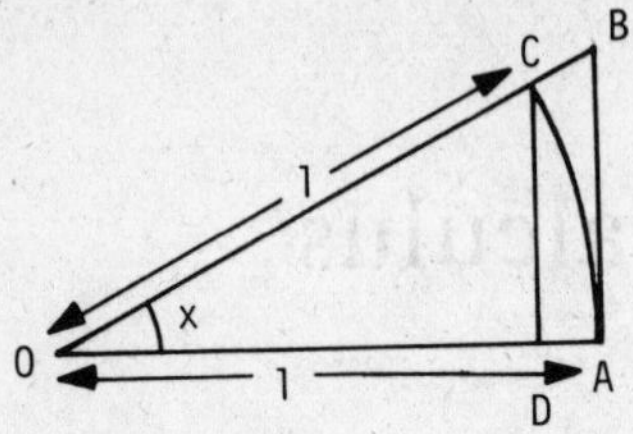

Figure 2.1

A formal definition of a limit is that f(x) tends to the limit L as x tends to a, if the difference between f(x) and L remains as small as we please so long as x remains sufficiently near to a while remaining distinct from a.

$$\lim_{x \to a} f(x) = L \tag{2.4}$$

A more difficult example, which we shall use later on, is

$$\lim_{x \to 0} \frac{\sin x}{x} \tag{2.5}$$

We can determine this limit by a geometrical method. Let the angle x be defined by an arc AC with unit radius (figure 2.1). The area of the sector OAC is

$$\pi \times 1^2 \times \frac{x}{2\pi} = \frac{x}{2}$$

We also calculate the areas of the triangles OAB and OCD

$$\Delta OAB = 1/2 \times 1 \times \tan x$$
$$\Delta OCA = 1/2 \times 1 \times \sin x$$

Inspection of figure 2.1 shows that

$$\Delta OAB \geqslant \text{sector } OAC \geqslant \Delta OCA \tag{2.6}$$

that is

$$\tan x \geqslant x \geqslant \sin x$$

which can be rewritten as

$$\frac{1}{\cos x} \geqslant \frac{x}{\sin x} \geqslant 1$$

or

$$\cos x \leqslant \frac{\sin x}{x} \leqslant 1$$

As x approaches zero, cos x approaches 1 so sin x/x is squeezed between unity and a function approaching unity so we can say that

$$\lim_{x \to 0} \frac{\sin x}{x} = 1 \tag{2.7}$$

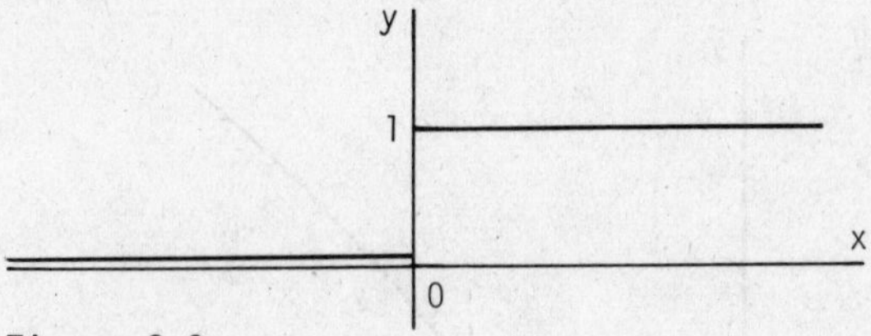

Figure 2.2

In the examples discussed so far, we obtain the same limit irrespective of whether we approach $x = a$ from values smaller than a or from values larger than a. There are cases where this is not so. If we consider the 'step function'

$$f(x) = 1 \text{ if } x \geqslant 0 \qquad (2.8)$$
$$= 0 \text{ if } x < 0$$

we see that as x approaches zero from the negative side, f(x) tends to zero whereas if x approaches zero from positive values, the limit is 1 (figure 2.2). Strictly speaking the limit does not exist in this case but we can write

$$\lim_{x \to 0_-} f(x) = 0; \quad \lim_{x \to 0_+} f(x) = 1 \qquad (2.9)$$

to indicate that two different limits exist.

We quote without proof three theorems about limits that will be useful in subsequent work. Suppose we have two functions f(x) and g(x) such that

$$\lim_{x \to a} f(x) = l \quad \text{and} \quad \lim_{x \to a} g(x) = m$$

then the following theorems are true.

Theorem 1

$$\lim_{x \to a} \left[f(x) + g(x)\right] = l + m \qquad (2.10)$$

Theorem 2

$$\lim_{x \to a} \left[f(x)g(x)\right] = lm \qquad (2.11)$$

Theorem 3

$$\lim_{x \to a} \frac{f(x)}{g(x)} = \frac{\lim_{x \to a} f(x)}{\lim_{x \to a} g(x)} = \frac{l}{m} \qquad (2.12)$$

provided that $\lim_{x \to a} g(x) \neq 0$.

2.2 CONTINUITY

In our first example, $y = x^2$, the function is defined at the value of $x (x = 3)$ of interest whereas y is not defined for

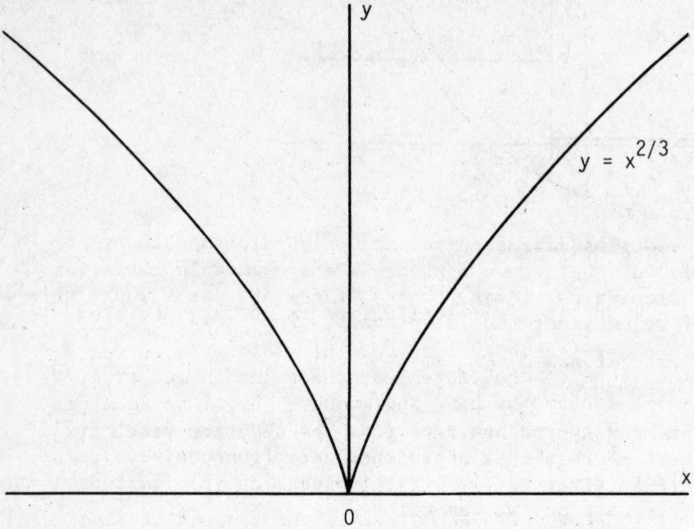

Figure 2.3

$y = (x^2 - 1)/(x - 1)$ at $x = 1$ or for $(\sin x)/x$ at $x = 0$. When $x = 3$, x^2 is, in fact, equal to 9; that is

$$\lim_{x \to 3} (x^2) = (x^2)_{x=3}$$

and we say that the function is *continuous* at $x = 3$. The formal definition of *continuity* is that the function $f(x)$ is continuous at $x = a$ if the limit $\lim_{x \to a} f(x)$ exists *and* equals $f(a)$.

Our other examples, 2.3, 2.5 and 2.8, are not continuous. Loosely speaking, a function is continuous if we can draw a graph of it without lifting the pencil from the paper. Even a function having a cusp, for example $y = x^{2/3}$ (figure 2.3), is continuous because $\lim_{x \to 0} x^{2/3} = 0$ and $y = 0$ for $x = 0$. $y = \sin x$ is continuous for all x but $y = \tan x$ has discontinuities for $x = n\pi/2$, where n is an integer.

2.3 THE DERIVATIVE

In section 1.1.2(i) we defined the slope of a straight line by the relation

$$\text{slope} = \frac{y_2 - y_1}{x_2 - x_1} \tag{2.13}$$

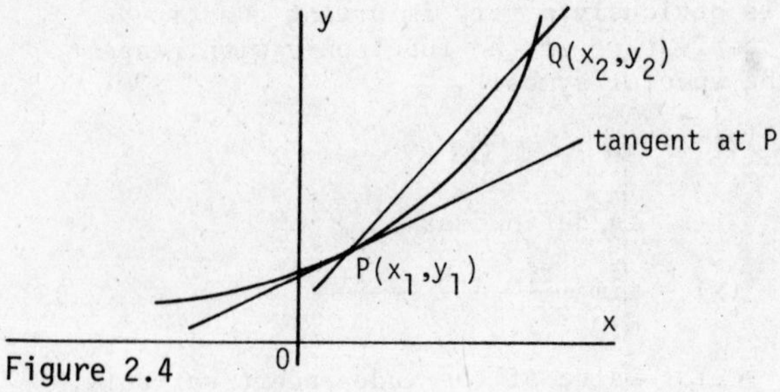

Figure 2.4

where (x_1, y_1) and (x_2, y_2) are two points on the line. This is obviously not applicable to a curve. The slope of a curve is given by the slope of the tangent at the point in question. We could draw the tangent by hand and measure the slope but this is a tedious and inaccurate procedure. We can, however, determine the slope quantitatively as a limit. Consider the point P (figure 2.4), having co-ordinates (x_1, y_1), on the curve $y = f(x)$. We require the slope of the tangent at P. If we take some other point Q near to P on the curve, we can readily calculate the slope of the chord PQ as

$$\text{slope of PQ} = \frac{f(x_2) - f(x_1)}{x_2 - x_1}$$

For the choice of Q shown in the figure, the slope of PQ is larger than the slope of the tangent at P. If we take another point $Q'(x_3, y_3)$ between P and Q, the slope of PQ' will be closer to the slope of the tangent at P than was the slope of PQ. We will get a better approximation to the slope at P by letting Q' approach closer to P. If we take a point $(x_1 + h, f(x_1 + h))$, where h is some small quantity, the slope of the chord is

$$\frac{f(x_1 + h) - f(x_1)}{(x_1 + h) - x_1} = \frac{f(x_1 + h) - f(x_1)}{h}$$

Intuitively we can say that the slope of the tangent at P will be given by the limit of the slope of the chord as h approaches zero; that is

$$\text{slope at P} = \lim_{h \to 0} \frac{f(x_1 + h) - f(x_1)}{h} \tag{2.14}$$

A formal definition is that given a curve $y = f(x)$, and P a point on the curve, the slope of the curve at P is the limit of the slope of lines between P and another point Q on the curve as Q approaches P.

The slope of a curve $y = f(x)$ is the rate at which y is changing as x changes - it is the *rate of change of y with respect to x*. This is obviously a very important quantity and is known as the *derivative* of the function y with respect to x. It is given the special symbol

$$\frac{dy}{dx} \quad \text{or} \quad \frac{df(x)}{dx} \quad \text{or} \quad f'(x)$$

The derivative of y = f(x) is defined as

$$\frac{dy}{dx} = \frac{df(x)}{dx} = f'(x) = \lim_{h\to 0}\left[\frac{f(x + h) - f(x)}{h}\right] \tag{2.15}$$

where x is some particular value of the independent variable. The quotient $[f(x + h) - f(x)]/h$ is known as the *Newton quotient*.

A function y = f(x) is said to be *differentiable* if it possesses a derivative and to be differentiable at a point x = a if dy/dx exists at that point. The process of obtaining the derivative is known as *differentiation*.

2.4 RULES FOR DIFFERENTIATION

In this section we develop methods for the differentiation of most types of function.

2.4.1 Derivatives of powers of x

To illustrate the use of equation 2.15 for the derivative we shall consider some simple examples.

(i) The derivative of a constant is zero

If y = a, then

$$\frac{dy}{dx} = \lim_{h\to 0}\left[\frac{f(x + h) - f(x)}{h}\right] = \lim_{h\to 0}\frac{0}{h} = 0 \tag{2.16}$$

(ii) $y = x$

$$\frac{dy}{dx} = \lim_{h\to 0}\left[\frac{f(x + h) - f(x)}{h}\right] = \lim_{h\to 0}\frac{(x + h - x)}{h}$$

$$= \lim_{h\to 0} 1 = 1 \tag{2.17}$$

(iii) $y = x^2$

$$\frac{dy}{dx} = \lim_{h\to 0}\left[\frac{f(x + h) - f(x)}{h}\right] = \lim_{h\to 0}\frac{(x + h)^2 - x^2}{h}$$

$$= \lim_{h\to 0}(2x + h) = 2x \tag{2.18}$$

(iv) $y = x^3$

$$\frac{dy}{dx} = \lim_{h\to 0}\left[\frac{(x+h)^3 - x^3}{h}\right] = \lim_{h\to 0}(3x^2 + 3xh + h^2) = 3x^2 \qquad (2.19)$$

(v) $y = x^n$ *(n a positive integer)*

We should expect, on the basis of the three previous derivatives, that $d/dx(x^n)$ would be nx^{n-1}. The derivative is given by

$$\frac{dy}{dx} = \lim_{h\to 0}\left[\frac{(x+h)^n - x^n}{h}\right]$$

Expanding $(x + h)^n$ by the binomial theorem (see chapter 7) gives

$$\frac{dy}{dx} = \lim_{h\to 0}\left[nx^{n-1} + \frac{n(n-1)}{2!}x^{n-1}h + \text{terms in } h^2, h^3, \text{etc.}\right]$$

$$= nx^{n-1} \qquad (2.20)$$

Although we have shown that $d/dx(x^n) = nx^{n-1}$ if n is a positive integer, the result is valid for all values of n. For example

$$\frac{d}{dx}(x^{3/2}) = 3/2x^{1/2}$$

$$\frac{d}{dx}(x^{-1/2}) = -1/2x^{-3/2}$$

2.4.2 The derivative of a sum

If $y = f(x) + g(x)$ then the derivative

$$\frac{dy}{dx} = \lim_{h\to 0}\left[\frac{f(x+h) + g(x+h) - f(x) - g(x)}{h}\right] \qquad (2.21)$$

which can be rewritten using equation 2.10 as

$$\frac{dy}{dx} = \lim_{h\to 0}\left[\frac{f(x+h) - f(x)}{h}\right] + \lim_{h\to 0}\left[\frac{g(x+h) - g(x)}{h}\right]$$

$$= \frac{df(x)}{dx} + \frac{dg(x)}{dx}$$

Thus the derivative of a sum of functions is equal to the sum of the individual derivatives. For example, if $y = x^4 + x^2$, $dy/dx = 4x^3 + 2x$.

2.4.3 The derivative of a product

If $y = f(x)g(x)$, then applying the basic definition of equation 2.15 gives

$$\frac{dy}{dx} = \lim_{h\to 0}\left[\frac{f(x+h)g(x+h) - f(x)g(x)}{h}\right]$$

$$= \lim_{h\to 0}\left[\frac{f(x+h)g(x+h) - f(x+h)g(x) + f(x+h)g(x) - f(x)g(x)}{h}\right]$$

Using equations 2.10 and 2.11 gives

$$\frac{dy}{dx} = \lim_{h\to 0} f(x+h) \lim_{h\to 0}\left[\frac{g(x+h) - g(x)}{h}\right]$$

$$+ \lim_{h\to 0} g(x) \lim_{h\to 0}\left[\frac{f(x+h) - f(x)}{h}\right]$$

$$= f(x)\frac{dg(x)}{dx} + g(x)\frac{df(x)}{dx}$$

that is

$$\frac{d}{dx}\left[f(x)g(x)\right] = f(x)\frac{dg(x)}{dx} + g(x)\frac{df(x)}{dx} \qquad (2.22)$$

We see at once that if we multiply a function $f(x)$ by a constant a, the derivative of $\left[af(x)\right]$ is simply $a\,df(x)/dx$ because the derivative of a constant is zero; for example

$$\frac{d}{dx}\left[(x^6 + x^{-1/2})(4x^2 + 3x + 1)\right]$$

$$= (x^6 + x^{-1/2})(4.2x + 3) + (6x^5 - 1/2x^{-3/2})(4x^2 + 3x + 1)$$

Relation 2.22 can be generalised to products of several functions. For example if $y = f(x)g(x)h(x)$, then

$$\frac{dy}{dx} = f(x)g(x)\frac{dh(x)}{dx} + f(x)h(x)\frac{dg(x)}{dx} + g(x)h(x)\frac{df(x)}{dx} \qquad (2.23)$$

2.4.4 The derivative of a quotient

The derivative of the quotient $y = f(x)/g(x)$ (provided $g(x) \neq 0$) is given by

$$\frac{dy}{dx} = \lim_{h\to 0}\left[\frac{f(x+h)}{g(x+h)} - \frac{f(x)}{g(x)}\right]/h$$

$$= \lim_{h\to 0}\left[\frac{f(x+h)g(x) - f(x)g(x+h)}{hg(x)g(x+h)}\right]$$

$$= \lim_{h\to 0}\left[\frac{f(x+h)g(x) - f(x)g(x) + f(x)g(x) - f(x)g(x+h)}{hg(x)g(x+h)}\right]$$

Using equations 2.10, 2.11 and 2.12 gives

$$\frac{dy}{dx} = \left[\lim_{h\to 0} g(x) \lim_{h\to 0}\{[f(x + h) - f(x)]/h\}\right.$$

$$\left. - \lim_{h\to 0}\{[g(x + h) - g(x)]/h\}\lim_{h\to 0} f(x)\right] \Big/ \lim_{h\to 0} g(x)g(x + h)$$

that is

$$\frac{dy}{dx} = \frac{g(x)(df(x)/dx) - f(x)\ (dg(x)/dx)}{[g(x)]^2} \qquad (2.24)$$

For example

$$\frac{d}{dx}\left(\frac{x^2 + 1}{3x^4 - 2x}\right) = \frac{(3x^4 - 2x)2x - (x^2 + 1)(3.4x^3 - 2)}{(3x^4 - 2x)^2}$$

2.4.5 The chain rule

The rules we have just developed do not enáble us to differentiate functions such as $y = (x^2 + 3x + 5)^{5/2}$. This is an example of a *function of a function*. If we denote $(x^2 + 3x + 5)$ by u, then we can write $y = u^{5/2}$, where u is the function of x, $g(x) = x^2 + 3x + 5$. Another example is $y = \sqrt{[(x + 1)/(x - 1)]}$. Here we let $u = g(x) = (x + 1)/(x - 1)$, so $y = u^{1/2}$. This problem occurs very commonly and we require the *chain rule* to differentiate functions of this type. Since the proof is rather involved we simply quote the rule.

If $y = f(u)$, where $u = g(x)$ then the derivative of y with respect to x is given by

$$\frac{dy}{dx} = \frac{dy}{du} \times \frac{du}{dx} \qquad (2.25)$$

Let us apply this to our examples. If $y = u^{5/2}$, where $u = x^2 + 3x + 5$ (that is $y = (x^2 + 3x + 5)^{5/2}$), then

$$\frac{dy}{dx} = \frac{dy}{du} \times \frac{du}{dx} = \frac{5u^{3/2}}{2}\quad (2x + 3)$$

that is

$$\frac{d}{dx}\left[(x^2 + 3x + 5)^{5/2}\right] = \frac{5}{2}(x^2 + 3x + 5)^{3/2}\ (2x + 3)$$

For $y = \sqrt{[(x + 1)/(x - 1)]}$, letting $u = (x + 1)/(x - 1)$ gives

$$\frac{d}{dx}\left[\sqrt{\left(\frac{x+1}{x-1}\right)}\right] = 1/2u^{-1/2}\frac{du}{dx}$$

$$= 1/2\left(\frac{x+1}{x-1}\right)^{-1/2}\left[\frac{(x-1)-(x+1)}{(x-1)^2}\right]$$

We can have more complicated examples such as

$$y = \cos\{\sqrt{[(x+1)/(x-1)]}\}$$

which is of the form $y = f(u)$ where $u = g(v)$ and $v = h(x)$. In this case

$$\frac{dy}{dx} = \frac{dy}{du} \times \frac{du}{dv} \times \frac{dv}{dx} \tag{2.26}$$

Here $y = \cos u$, $u = v^{1/2}$,

$$v = \frac{x+1}{x-1}$$

so

$$\frac{dy}{dx} = \frac{d}{du}(\cos u)\ 1/2\left(\frac{x+1}{x-1}\right)^{-1/2}\left[\frac{(x-1)-(x+1)}{(x-1)^2}\right]$$

The derivative of the cosine function will be discussed in the next section. The rules we have derived so far are sufficient for us to be able to differentiate any algebraic function.

2.4.6 Derivatives of the trigonometric functions

Applying the standard definition of equation 2.15 to $y = \sin x$ gives the expression

$$\frac{d}{dx}(\sin x) = \lim_{h\to 0}\left[\frac{\sin(x+h) - \sin x}{h}\right]$$

Expanding $\sin(x + h)$ by formula 1.26 gives

$$\frac{d}{dx}(\sin x) = \lim_{h\to 0}\left[\frac{\sin x \cos h + \sin h \cos x - \sin x}{h}\right]$$

$$= \lim_{h\to 0}(\sin x) \lim_{h\to 0}\left(\frac{\cos h - 1}{h}\right)$$

$$+ \lim_{h\to 0}\frac{\sin h}{h} \lim_{h\to 0}\cos x$$

It can be proved rigorously that $\lim_{h\to 0}[(\cos h - 1)/h]$ is zero and we have shown that

$$\lim_{h\to 0}\frac{\sin h}{h} = 1 \quad \text{so} \quad \frac{d}{dx}(\sin x) = \cos x \tag{2.27}$$

The derivatives of cos x can be derived by using equation 1.22 for cos x in terms of $\sin(x + \pi/2)$

$$\frac{d}{dx}(\cos x) = \frac{d}{dx}\left[\sin\left(\frac{\pi}{2} + x\right)\right] = \cos\left(x + \frac{\pi}{2}\right) = -\sin x$$

that is

$$\frac{d}{dx}(\cos x) = -\sin x \qquad (2.28)$$

The derivatives of other trigonometric functions can be derived from these two basic derivatives.

$$\frac{d}{dx}(\tan x) = \frac{d}{dx}\left(\frac{\sin x}{\cos x}\right) = \frac{\cos x \times \cos x - \sin x\,(-\sin x)}{\cos^2 x}$$

Therefore

$$\frac{d}{dx}(\tan x) = \frac{1}{\cos^2 x} = \sec^2 x \qquad (2.29)$$

$$\frac{d}{dx}(\sec x) = \frac{d}{dx}\left(\frac{1}{\cos x}\right) = \sec x \tan x$$

$$\frac{d}{dx}(\operatorname{cosec} x) = \frac{d}{dx}\left(\frac{1}{\sin x}\right) = -\operatorname{cosec} x \cot x$$

$$\frac{d}{dx}(\cot x) = \frac{d}{dx}\left(\frac{\cos x}{\sin x}\right) = -\operatorname{cosec}^2 x \qquad (2.30)$$

We shall often have to use the other rules we have developed; for example

$$\frac{d}{dx}\left[(\sin x)^2\right] = 2 \sin x \cos x$$

$$\frac{d}{dx}\left[\frac{\sin x}{x}\right] = \frac{x \cos x - \sin x \times 1}{x^2}$$

$$\frac{d}{dx}\left[\sin(\sin x)\right] = \cos(\sin x) \times \cos x$$

2.4.7 The exponential function

In section 1.1.4 we defined the exponential function in terms of the infinite series

$$\exp(x) = 1 + \frac{x}{1!} + \frac{x^2}{2!} + \frac{x^3}{3!} + \frac{x^4}{4!} + \ldots$$

If we differentiate this term by term we obtain

$$\frac{d}{dx}\exp(x) = 0 + 1 + \frac{2x}{2!} + \frac{3x^2}{3!} + \frac{4x^3}{4!} + \ldots$$

$$= 1 + \frac{x}{1!} + \frac{x^2}{2!} + \frac{x^3}{3!} + \ldots$$

that is

$$\frac{d}{dx}(\exp(x)) = \exp(x) \qquad (2.31)$$

This is a very important result. Indeed we could have defined the exponential function as that function whose derivative is equal to itself.

We use the chain rule for the differentiation of $y = \exp[f(x)]$; for example

$$\frac{d}{dx}[\exp(ax)] = a\exp(ax) \qquad (2.32)$$

The derivative of exp(ax) illustrates the important mathematical idea of an eigenfunction of an operator. d/dx is an *operator*, which operates on the function exp(ax) to give the function multiplied by a constant which is known as the *eigenvalue*. We say that exp(ax) is an *eigenfunction* of the operator d/dx. Other examples of derivatives of functions of the exponential are

$$\frac{d}{dx}\left[\exp\left(\frac{1}{x}\right)\right] = \frac{-1}{x^2}\exp\left(\frac{1}{x}\right)$$

$$\frac{d}{dx}[\exp(4x^2 + 2x)] = (8x + 2)\exp(4x^2 + 2x)$$

2.4.8 The logarithmic function

One way of obtaining the derivative of ln x is to rewrite it in the form

$$x = \exp(\ln x)$$

and differentiate both sides. Thus

$$\frac{d(x)}{dx} = \frac{d}{dx}\exp(\ln x)$$

that is

$$1 = \exp(\ln x)\frac{d}{dx}(\ln x)$$

Thus

$$\frac{d}{dx}(\ln x) = \frac{1}{\exp(\ln x)} = \frac{1}{x} \qquad (2.33)$$

The simplicity of this result is one reason for preferring logarithms to the base e. Derivatives of $\ln[f(x)]$ are obtained by using the chain rule; for example

$$\frac{d}{dx}\ln(x^2 + 2x) = \frac{1}{(x^2 + 2x)}(2x + 2)$$

$$\frac{d}{dx}\ln\left(\frac{x}{2 + 3x}\right) = \frac{2 + 3x}{x}\left[\frac{(2 + 3x)1 - x \times 3}{(2 + 3x)^2}\right]$$

2.4.9 The generalised exponential a^x

We can differentiate a^x by expressing a in terms of e thus, a = exp (ln a). Therefore

$$a^x = [\exp(\ln a)]^x = \exp(x \ln a)$$

and

$$\frac{d}{dx}(a^x) = \ln a \times \exp(x \ln a) = a^x \times \ln a \qquad (2.34)$$

For example

$$\frac{d}{dx}(3^{2x}) = 3^{2x} \times 2 \ln 3$$

2.4.10 Hyperbolic functions

The derivatives of the hyperbolic functions follow easily from the definitions of the functions in equations 1.39, 1.40

$$\frac{d}{dx}(\cosh x) = \frac{d}{dx}\left[\frac{1}{2}(e^x + e^{-x})\right] = \frac{1}{2}(e^x - e^{-x}) = \sinh x \qquad (2.35)$$

$$\frac{d}{dx}(\sinh x) = \frac{d}{dx}\left[\frac{1}{2}(e^x - e^{-x})\right] = \frac{1}{2}(e^x + e^{-x}) = \cosh x \qquad (2.36)$$

$$\frac{d}{dx}(\tanh x) = \frac{d}{dx}\left[\frac{\sinh x}{\cosh x}\right] = \frac{\cosh^2 x - \sinh^2 x}{\cosh^2 x} = \frac{1}{\cosh^2 x} \qquad (2.37)$$

2.4.11 Inverse trigonometric functions

If we have a function y = f(x) and define the inverse function x = g(y) as in section 1.1.7, it can be shown that the derivative of g with respect to y is given by

$$\frac{dg(y)}{dy} = 1\bigg/\frac{df(x)}{dx} \qquad (2.38)$$

that is

$$\frac{dx}{dy} = 1\bigg/\frac{dy}{dx}$$

We now apply this to the inverse trigonometric functions defined in section 1.1.7. If

$$y = \sin^{-1} x \text{ for } -\pi/2 \leqslant y \leqslant \pi/2$$

then

$$x = \sin y$$

and

$$\frac{dx}{dy} = \cos y = +\surd(1 - \sin^2 y) = +\surd(1 - x^2)$$

where we have taken the positive square root because cos y is positive for $-\pi/2 \leqslant y \leqslant \pi/2$. Using equation 2.38 gives

$$\frac{d}{dx}(\sin^{-1} x) = \frac{1}{\sqrt{(1 - x^2)}} \tag{2.39}$$

A more general form is $d/dx\left[\sin^{-1}(x/a)\right]$, which is obtained from x = a sin y as follows

$$\frac{dx}{dy} = a \cos y = a\sqrt{\left(1 - \frac{x^2}{a^2}\right)} = \sqrt{(a^2 - x^2)}$$

that is

$$\frac{d}{dx}\left[\sin^{-1}\left(\frac{x}{a}\right)\right] = \frac{1}{\sqrt{(a^2 - x^2)}} \tag{2.40}$$

Similarly

$$\frac{d}{dx}\left[\cos^{-1}\left(\frac{x}{a}\right)\right] = -\frac{1}{\sqrt{(a^2 - x^2)}} \tag{2.41}$$

The same general method can be used to differentiate the inverse tangent function $\tan^{-1}(x/a)$. Letting

$$x = a \tan y$$

$$\frac{dx}{dy} = a \sec^2 y = a\left(1 + \frac{x^2}{a^2}\right) = \frac{a^2 + x^2}{a}$$

Therefore

$$\frac{d}{dx}\tan^{-1}\left(\frac{x}{a}\right) = \frac{a}{a^2 + x^2} \tag{2.42}$$

The derivatives of the other inverse trigonometric functions are

$$\frac{d}{dx}(\cot^{-1} x) = -\frac{1}{1 + x^2};\ \frac{d}{dx}(\sec^{-1} x) = \frac{1}{|x|\sqrt{(x^2 - 1)}}$$

$$\frac{d}{dx}(\mathrm{cosec}^{-1} x) = -\frac{1}{|x|\sqrt{(x^2 - 1)}} \tag{2.43}$$

where $|x|$ is the *modulus* of x, which is equal to x if $x > 0$ and to $-x$ if $x < 0$.

2.5 HIGHER DERIVATIVES

The symbol $f'(x)$ for the derivative indicates that the derivative is also a function of x, which can, therefore, be differentiated again. The *second derivative* is given the symbols d^2y/dx^2 or $f''(x)$.

$$\frac{d^2y}{dx^2} \equiv f''(x) = \frac{d}{dx}\left(\frac{dy}{dx}\right) \equiv \frac{d}{dx}\left[f'(x)\right] \tag{2.44}$$

We can define higher derivatives still: the third derivative is d^3y/dx^3 or $f'''(x)$. For example, if

$$y = x^4 + x^3 + x^2 + x$$

$$f'(x) \equiv \frac{dy}{dx} = 4x^3 + 3x^2 + 2x + 1$$

$$f''(x) \equiv \frac{d^2y}{dx^2} = 12x^2 + 6x + 2$$

$$f'''(x) \equiv \frac{d^3y}{dx^3} = 24x + 6$$

$$f^{(4)}(x) \equiv \frac{d^4y}{dx^4} = 24$$

But

$$f^{(5)}(x) \equiv \frac{d^5y}{dx^5} = 0$$

The $(n + 1)$th derivative of a polynomial of degree n is zero.

You should note that although

$$\frac{dx}{dy} = \frac{1}{(dy/dx)}$$

$$\frac{d^2x}{dy^2} \text{ is \textit{not} equal to } \frac{1}{(d^2y/dx^2)}$$

2.6 APPLICATIONS OF DIFFERENTIATION

2.6.1 Rate of change

The derivative of the function $y = f(x)$ is the rate of change of y with respect to change in x. Thus the derivative can be used to describe any nonstationary system. If, in radioactive decay, the amount of material x left at time t is given by $x = ae^{-\lambda t}$, where a is the initial amount and λ is a constant, the rate of decay is given by dx/dt

$$\frac{dx}{dt} = -\lambda ae^{-\lambda t} = -\lambda x$$

Thus the rate of decay is proportional to the amount present at time t.

If the position of a particle at time t is given by $x = f(t)$, the velocity is given by dx/dt and the acceleration, which is the rate of change of velocity with respect to time, is given by the second derivative d^2x/dt^2.

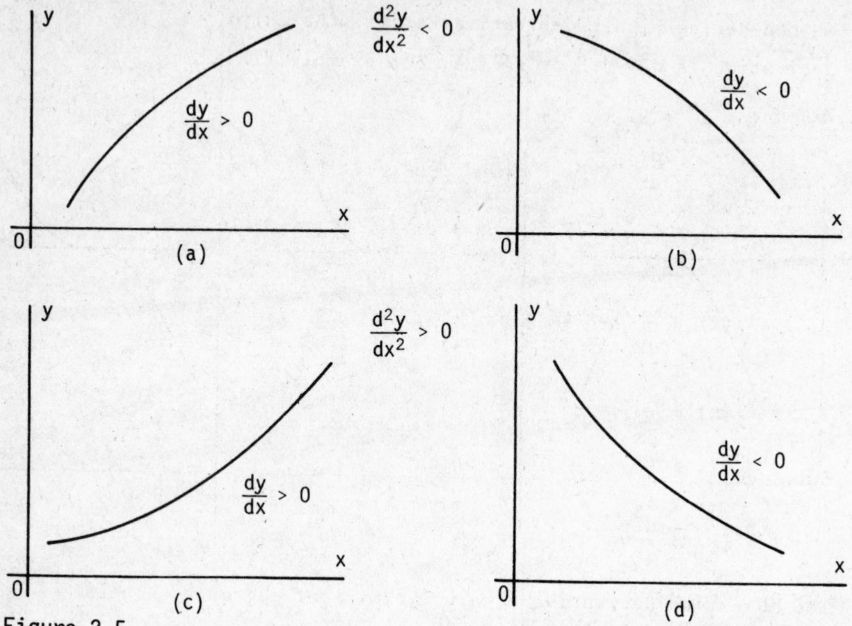

Figure 2.5

2.6.2 Slope of a curve, maxima and minima

We have seen in section 2.3 that the derivative of a function $y = f(x)$ at $x = x_1$ gives the slope of the curve at that point. Often we are not so much interested in the actual value of the slope as in whether the curve is increasing or decreasing from left to right or whether it is concave or convex towards the x-axis. A positive slope (figure 2.5a, c) indicates that as x increases y increases, whereas a negative slope (figure 2.5b, d) is indicative of y decreasing with increasing x. Thus the *sign of the first derivative* tells us whether the function is increasing or decreasing as x increases. The second derivative also gives us valuable information. It tells us the *slope of the slope* or whether the curve $y = f(x)$ is concave or convex towards the x-axis. If d^2y/dx^2 is positive, the slope dy/dx increases as x increases and the curve is convex towards the x-axis (figure 2.5c, d), whereas if d^2y/dx^2 is negative, then the slope dy/dx decreases as x increases and the curve is concave towards the x-axis (figure 2.5a, b).

If the derivative is zero, the tangent is horizontal and we can have one of the three possibilities shown in figure 2.6.

Such points are called *turning points*. The three possibilities shown in figure 2.6 correspond to a *maximum* (a), *a minimum* (b) or a *point of inflection* (c). We can distinguish between these possibilities by using the second derivative. A *maximum* occurs when the slope decreases from a positive value to zero and then becomes negative as x

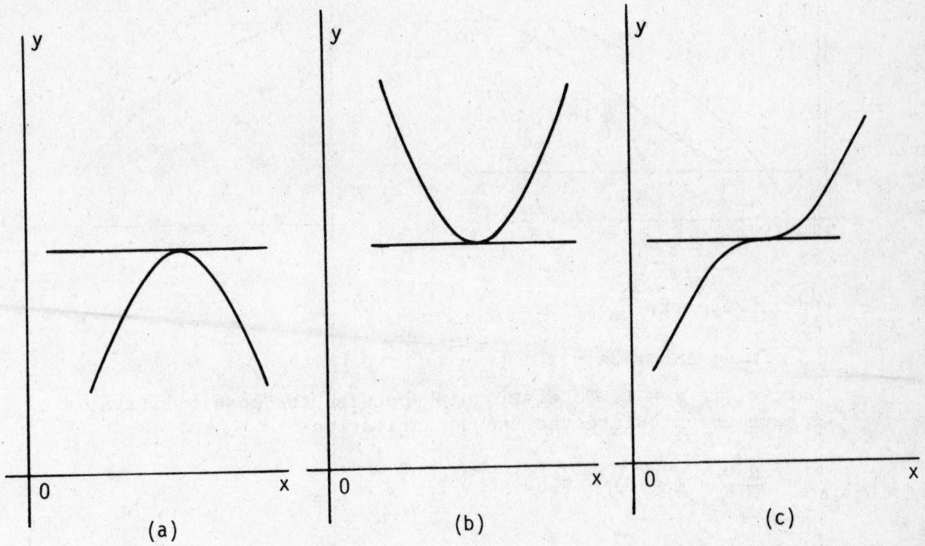

Figure 2.6

increases. Thus dy/dx decreases as x increases and the second derivative is therefore *negative*. On the other hand, at a *minimum*, the slope increases from a negative value to zero and then becomes positive as x increases; that is, it is characterised by an increasing slope dy/dx, and d^2y/dx^2 is *positive*. At the *point of inflection* in figure 2.6(c), the slope decreases to zero and then starts to increase. Thus to the left of the point of inflection d^2y/dx^2 is negative and to the right it is positive, so at the point of inflection d^2y/dx^2 is *zero*.

It is possible for d^2y/dx^2 to be zero without dy/dx being zero. This also corresponds to a point of inflection because the curve is changing from being concave upwards to being concave downwards (figure 2.7).

Strictly speaking we have been discussing *relative* or *local* rather than *absolute* maxima or minima. A function f(x) has a *relative or local maximum* at x = a if $f(a) \geq f(a + h)$ for all positive and negative values of h sufficiently near zero whereas f(x) has an *absolute maximum* at x = a if $f(a) > f(x)$ for all x.

The function

$$y = \frac{x^2}{2} - 3x + 3 \ln x + \frac{1}{x} \qquad (x > 0)$$

has turning points for the values of x for which dy/dx is zero

$$\frac{dy}{dx} = x - 3 + \frac{3}{x} - \frac{1}{x^2}$$

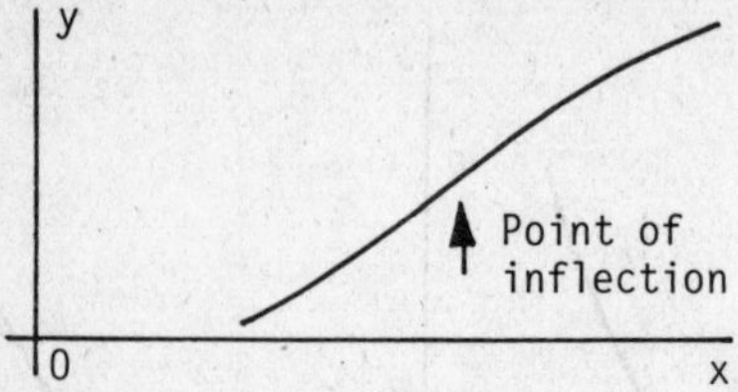

Figure 2.7

and is zero if

$$x^3 - 3x^2 + 3x - 1 = (x - 1)^3 = 0$$

that is, if x = 1. To distinguish between the possibilities, we have to calculate the second derivative

$$\frac{d^2y}{dx^2} = 1 - \frac{3}{x^2} + \frac{2}{x^3} = 0 \qquad \text{for } x = 1$$

so we have a point of inflection.

The velocity v of an autocatalytic reaction is given by

$$v = kx(a - x)$$

where a is the initial concentration of the reactive material, x is the amount decomposed at time t and k is a constant. The rate will be a maximum when dv/dx is zero and d^2v/dx^2 is negative. Differentiating, we have

$$\frac{dv}{dx} = ka - 2kx$$

which is zero for x = a/2, that is when half of the starting material has been used up. $d^2v/dx^2 = -2k$, which is obviously negative for positive values of k.

At constant pressure, the volume V of 1 gram of water as a function of temperature T is given by a relation of the form

$$V = a + bT + cT^2 + dT^3$$

The *coefficient of expansion* α is given by

$$\alpha = \frac{1}{V_0}\left(\frac{dV}{dT}\right)_P$$

where V_0 is the volume at 0°C. The volume will be a minimum (the density will be a maximum) when dV/dT = 0, that is for the value of T that satisfies the equation

$$b + 2cT + 3\,dT^2 = 0$$

and gives a positive second derivative 2c + 6 dT.

2.6.3 Curve tracing

It is often useful to be able to draw a sketch showing the essential features of a function $y = f(x)$ without actually having to draw an accurate graph. We shall illustrate the procedure with the function

$$y = \frac{x^2 - 3x + 2}{x^2 + 3x + 2}$$

(i) Find the values of x for which y = 0 (approximately if necessary).

$$f(x) = 0 \text{ for } x = 1, 2$$

(ii) Find the value of y when x = 0.

$$f(0) = 1$$

(iii) Investigate what happens as x tends to $\pm\infty$.
As $x \to \infty$, $y \to 1$ from below (that is from $y < 1$). As $x \to -\infty$, $y \to 1$ from above (that is from $y > 1$). Thus as $x \to \infty$, the curve approaches more closely to the line $y = 1$. Such a line is known as a *horizontal asymptote*.
(iv) Are there any values of x for which y becomes infinite?
If $x \to -1$ or -2, y becomes infinite. Looking at this more carefully shows that if x is a little smaller than -1, y approaches $-\infty$, but if x is a little larger than -1, y approaches ∞. Similarly if x approaches -2 from $x < -2$, y tends to ∞, but if x approaches -2 from $x > -2$ then y tends to $-\infty$. The lines $x = 1$, $x = -2$ are *vertical asymptotes*.
(v) Determine the turning points.

$$\frac{dy}{dx} = \frac{6(x^2 - 2)}{(x^2 + 3x + 2)^2}$$

is zero for $x = \pm\sqrt{2}$, and the turning points are at approximately $(\sqrt{2}, -0.029)$ and $(-\sqrt{2}, -34)$. The second derivative

$$\frac{d^2y}{dx^2} = \frac{12(-x^3 + 6x + 6)}{(x^2 + 3x + 2)^3}$$

is positive for $x = +\sqrt{2}$ (that is, it is a minimum) and negative for $x = -\sqrt{2}$ (a maximum).
(vi) Is the second derivative zero?

$$\frac{d^2y}{dx^2} \text{ is zero when } x \approx 2.87$$

so there is a point of inflection in addition to the turning points previously obtained.

The resulting sketch is shown in figure 2.8.

One equation of state for a real gas is the van der Waals

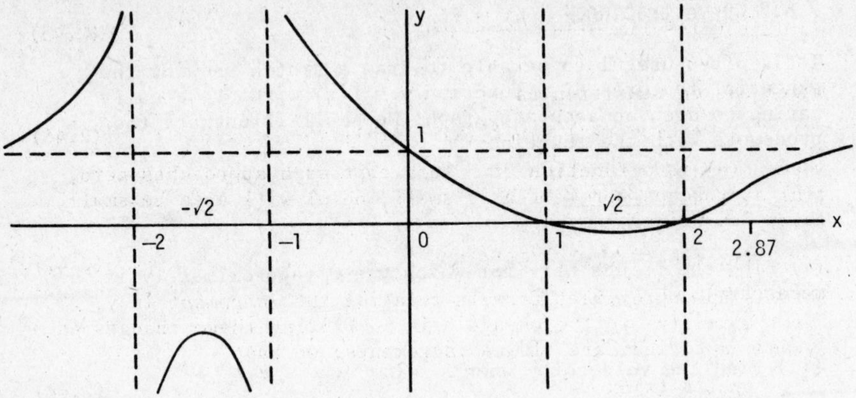

Figure 2.8

equation

$$\left(P + \frac{n^2 a}{V^2}\right)(V - nb) = nRT$$

where P is the pressure, V the volume, T the temperature, n the number of moles of gas, R the gas constant and a and b constants. This does not accurately represent the PVT behaviour of a real gas near the point of liquefaction but it can be used to determine the *critical constants* by finding the values of P, V and T, P_c, V_c, T_c for which $dP/dV = 0$ and $d^2P/dV^2 = 0$, that is, the point at which the maximum and minimum merge into a point of inflection. Solving the equations

$$P_c = \frac{RT_c}{V_c - b} - \frac{a}{V_c^2}$$

$$\frac{dP}{dV} = 0 = \frac{-RT_c}{(V_c - b)^2} + \frac{2a}{V_c^3}$$

$$\frac{d^2P}{dV^2} = 0 = \frac{2RT_c}{(V_c - b)^3} - \frac{6a}{V_c^4}$$

gives

$$T_c = \frac{8a}{27bR}, \quad V_c = 3b, \quad P_c = \frac{a}{27b^2}.$$

2.7 INCREMENTS AND DIFFERENTIALS

We have defined the derivative of $y = f(x)$ by the relation

$$f'(x) = \lim_{h\to 0} \frac{f(x + h) - f(x)}{h} \tag{2.45}$$

which can be rewritten as

$$f(x + h) - f(x) = h\left[f'(x) + \phi(h)\right] \tag{2.46}$$

where $\phi(h)$ is a function of h such that as h approaches zero, $\phi(h)$ approaches zero. If h is small, $h\phi(h)$ will also be small, so we can write

$$f(x + h) - f(x) \approx hf'(x) \tag{2.47}$$

This is an approximate formula relating the *increment* in y, $f(x + h) - f(x)$ to the change h in x. Writing these changes as Δy and Δx to indicate finite increments, we have

$$\Delta y \approx f'(x)\Delta x \tag{2.48}$$

We demonstrate the validity of this geometrically in figure 2.9, where the change in y calculated by the formula and the true change are indicated by Δy_{calc} and Δy_{true}.

For example we frequently require the volume of a thin spherical shell with internal radius r and thickness Δr. The volume of a sphere of radius r is $4/3\pi r^3$, so using equation 2.48 the volume of the thin shell is given by

$$\Delta V \approx \frac{d}{dr}\left(\frac{4}{3}\pi r^3\right)\Delta r \approx 4\pi r^2 \Delta r \tag{2.49}$$

The true volume is

$$\Delta V = \frac{4}{3}\pi(r + \Delta r)^3 - \frac{4}{3}\pi r^3 = 4\pi r^2\Delta r + 4\pi r(\Delta r)^2 + \frac{4}{3}\pi(\Delta r)^3 \tag{2.50}$$

Thus equation 2.48 neglects powers of Δx higher than the first and is therefore only valid for *small* changes in Δx.

This approximate formula for increments should not be confused with an apparently similar formula involving differentials. We have previously taken dy/dx as an entity, although we have taken its reciprocal to obtain the derivative of an inverse function. However, if we let the *differential of x*, dx, assume some arbitrary value, then we can

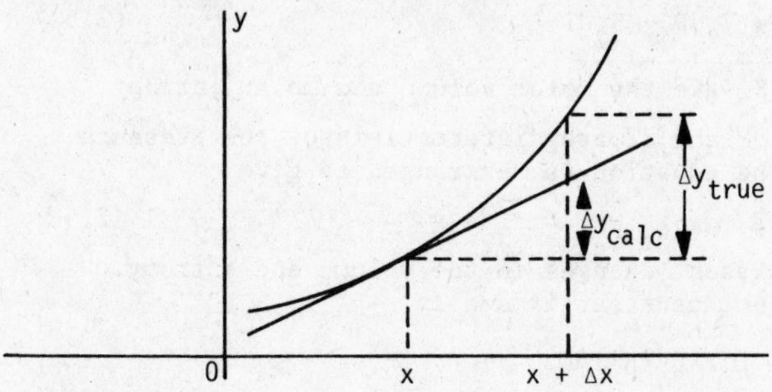

Figure 2.9

define the *differential of y*, dy, in terms of it by the relation

$$dy = f'(x)\ dx \tag{2.51}$$

This is an exact relation defining dy in terms of some number dx. If dx is a large number, then dy will bear no resemblance to the change in f(x) as x changes from x to x + dx.

The differential of the volume dV is given by

$$dV = (4\pi r^2)dr$$

and comparison with equation 2.50 makes it clear that if dr is a large number dV will not in any sense correspond to the volume change resulting from a change dr in the radius.

It is very common to derive by physical or chemical arguments a relation such as equation 2.48 and then say that if Δx and Δy tend to zero, equation 2.48 becomes equation 2.51 and we have an expression for the derivative.

Suppose we have a quantity of gas at pressure P in a cylinder of cross-section A and that we allow the gas to expand by moving the piston through a length Δl. Assuming that the pressure remains essentially constant during the process, the work done by the gas, ΔW, is given by the force (PA) multiplied by the distance moved Δl.

$$\Delta w \approx PA\Delta l$$

But $A\Delta l$ is the change in volume ΔV, so

$$\Delta w \approx P\Delta V$$

We then say that as $\Delta V \to 0$, we can write this as

$$dw = PdV$$

Thus we have expressed our physical problem in terms of a differential expression. We shall consider how we go from dw to the function w in chapter 3.

The student should be most careful to distinguish between differentials and increments, particularly in expressions that contain both. An example from thermodynamics is the Clapeyron-Clausius equation. The derivation proceeds through the relation

$$V_1 dP - S_1 dT = V_2 dP - S_2 dT \tag{2.52}$$

where V_1, V_2, S_1, S_2 are the molar volume and molar entropy in two phases and dP and dT are differentials of the pressure and temperature. The equation is rearranged to give

$$\Delta V\ dP = \Delta S\ dT \tag{2.53}$$

Here ΔV and ΔS represent changes in the volume and entropy. These changes are not necessarily small.

2.8 DIFFERENTIATION OF IMPLICIT FUNCTIONS

If we wish to find the derivative of the implicit function

$$y^2 - 2xy + 1 = 0 \tag{2.54}$$

we could solve for y as a function of x and then differentiate. However, if we have the function

$$x^5 + 4xy^3 - 3y^5 = 2 \tag{2.55}$$

we cannot do this.

One approach is to simply differentiate term by term with respect to x, regarding y as a function of x and using the chain rule when differentiating powers or functions of y; for example

$$\frac{d}{dx}(y^2) - \frac{d}{dx}(2xy) + \frac{d}{dx}(1) = 0$$

gives

$$2y\frac{dy}{dx} - \left[2y + 2x\frac{dy}{dx}\right] = 0$$

that is

$$\frac{dy}{dx} = \frac{y}{y - x} \text{ provided that } y \neq x \tag{2.56}$$

On differentiating equation 2.55 by this method we get

$$5x^4 + \left[4y^3 + 4x \times 3y^2\frac{dy}{dx}\right] - 3 \times 5y^4\frac{dy}{dx} = 0$$

Thus, if $12xy^2 - 15y^4 \neq 0$, then

$$\frac{dy}{dx} = -\frac{(5x^4 + 4y^3)}{12xy^2 - 15y^4} \tag{2.57}$$

2.9 LOGARITHMIC DIFFERENTIATION

The differentiation of a complicated product or quotient can often be made easier by taking logarithms and then differentiating as an implicit function. If

$$y = \frac{(3x^2 + 2x + 4)^{3/2}}{(x^4 + 5x^2 + 2x)^2(x + 1)}$$

then

$$\ln y = \frac{3}{2}\ln(3x^2 + 2x + 4) - 2\ln(x^4 + 5x^2 + 2x) - \ln(x + 1)$$

and

$$\frac{1}{y}\frac{dy}{dx} = \frac{3}{2}\frac{(6x + 2)}{(3x^2 + 2x + 4)} - \frac{2(4x^3 + 10x + 2)}{x^4 + 5x^2 + 2x} - \frac{1}{x + 1}$$

so

$$\frac{dy}{dx} = \frac{(3x^2 + 2x + 4)^{3/2}}{(x^4 + 5x^2 + 2x)^2(x + 1)}\left[\frac{3}{2}\frac{(6x + 2)}{(3x^2 + 2x + 4)} - \frac{2(4x^3 + 10x + 2)}{x^4 + 5x^2 + 2x} - \frac{1}{x + 1}\right] \quad (2.58)$$

In general, if

$$y = [u(x)]^a[v(x)]^b[w(x)]^c \ldots$$

then

$$\ln y = a \ln u(x) + b \ln v(x) + c \ln w(x) + \ldots$$

and

$$\frac{1}{y}\frac{dy}{dx} = \frac{a}{u(x)}\frac{du(x)}{dx} + \frac{b}{v(x)}\frac{dv(x)}{dx} + \frac{c}{w(x)}\frac{dw(x)}{dx} + \ldots \quad (2.59)$$

This method provides an alternative route to the derivative of a^x.

If $y = a^x$

$$\ln y = x \ln a$$

and

$$\frac{1}{y}\frac{dy}{dx} = \ln a$$

so that

$$\frac{d}{dx}(a^x) = a^x \ln a$$

The derivative of x^x can be obtained similarly

If $y = x^x$, then

$$\ln y = x \ln x$$

and

$$\frac{1}{y}\frac{dy}{dx} = 1 + \ln x$$

so that

$$\frac{dy}{dx} = x^x (1 + \ln x)$$

2.10 PROBLEMS FOR SOLUTION

1. Evaluate the limits:

(i) $\lim_{x\to 3} \frac{x^2 - 9}{x + 3}$; (ii) $\lim_{x\to 1} \frac{3}{x + 2}$

2. Do the following limits exist?

(i) $\lim_{x\to 3} \frac{x^2 - 9}{x - 3}$; (ii) $\lim_{x\to 3} \frac{1}{x - 3}$.

3. Find the derivatives of the following functions from first principles:

(i) $x^2 + 1$; (ii) x^3; (iii) $2x^2 - 3x$; (iv) $\frac{1}{x + 1}$.

4. Find the slopes of the following curves at the points indicated.

(i) $y = x^{2/3}$ (8, 4); (ii) $y = \frac{3x^2}{5} - 2x^8$ $\left(1, -\frac{7}{5}\right)$.

5. Differentiate the following functions with respect to x:

(i) $7x^3 + 4x^2$; (ii) $2x^{1/3}$; (iii) $\frac{1}{2} x^{-3/4}$; (iv) $(2x^2 - 1)(x^2 + 4)$;

(v) $(2x - 5)(3x^4 + 5x + 2)$; (vi) $(x - 1)(x + 1)(x^2 + 1)$;

(vii) $2x^{3/2}(\sqrt{x} + 2)(\sqrt{x} - 1)$; (viii) $\frac{2x + 1}{x + 1}$; (ix) $\frac{1}{1 - 3x^2}$;

(x) $\frac{x(x - 1)}{x - 2}$; (xi) $(1 - 5x)^8$; (xii) $\sqrt{\left(\frac{x}{1 - x}\right)}$;

(xiii) $(1 - 2x^2)^{2n}$; (xiv) $\sin 3x + \cos 3x$; (xv) $\sin^3 x + \cos^3 x$;
(xvi) $\sin x^3 + \cos x^3$; (xvii) $\cot (5x + 1)$; (xviii) $\operatorname{cosec} 2x^2$;
(xix) $\exp (5x)$; (xx) $\exp (5 - 2x)$; (xxi) $\ln (x/a)$;
(xxii) $\ln (\cos x)$; (xxiii) $\ln (x^3 + 3)$; (xxiv) $x \ln (\sin x)$;
(xxv) $\exp (\cos x)$; (xxvi) 3^x; (xxvii) $2^{\sec x}$; (xxviii) $\exp (\sqrt{x})$.

6. A particle is moving so that in time t it has travelled a distance s given by

$$s = t^3 - 2t + 1$$

If acceleration is defined as the rate of change of velocity with respect to time, at what time is the acceleration equal to zero?

7. Find the turning points of the following functions:

(i) $y = x^3 - 5x^2 + 3x$; (ii) $y = \frac{x}{1 + x^2}$;

(iii) $y = x^4 - 4x^3 + 4x + 7$.

8. The concentration b of B in the successive first-order reactions

$$A \rightarrow B \rightarrow C$$

is given by

$$b = a_0 \left(\frac{k_1}{k_2 - k_1}\right) \left[\exp(-k_1 t) - \exp(-k_2 t)\right]$$

Show that the concentration of b is a maximum when $t = (k_1/k_2) \ln (k_2/k_1)$.

9. The probability P of finding an electron in the 1s orbital in the hydrogen atom at a distance r from the nucleus is given by

$$P = 4\pi r^2 \left[\frac{1}{\pi a_0^2} \exp(-2r/a_0)\right]$$

where a_0 is a constant. Show that the maximum probability occurs when $r = a_0$.

10. The probability P of a molecule of mass m in a gas at temperature T having a speed c is given by

$$P = \left(\frac{m}{2\pi kT}\right)^{3/2} \exp(-mc^2/2kT)\, c^2$$

where k is the Boltzmann constant. Show that the maximum probability is for $c = \sqrt{(2kT/m)}$

11. Differentiate with respect to x:

(i) $\sin^{-1}(4x)$; (ii) $\tan^{-1}(x/a)$; (iii) $\cos^{-1}\left(\frac{x^2 + 1}{x^2 - 1}\right)$;
(iv) $\cos^{-1}(x/3)$.

12. Sketch the curves:

(i) $y = \frac{x - 3}{(x - 2)^2}$; (ii) $y = \frac{x^2 - 4}{x(x - 1)}$; (iii) $y = \frac{x^2(1 - x)}{(1 + x)}$.

13. Find dy/dx for the following functions:

(i) $3x^2 + 7xy + 9y^2 = 6$; (ii) $(x^2 + y^2)^2 - (x^2 - y^2) = 0$;
(iii) $x^3 + y^3 = 3xy$.

14. Find dy/dx by the method of logarithmic differentiation for the following functions:

(i) $\left[\frac{x(x + 1)(x - 2)}{(x^2 + 1)(2x + 3)}\right]^{1/2}$; (ii) $(\sin x)^{\tan x}$;

(iii) $\frac{x(x^2 + 1)^{1/2}}{(x + 1)^{2/3}}$.

3

Integration

In the previous chapter we discussed the derivative dy/dx of the function y = F(x). We shall often encounter the reverse problem - given a function f(x), which represents the rate of change of some quantity with respect to x, what is the function F(x) such that

$$f(x) = \frac{dF(x)}{dx} \text{ ?} \tag{3.1}$$

The process of working back from the derivative of F(x) to the function F(x) itself is known as *integration* and has many important applications in physical science.

3.1 THE INDEFINITE INTEGRAL

If F(x) and f(x) are two functions such that equation 3.1 holds, then F(x) is said to be the *indefinite integral* of f(x) and is written

$$F(x) = \int f(x)\,dx \tag{3.2}$$

f(x) is known as the *integrand* and $\int$ is the *integral sign* that is used to represent this process. It is assumed that f(x) is defined over some interval a < x < b and that F(x) is differentiable in this interval.

The reason that F(x) is referred to as the indefinite integral is as follows. Suppose that there is some other function G(x), which is also an indefinite integral of f(x); that is

$$\frac{dG(x)}{dx} = f(x) \tag{3.3}$$

Thus

$$\frac{dF(x)}{dx} - \frac{dG(x)}{dx} = 0$$

that is

$$\frac{d}{dx}\left[F(x) - G(x)\right] = 0 \tag{3.4}$$

$[F(x) - G(x)]$ is a function whose derivative is zero and must therefore be a constant. Thus the functions F(x) and G(x) can only differ by a constant

$$F(x) = G(x) + c \tag{3.5}$$

Hence we can add an arbitrary constant c to the integral and it is therefore 'indefinite'.

We can rewrite this using the differential of F(x) because from equation 3.1

$$dF(x) = F(x)\ dx \tag{3.6}$$

$$\int dF(x) = \int f(x)\ dx = F(x) + c \tag{3.7}$$

Thus when we integrate the differential of a function we obtain the function itself plus an arbitrary constant.

3.2 METHODS OF INTEGRATION

Integration is the *inverse* of differentiation. Whereas there are definite rules for the differentiation of any function, there are no such rules for integration. Some integrals are of a *standard form* and can be integrated on inspection, others can be readily converted into standard forms by various techniques but many integrals cannot be integrated analytically at all. For example, the integral $\int \exp(-x^2)dx$, which occurs frequently in statistical thermodynamics, the kinetic theory of gases and statistics cannot be integrated analytically.

One general point is that an integral is unaffected by multiplication by a constant. Thus

$$\int af(x)\ dx = a\int f(x)\ dx \tag{3.8}$$

Another elementary rule is that we can obtain the integral of a sum by integrating each factor separately

$$\int [f(x) + g(x) + h(x)]dx = \int f(x)\ dx + \int g(x)\ dx + \int h(x)\ dx \tag{3.9}$$

3.2.1 Standard Integrals

In many cases a function can be recognised as the derivative of some other function and thus can be integrated easily. Such integrals are known as *standard integrals* and a list of the commoner ones is given below.

(i) $$\int x^n\ dx = \frac{x^{n+1}}{n+1} + c \quad (n \neq -1) \tag{3.10}$$

This is true for nonintegral as well as integral values of n. For example

$$\int x^{1/2}\ dx = 2/3x^{3/2} + c$$

$$\int x^{-1/2}\ dx = 2x^{1/2} + c$$

(ii) $$\int \frac{1}{x}\ dx = \ln x + c \tag{3.11}$$

(iii) Trigonometric functions

$$\int \sin ax\, dx = -\frac{1}{a}\cos ax + c \qquad (3.12)$$

$$\int \cos ax\, dx = \frac{1}{a}\sin ax + c \qquad (3.13)$$

$$\int \sec^2 ax\, dx = \frac{1}{a}\tan ax + c \qquad (3.14)$$

$$\int \sec ax \tan ax\, dx = \frac{1}{a}\sec ax + c \qquad (3.15)$$

$$\int \operatorname{cosec} ax \cot ax\, dx = -\frac{1}{a}\operatorname{cosec} ax + c \qquad (3.16)$$

$$\int \operatorname{cosec}^2 ax\, dx = -\frac{1}{a}\cot ax + c \qquad (3.17)$$

(iv) Exponential functions

$$\int e^{ax} dx = \frac{1}{a} e^{ax} + c \qquad (3.18)$$

$$\int a^x dx = \frac{a^x}{\ln a} + c, \quad a \neq 1 \qquad (3.19)$$

(v) Inverse trigonometric functions

$$\int \frac{dx}{\sqrt{(a^2 - x^2)}} = \sin^{-1}\left(\frac{x}{a}\right) \quad \text{or} \quad -\cos^{-1}\left(\frac{x}{a}\right) \qquad (3.20)$$

$$\int \frac{dx}{a^2 + x^2} = \frac{1}{a}\tan^{-1}\left(\frac{x}{a}\right) + c \qquad (3.21)$$

(vi) Hyperbolic functions

$$\int \sinh ax\, dx = \frac{1}{a}\cosh ax + c \qquad (3.22)$$

$$\int \cosh ax\, dx = \frac{1}{a}\sinh ax + c \qquad (3.23)$$

An extensive collection can be found in Dwight (1961).

3.2.2 Method of Substitution

Integrals can often be reduced to a standard form by a suitable change of variable.

(i) Elementary substitutions

In the integral

$$I = \int \frac{dx}{\sqrt{(ax + b)}}$$

we see that dx is equivalent to 1/a d(ax + b). If we let u = ax + b then dx = (1/a) du and the integral can be rewritten as

$$I = \int \frac{(1/a)du}{u^{1/2}} = \frac{1}{a} \times 2u^{1/2} = \frac{2}{a}(ax + b)^{1/2} + c \qquad (3.24)$$

Thus the *substitution* u = ax + b transforms the original integral into a relatively trivial one. It is important to note that dx must also be transformed into a function of a and du. The above integral is a particular case of the more general integral $\int (ax + b)^n dx$. Applying the same substitution u = ax + b gives

$$\int (ax + b)^n dx = \int \frac{u^n}{a} du = \frac{u^{n+1}}{a(n + 1)} = \frac{(ax + b)^{n+1}}{a(n + 1)} + c \qquad (3.25)$$

An example of another elementary type is

$$\int (x^3 + 6x^2 + 9x + 7)^{10}(x^2 + 4x + 3)dx$$

where we note that

$$x^2 + 4x + 3 = 1/3d(x^3 + 6x^2 + 9x + 7)$$

Making the substitution

$$u = x^3 + 6x^2 + 9x + 7$$

$$du = (3x^2 + 12x + 9)dx$$

yields

$$I = \int u^{10} 1/3du = \frac{u^{11}}{3 \times 11} = \frac{(x^3 + 6x^2 + 9x + 7)^{11}}{3 \times 11} + c \qquad (3.25)$$

These integrals all have the general form

$$I = \int [f(x)]^n af'(x)\, dx \qquad (3.26)$$

and can be integrated by the substitution

$$u = f(x),\ f'(x)\, dx = du$$

If n = -1 the result is a logarithmic function; for example

$$\int \frac{x\, dx}{1 + x^2}$$

Letting $u = 1 + x^2$, x dx = 1/2 du and

$$\int \frac{x\, dx}{1 + x^2} = \int \frac{1/2\, du}{u} = 1/2 \ln u + c$$

An example from second-order kinetics is the integral

$$\int \frac{dx}{(a - x)^2}$$

which can be integrated by making the substitution $u = a - x$ and $dx = -du$. Thus

$$\int \frac{dx}{(a-x)^2} = -\int \frac{du}{u^2} = \frac{1}{u} + c = \frac{1}{a-x} + c$$

Another integral that can be solved by an elementary substitution is $\int (2J + 1) \exp [-BJ(J + 1)/kT] dJ$, which occurs in statistical thermodynamics. Here $(2J + 1)dJ$ is the differential of $J(J + 1)$, so the substitution $u = J(J + 1)$ gives

$$\int \exp(-Bu/kT)\,du = -\frac{kT}{B} \exp(-Bu/kT)$$

With a little practice these integrals can usually be done on inspection without resorting to a formal substitution.

(ii) Trigonometric substitution

Often the substitution of a trigonometric function reduces the integral to a standard form, for example $\int dx/\sqrt{(a^2 - x^2)}$. This is, of course, a standard integral, but it can be integrated from first principles as follows. Letting $x = a \sin u$, $dx = a \cos u\,du$, which gives

$$\int \frac{dx}{\sqrt{(a^2 - x^2)}} = \int \frac{a \cos u\, du}{a \cos u} = \int du = u = \sin^{-1}\left(\frac{x}{a}\right) + c \tag{3.27}$$

This substitution is of considerable value for integrals containing $\sqrt{(a^2 - x^2)}$. In the calculation of the area of a semicircle in section 3.6.1 we shall require the integral $\int\sqrt{(a^2 - x^2)}\,dx$, which can be integrated as follows

$$\int\sqrt{(a^2 - x^2)}dx = \int\sqrt{(a^2 - a^2 \sin^2 u)}a \cos u\, du$$

$$= \int a^2 \cos^2 u\, du \tag{3.28}$$

This can be integrated by using the trigonometric relationship $\cos^2 u = 1/2(1 + \cos 2u)$ (this will be discussed in more detail in the next section)

$$I = \int 1/2a^2 (1 + \cos 2u)du = \frac{a^2}{4} \sin 2u + \frac{a^2 u}{2}$$

$$= \frac{x}{2}\sqrt{(a^2 - x^2)} + \frac{a^2}{2} \sin^{-1}\left(\frac{x}{a}\right) + c \tag{3.29}$$

If the integrand involves $\sqrt{(1 + x^2)}$, the substitution $x = \tan u$ may be useful; for example

$$\int \frac{dx}{x^2\sqrt{(1 + x^2)}}$$

If $x = \tan u$, $dx = \sec^2 u\, du$ and

$$I = \int \frac{\sec^2 u \, du}{\tan^2 u \sec u} = \int \frac{\cos^3 u \, du}{\cos^2 u \sin^2 u} = \int \frac{\cos u \, du}{\sin^2 u}$$

$$= \int \frac{d(\sin u)}{\sin^2 u} = - \frac{1}{\sin u} = - \frac{\sqrt{(1 + x^2)}}{x} + c \qquad (3.30)$$

The integral

$$\int \frac{dx}{(a^2 + x^2)^{3/2}}$$

arises in the calculation of the magnetic induction at the centre of a short solenoid. The substitution $z = a \tan u$ reduces the integral to $1/a^2 \int \cos u \, du$.

Unfortunately there are no general rules for making substitutions and one has to rely on experience and trial and error.

A different type of substitution is useful for integrals involving sines or cosines such as

$$\int \operatorname{cosec} x \, dx = \int \frac{dx}{\sin x} \quad \text{or} \quad \int \frac{dx}{a + b \sin x}$$

From equation 1.27

$$\sin 2x = 2 \sin x \cos x; \ \cos 2x = \cos^2 x - \sin^2 x$$

we easily obtain a formula for tan 2x

$$\tan 2x = \frac{2 \tan x}{1 - \tan^2 x} \qquad (3.31)$$

The relation $\sec^2 A = \tan^2 A + 1$ gives us the following expression for cos 2x

$$\cos 2x = \frac{1 - \tan^2 x}{1 + \tan^2 x} \qquad (3.32)$$

and hence

$$\sin 2x = \frac{2 \tan x}{1 + \tan^2 x} \qquad (3.33)$$

If we let $t = \tan x/2$, then we can write expressions for cos x, sin x and dx in terms of t

$$\cos x = \frac{1 - t^2}{1 + t^2}; \ \sin x = \frac{2t}{1 + t^2}; \ dx = \frac{2 \, dt}{1 + t^2} \qquad (3.34)$$

which are useful for integration by substitution; for example

$$\int \operatorname{cosec} x \, dx = \int \frac{dx}{\sin x} = \int \frac{2dt/(1 + t^2)}{2t/(1 + t^2)} = \int \frac{2dt}{2t}$$

$$= \ln t = \ln \tan \left(\frac{x}{2}\right) + c \qquad (3.35)$$

$$\int \frac{dx}{a + b \sin x} = \int \frac{\dfrac{2\,dt}{1 + t^2}}{a + [b2t/(1 + t^2)]} = \int \frac{2\,dt}{a + 2bt + at^2} \tag{3.36}$$

which can be integrated by methods to be discussed in section 3.2.5.

(iii) Algebraic substitution

Integrals involving square roots may sometimes be simplified by the substitution $u = \sqrt{(\ \ )}$. For example in $\int x\sqrt{(4x + 1)}\,dx$, let $u = \sqrt{(4x + 1)}$; that is $x = 1/4(u^2 - 1)$ and $dx = 1/2\,u\,du$. Making the substitution gives

$$I = \int \frac{1}{4}(u^2 - 1)u \times \frac{1}{2} u\,du = \frac{1}{8}\int (u^4 - u^2)\,du$$

$$= \frac{1}{8 \times 5} u^5 - \frac{1}{8 \times 3} u^3 = \frac{1}{40}(4x + 1)^{5/2} - \frac{1}{24}(4x + 1)^{3/2} + c \tag{3.37}$$

In the integral $\int x^3\sqrt{(1 - x^2)}\,dx$, we let $u = \sqrt{(1 - x^2)}$; that is $x = \sqrt{(1 - u^2)}$;

$$dx = -\frac{u\,du}{\sqrt{(1 - u^2)}}$$

$$I = \int \frac{(1 - u^2)^{3/2} u(-u)\,du}{\sqrt{(1 - u^2)}} = -\int (1 - u^2)u^2\,du$$

$$= -\frac{u^3}{3} + \frac{u^5}{5} = \frac{(1 - x^2)^{5/2}}{5} - \frac{(1 - x^2)^{3/2}}{3} + c \tag{3.38}$$

$\int dx/(\sqrt{x} + 2)$ can be integrated by making the substitution

$u = \sqrt{x}$, so $x = u^2$ and $dx = 2\,u\,du$

$$I = \int \frac{2u\,du}{u + 2} = \int \left[\frac{2(u + 2) - 4}{u + 2}\right] du$$

$$= \int 2\,du - 4\int \frac{du}{u + 2} = 2u - 4\ln(u + 2) \tag{3.39}$$

$$= 2\sqrt{x} - 4\ln(\sqrt{x} + 2) + c$$

3.2.3 Transformation of trigonometric integrands

Some of the trigonometric formulae given in section 1.1.3 may be useful in the simplification of trigonometric integrands. A few examples will illustrate this

$$\int \tan x\,dx = \int \frac{\sin x}{\cos x}\,dx = \int \frac{-d(\cos x)}{\cos x} = -\ln(\cos x)$$

$$= \ln(\sec x) + c \tag{3.40}$$

The integral $\int \sin^2 x\, dx$, which occurs in the normalisation of wavefunctions for a particle in a box, for example, can be integrated thus

$$\int \sin^2 x\, dx = \int \frac{1}{2}(1 - \cos 2x)\, dx = \frac{x}{2} - \frac{\sin 2x}{2} + c \quad (3.41)$$

Also

$$\int \cos^3 x\, dx = \int \frac{1}{4}(\cos 3x + 3\cos x)\, dx = \frac{1}{12}\sin 3x + \frac{3}{4}\sin x + c \quad (3.42)$$

If the integrand is a product of two sines, two cosines or a sine and a cosine, we can use equations 1.28; for example

$$\int \sin 6x \cos 2x\, dx = \int \frac{1}{2}(\sin 8x + \sin 4x)\, dx$$

$$= -\frac{1}{16}\cos 8x - \frac{1}{8}\cos 4x + c \quad (3.43)$$

Integrals of this type are useful in Fourier analysis (see chapter 8).

Other cases are less obvious and may require a little experimentation. For example

$$\int \frac{\sin^5 x}{\cos^4 x}\, dx = \int \frac{(1 - \cos^2 x)^2}{\cos^4 x}\sin x\, dx$$

$$= -\int \frac{(1 - \cos^2 x)^2}{\cos^4 x}\, d(\cos x)$$

$$= -\int \frac{d(\cos x)}{\cos^4 x} + \int \frac{2\, d(\cos x)}{\cos^2 x} - \int d(\cos x)$$

$$= \frac{1}{3\cos^3 x} - \frac{2}{\cos x} - \cos x + c \quad (3.44)$$

$$\int \frac{dx}{\sin^2 x \cos^2 x} = \int \frac{4\, dx}{(\sin 2x)^2} = \int 4(\operatorname{cosec} 2x)^2\, dx$$

$$= -2\cot 2x + c \quad (3.45)$$

3.2.4 Integration by Parts

One of the most useful and powerful integration techniques is *integration by parts*. The derivative of the product u(x)v(x) was given in section 2.4.3 as

$$\frac{d}{dx}\left[u(x)v(x)\right] = u(x)\frac{dv(x)}{dx} + v(x)\frac{du(x)}{dx} \quad (3.46)$$

Let us now integrate this expression to give

$$\int \frac{d\left[u(x)v(x)\right]}{dx}\, dx = \int u(x)\frac{dv(x)\, dx}{dx} + \int v(x)\frac{du(x)\, dx}{dx}$$

which, on rearrangement, gives the integration by parts formula

$$\int u(x)\,dv(x) = u(x)v(x) - \int v(x)\,du(x) \tag{3.47}$$

This is frequently useful for transforming an integral $\int u(x)\,dv(x)$ that we cannot integrate into $\int v(x)\,du(x)$, which may be integrable.

Consider the integral $\int x \cos x\,dx$. Letting $u = x$, $dv = \cos x\,dx$ gives $du = dx$ and $v = \sin x$. Putting this into equation 3.47 gives

$$\int x \cos x\,dx = x \sin x - \int \sin x\,dx = x \sin x + \cos x + c \tag{3.48}$$

One has to be careful to make the correct choice for u and dv, since otherwise no simplification results. If we had taken $u = \cos x$ and $dv = x\,dx$ the result would have been

$$I = \frac{x^2}{2} \cos x + \int \frac{x^2}{2} \sin x\,dx$$

It may be necessary to experiment with the various possibilities befoie reaching a solution.

The integral $\int r \exp(-kr)dr$, which occurs in Debye-Hückel theory, can be integrated by parts to give $-(1/k)r \exp(-kr) - (1/k^2) \exp(-kr)$. The logarithmic and inverse trigonometric functions can be integrated by parts as follows. For $\int \ln x\,dx$ let $u = \ln x$, $dv = dx$ so that $du = (1/x)dx$ and $v = x$.

$$\int \ln x\,dx = x \ln x - \int \frac{x}{x}\,dx = x \ln x - x + c \tag{3.49}$$

In the case of $\int \cos^{-1} x\,dx$, let $u = \cos^{-1} x$ and $v = x$. Therefore

$$du = -\frac{dx}{\sqrt{(1 - x^2)}} \qquad dv = dx$$

to give

$$\int \cos^{-1} x\,dx = x \cos^{-1} x + \int \frac{x\,dx}{\sqrt{(1 - x^2)}}$$

$$= x \cos^{-1} x - (1 - x^2)^{1/2} + c \tag{3.50}$$

Repeated application of the method may be required to yield the final result. For example

$$\int x^2 \sin x\,dx = x^2 (-\cos x) - \int (-\cos x) 2x\,dx$$

But from equation 3.48

$$\int x \cos x\,dx = x \sin x + \cos x$$

so

$$\int x^2 \sin x\,dx = -x^2 \cos x + 2x \sin x + 2 \cos x + c \tag{3.51}$$

$\int x^3 \sin x \, dx$ would require a threefold integration by parts. Sometimes a second integration may yield the original integral but rearrangement of the resulting expression will give the required result. For example

$$\int e^x \cos x \, dx = e^x \sin x - \int \sin x \, e^x \, dx$$

But

$$\int e^x \sin x \, dx = -e^x \cos x + \int \cos x \, e^x \, dx$$

giving

$$\int e^x \cos x \, dx = \frac{1}{2}(e^x \sin x + e^x \cos x) + c \tag{3.52}$$

Reduction formulae

The repeated use of integration by parts can be formalised by the introduction of a *reduction formula*. Consider the integral $I_n = \int x^n e^x \, dx$. Integrating by parts once gives the result

$$I_n = x^n e^x - n \int x^{n-1} e^x \, dx$$

that is

$$I_n = x^n e^x - nI_{n-1} \tag{3.53}$$

This is known as a *reduction formula* because it expresses $\int x^n e^x \, dx$ in terms of $\int x^{n-1} e^x \, dx$. So if we have to integrate, say, $\int x^6 e^x \, dx$, we can write down $I_6 = \int e^x x^6 \, dx = e^x x^6 - 6I_5$.

Using the reduction formula we can write

$$I_5 = x^5 e^x - 5I_4$$

$$I_4 = x^4 e^x - 4I_3$$

$$I_3 = x^3 e^x - 3I_2$$

$$I_2 = x^2 e^x - 2I_1$$

$$I_1 = xe^x - 1I_0$$

where $I_0 = \int e^x \, dx$. This method is useful for integrals of the type $\int \exp(-kr) r^n \, dr$, which occur in quantum mechanics.

A slightly different case is the integral $\int \sin^n x \, dx$. Letting $u = \sin^{n-1} x$ and $dv = \sin x \, dx$, $du = (n - 1)\sin^{n-2} x \cos x \, dx$ and $v = -\cos x$

$$I_n = \int \sin^n x\, dx = -\cos x \sin^{n-1} x + (n-1)\int \sin^{n-2} x \cos^2 x\, dx$$

$$= -\cos x \sin^{n-1} x + (n-1)\int \sin^{n-2} x(1 - \sin^2 x)dx$$

Rearranging gives

$$I_n = -\frac{1}{n}\sin^{n-1} x \cos x + \frac{(n-1)}{n} I_{n-2} \qquad (3.54)$$

In this case the reduction formula reduces the order of the integral by two.

3.2.5 Integration of algebraic fractions

(i) Rational fractions

Before attempting to integrate a rational algebraic fraction it is essential to express the fraction in such a way that the numerator is of lower degree than the denominator. For example

$$\int \left(\frac{3x+1}{2x-3}\right) dx = \int \left[\frac{3/2\ (2x-3) + 11/2}{2x-3}\right] dx$$

$$= \frac{3}{2}\int dx + \frac{11}{2}\int \frac{dx}{2x-3}$$

$$\int \left(\frac{x^2+2x+3}{x^2-x-2}\right) dx = \int \left[\frac{(x^2-x-2) + (3x+5)}{x^2-x-2}\right] dx$$

$$= \int dx + \int \left(\frac{3x+5}{x^2-x-2}\right) dx$$

$$\int \left(\frac{x^3+x^2-x+2}{x^2-2x+4}\right) dx = \int \left[\frac{x(x^2-2x+4) + (3x^2-5x+2)}{x^2-2x+4}\right] dx$$

$$= \int x\, dx + \int \left[\frac{3(x^2-2x+4) + (x-10)}{x^2-2x+4}\right] dx$$

$$= \int x\, dx + \int 3\, dx + \int \frac{(x-10)\, dx}{x^2-2x+4}$$

(ii) Rational fractions with linear denominator

If the denominator is linear, the fraction can be readily integrated to give a logarithmic function

$$\int \frac{(3x+1)}{2x-3} dx = \frac{3}{2}\int dx + \frac{11}{2}\int \frac{dx}{2x-3}$$

$$= \frac{3}{2}x + \frac{11}{4}\ln(2x-3) + c \qquad (3.55)$$

$$\int \frac{x^2}{x+1} dx = \int (x-1)dx + \int \frac{dx}{x+1}$$

$$= \frac{x^2}{2} - x + \ln(x+1) + c \qquad (3.56)$$

(iii) Rational fractions with quadratic denominator

The method used for the integration of a fraction with a quadratic denominator depends on whether the denominator can be factorised into two different factors, into a perfect square or not at all.

A. Two different factors in the denominator. Consider the integral

$$\int \frac{(-3x - 7)}{2x^2 + x - 3} dx = \int \frac{(-3x - 7)\,dx}{(2x + 3)(x - 1)}$$

The technique used for this case is to rewrite the fraction as a sum of *partial fractions*. We require numbers A and B such that

$$\frac{-3x - 7}{(2x + 3)(x - 1)} = \frac{A}{2x + 3} + \frac{B}{x - 1}$$

Adding the fractions on the right-hand side, we get

$$\frac{-3x - 7}{(2x + 3)(x - 1)} = \frac{A(x - 1) + B(2x + 3)}{(2x + 3)(x - 1)}$$

that is, we require

$$A(x - 1) + B(2x + 3) \equiv -3x - 7 \qquad (3.58)$$

This is an *identity* and is valid for all values of x. By a judicious choice of values of x we can easily evaluate A and B. If we let $x = 1$, we get

$$A \times 0 + B \times 5 = -10$$

that is, $B = -2$, and taking $x = -3/2$ gives

$$A(-5/2) + B \times 0 = -5/2$$

that is $A = 1$.

Thus we can rewrite the integral in terms of the partial fractions

$$\int \frac{(-3x - 7)dx}{(2x + 3)(x - 1)} = \int \frac{dx}{2x + 3} - 2\int \frac{dx}{x - 1}$$
$$= 1/2 \ln(2x + 3) - 2 \ln(x - 1) + c \qquad (3.59)$$

This type of integral occurs in the treatment of a second-order reaction in which the rate of reaction is given by

$$\frac{dx}{dt} = k(a - x)(b - x) \qquad (3.60)$$

where k is a constant and a and b are the concentrations of the reactants at time $t = 0$. Rearranging and integrating gives

$$\int k\,dt = \int \frac{dx}{(a - x)(b - x)} \qquad (3.61)$$

Expressing the fraction in terms of partial fractions

$$\frac{1}{(a - x)(b - x)} = \frac{A}{(a - x)} + \frac{B}{(b - x)} = \frac{A(b - x) + B(a - x)}{(a - x)(b - x)}$$

and equating the numerators gives

$$A = -\frac{1}{a - b} \text{ and } B = \frac{1}{a - b}$$

Therefore

$$\int \frac{dx}{(a - x)(b - x)} = \frac{1}{a - b}\left(-\int \frac{dx}{a - x} + \int \frac{dx}{b - x}\right)$$

$$= \frac{1}{a - b}\left[\ln(a - x) - \ln(b - x)\right] + c \qquad (3.62)$$

B. Denominator is a perfect square

We have already discussed an integral of this type in section 3.2.2, when we considered the integral

$$kt = \int \frac{dx}{(a - x)^2} \qquad (3.63)$$

which arises in second-order kinetics. In this case the integration is trivial and yields

$$kt = \frac{1}{a - x} + c \qquad (3.64)$$

However, if the numerator is a linear function rather than a constant as in the last example, the fraction has to be split into partial fractions in a slightly different way. In the case of $\int[(1 + x)/(1 - x)^2]dx$, let us write the fraction as

$$\frac{1 + x}{(1 - x)^2} = \frac{A}{1 - x} + \frac{B}{(1 - x)^2}$$

that is

$$1 + x = A(1 - x) + B$$

We readily see that $A = -1$ and $B = 2$ so

$$\int \frac{(1 + x)dx}{(1 - x)^2} = -\int \frac{dx}{1 - x} + 2\int \frac{dx}{(1 - x)^2}$$

$$= \ln(1 - x) + \frac{2}{1 - x} + c \qquad (3.65)$$

C. Denominator cannot be factorised

We shall first of all discuss integrals of the type $\int dx/(ax^2 + bx + c)$ and then show how integrals of the form $\int[(Ax + B)\,dx/(ax^2 + bx + c)]$ can be reduced to this form. If in $\int[dx/(ax^2 + bx + c)]$, $b = 0$, and a and c are both positive, then the integral is a standard form, which gives an inverse tangent function. For example

$$\int \frac{dx}{2x^2 + 3} = \frac{1}{2}\int \frac{dx}{x^2 + 3/2} = \frac{1}{2}\sqrt{\left(\frac{2}{3}\right)}\tan^{-1}\left(\frac{x\sqrt{2}}{\sqrt{3}}\right) + c \qquad (3.66)$$

If b is nonzero, then $ax^2 + bx + c$ can be reduced to the sum or difference of two squares by *completing the square* as follows

$$a\left(x^2 + \frac{b}{a}x + \frac{c}{a}\right) = a\left[\left(x + \frac{b}{2a}\right)^2 + \frac{c}{a} - \frac{b^2}{4a^2}\right] \qquad (3.67)$$

If the result is the sum of two squares, the integral is an inverse tangent whereas the difference between two squares can be treated by partial fractions. For example

$$\int \frac{dx}{x^2 + 4x + 6} = \int \frac{dx}{(x + 2)^2 + 2} = \frac{1}{\sqrt{2}} \tan^{-1}\left(\frac{x + 2}{\sqrt{2}}\right) \qquad (3.68)$$

$$\int \frac{dx}{x^2 + 6x - 4} = \int \frac{dx}{(x + 3)^2 - 13} = \int \frac{dx}{(x + 3 + \sqrt{13})(x + 3 - \sqrt{13})}$$

$$= \frac{1}{2\sqrt{13}}\left[\int \frac{dx}{x + 3 - \sqrt{13}} - \int \frac{dx}{x + 3 + \sqrt{13}}\right]$$

$$= \frac{1}{2\sqrt{13}} \ln\left(\frac{x + 3 - \sqrt{13}}{x + 3 + \sqrt{13}}\right) \qquad (3.69)$$

Integration of the rate equation for opposing first-order and second-order reactions gives the integral $\int [dx/(k_1(a - x) - k_2x^2)]$, which is of this type.

If the numerator is linear, the integral can be reduced to the above type by expressing the numerator as a multiple of the derivative of the denominator plus a constant. For example

$$\int \frac{(4x + 5)dx}{3x^2 + x + 3} = \int \frac{2/3\ d(3x^2 + x + 3)}{3x^2 + x + 3} + \int \frac{13/3\ dx}{3x^2 + x + 3}$$

$$= \frac{2}{3} \ln (3x^2 + x + 3) + \frac{13}{9} \int \frac{dx}{x^2 + (x/3) + 1}$$

$$= \frac{2}{3} \ln (3x^2 + x + 3) + \frac{13}{9} \int \frac{dx}{(x + 1/6)^2 + 35/36}$$

$$= \frac{2}{3} \ln (3x^2 + x + 3) + \frac{26}{3\sqrt{35}} \tan^{-1}\left(\frac{6x + 1}{\sqrt{35}}\right) \qquad (3.70)$$

(iv) Rational fractions with cubic denominator

If the denominator is factorisable at all, the integral can be split up into integrals of the type discussed in sections (ii) and (iii) above. For example

$$\int \frac{(x^2 - 3)\ dx}{(x - 1)(x - 2)(x - 3)} = A \int \frac{dx}{x - 1} + B \int \frac{dx}{x - 2} + C \int \frac{dx}{x - 3}$$

where A, B and C are obtained from the identity

$$(x^2 - 3) = A(x - 2)(x - 3) + B(x - 1)(x - 3) + C(x - 1)(x - 2)$$

by taking x = 1, 2 and 3 in turn. The result is

$$\int \frac{(x^2 - 3)\,dx}{(x - 1)(x - 2)(x - 3)} = -\int \frac{dx}{x - 1} + 3\int \frac{dx}{x - 3} - \int \frac{dx}{x - 2}$$

$$= -\ln(x - 1) - \ln(x - 2) + 3\ln(x - 3) \qquad (3.71)$$

This method can be applied to the rate equation for third-order kinetics (Problem 11.8).

If factorisation gives repeated factors, the procedure is analogous to the quadratic case. For example

$$\int \frac{x\,dx}{(x + 1)^2(x - 1)} = A\int \frac{dx}{(x + 1)^2} + B\int \frac{dx}{x + 1} + C\int \frac{dx}{x - 1}$$

where A, B and C are such that

$$A(x - 1) + B(x + 1)(x - 1) + C(x + 1)^2 = x$$

that is

$$\int \frac{x\,dx}{(x + 1)^2(x - 1)} = \frac{1}{2}\int \frac{dx}{(x + 1)^2} - \frac{1}{4}\int \frac{dx}{(x + 1)} + \frac{1}{4}\int \frac{dx}{x - 1}$$

$$= -\frac{1}{2} \times \frac{1}{(x + 1)} + \frac{1}{4}\ln\frac{x - 1}{x + 1} + c \qquad (3.72)$$

The integral $\int[x\,dx/(1 + cx)^3]$, which occurs in the theory of activity coefficients, may be integrated by expressing $[x/(1 + cx)^3]$ as

$$\frac{x}{(1 + cx)^3} = \frac{1}{c} \times \frac{1}{(1 + cx)^2} - \frac{1}{c} \times \frac{1}{(1 + cx)^3}$$

and integrating to give

$$\int \frac{x\,dx}{(1 + cx)^3} = \frac{1}{c^2}\left[\frac{-1}{(1 + cx)} + \frac{1}{2(1 + cx)^2}\right]$$

A nonfactorisable quadratic term in the denominator is treated by the methods of section (iii)C above.

(v) Irrational fractions

Integrals of the type

$$\int \frac{dx}{\sqrt{(a^2 - x^2)}}, \quad \int \frac{dx}{\sqrt{(x^2 - a^2)}} \quad \text{and} \quad \int \frac{dx}{\sqrt{(a^2 + x^2)}}$$

are standard forms, which give inverse trigonometric or inverse hyperbolic functions.

If we have $\int[dx/\sqrt{(ax^2 + bx + c)}]$, this can be transformed into one of the above standard forms by completing the square; for example

$$\int \frac{dx}{\sqrt{(4 - 2x - x^2)}} = \int \frac{dx}{\sqrt{[5 - (x + 1)^2]}} = \sin^{-1}\left(\frac{x + 1}{\sqrt{5}}\right) + c \qquad (3.73)$$

An example is the integral

$$\int \frac{du}{\sqrt{[(2mE/l^2) - (2mV/l^2) - u^2]}}$$

from the theory of the motion of a particle of mass m with angular momentum l and energy E subject to a potential V(r), where $u = 1/r$. For an inverse-square law of force, V is proportional to u and the integral is of the form $\int[dx/\sqrt{(ax^2 + bx + c)}]$.

If the numerator is a linear function, we can use the approach of page 58 and write it in terms of the derivative of the function under the square-root sign; for example

$$\int \frac{(2x + 3)\,dx}{\sqrt{(1 - x - x^2)}} = -\int \frac{d(1 - x - x^2)}{\sqrt{(1 - x - x^2)}} + 2\int \frac{dx}{\sqrt{(1 - x - x^2)}}$$

$$= -2\sqrt{(1 - x - x^2)} + 2\int \frac{dx}{\sqrt{[5/4 - (x + 1/2)^2]}}$$

$$= -2\sqrt{(1 - x - x^2)} + 2\sin^{-1}\left(\frac{2x + 1}{\sqrt{5}}\right) + c \qquad (3.74)$$

We have already seen that substitution may be useful for irrational functions. Another substitution that is sometimes useful is $x = 1/u$, $dx = -du/u^2$. For example

$$\int \frac{dx}{x\sqrt{(x^2 - x - 1)}} = -\int \frac{du}{\sqrt{(1 - u - u^2)}} = \cos^{-1}\left(\frac{2u + 1}{\sqrt{5}}\right)$$

$$= \cos^{-1}\left(\frac{2 + x}{x\sqrt{5}}\right) + c \qquad (3.75)$$

3.3 THE PARTICULAR INTEGRAL

The indefinite integral includes an arbitrary constant. However, in any particular chemical or physical problem we shall wish to assign a value to this constant so that we may make calculations. In order to do this we need an additional piece of information from the problem itself. For example in the second-order kinetic equation 3.61

$$\frac{dx}{dt} = k(a - x)(b - x)$$

integration yielded equation 3.62

$$kt = \frac{1}{a - b}\ln\left(\frac{a - x}{b - x}\right) + c$$

a and b are the concentrations of the reactants A and B at time 0, that is when t = 0, x = 0, so

$$0 = \frac{1}{a - b} \ln \frac{a}{b} + c$$

that is

$$c = -\frac{1}{a - b} \ln \frac{a}{b} = \frac{1}{a - b} \ln \frac{b}{a} \qquad (3.76)$$

When c is given a particular value, the result is known as a *particular integral*.

3.4 THE DEFINITE INTEGRAL

This is a very important entity, which is defined as follows. If there is some function F(x) which is differentiable in the interval $a \leqslant x \leqslant b$ and has the derivative f(x), then the *definite integral* of f(x) with respect to x over the interval is given by F(b) - F(a) and is written

$$F(b) - F(a) = \int_a^b f(x)dx \qquad (3.77)$$

where a and b are the *limits* of integration, b usually being larger than a.

Suppose we require the definite integral $\int_1^2 (x^2 + 3x - 5)\, dx$. We know that

$$\int (x^2 + 3x - 5)\, dx = \frac{x^3}{3} + \frac{3x^2}{2} - 5x + c$$

that is

$$F(x) = \frac{x^3}{3} + \frac{3x^2}{2} - 5x + c$$

If x = 2, F(2) = -4/3 + c and for x = 1, F(x) = - 19/6 + c so

$$\int_1^2 (x^2 + 3x - 5)\, dx = \left(-\frac{4}{3} + c\right) - \left(-\frac{19}{6} + c\right) = \frac{11}{6} \qquad (3.78)$$

When writing down the definite integral of a function, we can omit the integration constant. A vertical line with the limits of integration indicates that we have to take the difference between the values of the functions at the limits; for example

$$\int_0^{\pi/6} \cos 3x\, dx = \frac{1}{3} \sin 3x \Big|_0^{\pi/6} = \frac{1}{3} \sin \frac{\pi}{2} - \frac{1}{3} \sin 0 = \frac{1}{3} \qquad (3.79)$$

3.4.1 Properties of Definite Integrals

Definite integrals have several important properties which are often useful in their evaluation.

(i) Interchanging the limits of integration merely changes the sign of the integral

$$\int_a^b f(x)dx = F(b) - F(a) = -\left[F(a) - F(b)\right]$$

$$= -\int_b^a f(x)\,dx \qquad (3.80)$$

(ii) The range of integration can be subdivided as follows

$$\int_a^b f(x)\,dx = \int_a^c f(x)\,dx + \int_c^b f(x)\,dx \qquad (3.81)$$

c may lie between a and b but not necessarily. This relation can be easily verified by putting in the appropriate values of F(x).

(iii) When we integrate by the method of substitution, we have to be most careful with the limits of integration. For example

$$\int_0^1 \frac{dx}{\sqrt{(1 - x^2)}}$$

can be integrated by using the substitution $x = \sin\theta$. However we have to change the limits from the values of x(0, 1) to the corresponding values of $\theta(0, \pi/2)$

$$\int_0^1 \frac{dx}{\sqrt{(1 - x^2)}} = \int_0^{\pi/2} d\theta = \theta\Big|_0^{\pi/2} = \frac{\pi}{2}$$

In general

$$\int_{x=a}^{x=b} f(x)\,dx = \int_{u=p}^{u=q} g(u)\,du \qquad (3.83)$$

where, if $u = \phi(x)$, $p = \phi(a)$ and $q = \phi(b)$.

(iv) In section 1.1.2 (ix), we defined even and odd functions as follows

$$\begin{array}{ll} \text{even function} & f(-x) = f(x) \\ \text{odd function} & f(-x) = -f(x) \end{array} \qquad (3.84)$$

For a symmetrical range of integration, the definite integrals of such functions simplify as follows

$$\text{even function} \quad \int_{-a}^{a} f(x)\,dx = 2\int_0^a f(x)\,dx$$

$$\text{odd function} \quad \int_{-a}^{a} f(x)\,dx = 0 \qquad (3.85)$$

Thus

$$\int_{-\pi}^{\pi} \cos x\,dx = 2\int_0^{\pi} \cos x\,dx$$

whereas $\int_{-\pi}^{\pi} \sin x\,dx = 0$. This is useful sometimes when considering the orthogonality of wavefunctions, for example in the particle in a box problem, where the wavefunction for a box of length ℓ is

$$\psi_n = \sqrt{\left(\frac{2}{\ell}\right)} \left(\frac{n\pi x}{\ell}\right)$$

where n is an integer. We can see by inspection that if n is odd and m even (or vice versa) that

$$\int_{-\ell/2}^{\ell/2} \psi_n \psi_m \, dx = 0$$

3.4.2 Improper integrals

So far we have restricted ourselves to finite limits and to functions that are finite throughout the range of integration. We are often interested in definite integrals for which one or both of the limits become infinite; for example in quantum mechanics integrals of the type $\int_0^\infty e^{-2kr} r^n dr$ often occur, as in the normalisation of the hydrogen radial wavefunction. We should also consider what happens when the integral becomes infinite in the range of integration. The term *improper integral* applies to both of these cases.

(i) Infinite range of integration

Suppose that the integral $\int_a^b f(x)\, dx$ exists when a and b are finite. The improper integral $\int_a^\infty f(x)\, dx$ is then given by the limit

$$\int_a^\infty f(x)\, dx = \lim_{b\to\infty} \int_a^b f(x)\, dx \qquad (3.86)$$

If the limit exists and is finite, the integral *converges* but if the limit tends to infinity or does not exist, the integral *diverges*. An example of a convergent integral is

$$\int_a^\infty \exp(-kx)\, dx = \lim_{b\to\infty} \int_a^b \exp(-kx)\, dx = \lim_{b\to\infty} \left[-\frac{1}{k} \exp(-kx) \Big|_a^b \right]$$

$$= \lim_{b\to\infty} \left[-\frac{1}{k} (\exp(-kb) - \exp(-ka)) \right] = \frac{1}{k} \exp(-ka)$$

The related integral

$$\int_a^\infty \exp(kx)\, dx = \lim_{b\to\infty} \int_a^b \exp(kx)\, dx = \lim_{b\to\infty} \left[\frac{1}{k} (\exp(kb) - \exp(ka)) \right] \qquad (3.88)$$

is divergent. An example for which the limit does not exist is

$$\int_a^\infty \cos x\, dx = \lim_{b\to\infty} \int_a^b \cos x\, dx$$

$$= \lim_{b\to\infty} (\sin b - \sin a) \qquad (3.89)$$

As $b\to\infty$, the integral oscillates between $-1 - \sin a$ and

1 - sin a and is said to diverge by oscillation

(ii) Integrand infinite in range of integration

Suppose that for $\int_a^b f(x)\,dx$, $f(x)\to\infty$ as $x\to a$. In such a case we again have to take a limit

$$\int_a^b f(x)\,dx = \lim_{\varepsilon\to 0} \int_{a+\varepsilon}^b f(x)\,dx \tag{3.90}$$

where ε is a small positive number. For example

$$\int_0^1 \frac{1}{x}\,dx = \lim_{\varepsilon\to 0} \int_\varepsilon^1 \frac{1}{x}\,dx = \lim_{\varepsilon\to 0} (\ln 1 - \ln \varepsilon) \tag{3.91}$$

As $\varepsilon\to 0$, $\ln \varepsilon$ tends to $-\infty$ so this integral diverges. On the other hand

$$\int_0^1 \frac{dx}{x^{1/2}} = \lim_{\varepsilon\to 0} \int_\varepsilon^1 \frac{dx}{x^{1/2}} = \lim_{\varepsilon\to 0} (2x^{1/2}|_\varepsilon^1) = 2 \tag{3.92}$$

and this integral converges. If the discontinuity occurs at some intermediate value of $x = c$, then the range of integration has to be split up as in equation 3.81 and the convergence of each part considered. Thus

$$\int_a^b f(x)\,dx = \lim_{\varepsilon\to 0} \left[\int_a^{c-\varepsilon} f(x)\,dx + \int_{c+\varepsilon}^b f(x)\,dx\right] \tag{3.93}$$

3.5 THE DEFINITE INTEGRAL AS A SUMMATION

Integration is a very valuable technique for calculations that can be expressed in terms of a summation. An important theorem relates the definite integral to the limit of a summation.

Suppose $f(x)$ is a function that is continuous for values of x such that $a \leqslant x \leqslant b$. We shall subdivide the interval a to b into n equal subintervals each of length Δx given by $\Delta x = (b - a)/n$, by the set of numbers $a < x_1 < x_2 \ldots < x_{n-1} < b$ (figure 3.1). Let $C_1, C_2 \ldots C_n$ be a set of n numbers, one in each sub-interval, such that

$$a \leqslant C_1 \leqslant x_1 \leqslant C_2 \leqslant x_2 \ldots x_{n-1} \leqslant C_{n-1} \leqslant b$$

We now calculate the sum

$$S_n = f(C_1)\Delta x + f(C_2)\Delta x + \ldots + f(C_n)\Delta x = \sum_{k=1}^n f(C_k)\Delta x$$

The *fundamental theorem of integral calculus* states that as the number of subintervals n approaches infinity

$$\lim_{n\to\infty} S_n = \lim_{n\to\infty} \sum_{k=1}^n f(C_k)\,\Delta x = \int_a^b f(x)\,dx \tag{3.94}$$

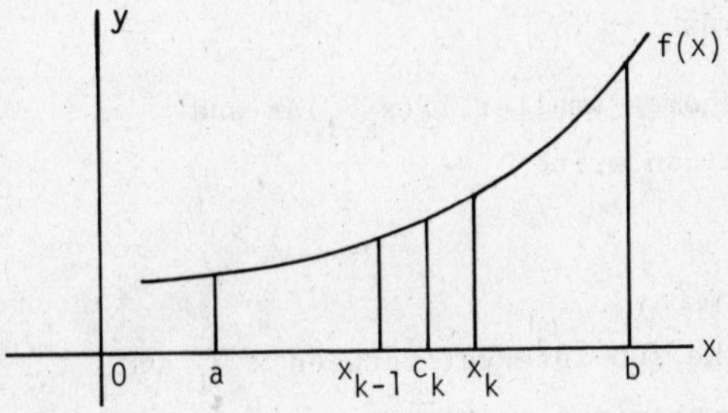

Figure 3.1

Any problem that can be expressed as a summation in this way can be solved by evaluation of the appropriate definite integral.

3.6 APPLICATIONS OF THE DEFINITE INTEGRAL

3.6.1 Area under a curve

The area under a curve can be found approximately by counting squares of graph paper or by cutting out the area in question and weighing it. A much more satisfactory method is to calculate the area exactly by integration.

Let us consider the area under the curve $y = f(x)$ between the values of $x = a$ and $x = b$. We assume that $f(x)$ is positive over this interval. If we now partition the interval into n sub-intervals as in the previous section, we can write the total area A as the sum of the areas under the curve for each sub-interval

$$A = \sum_{k=1}^{n} A_k$$

where A_k is the area under the curve between x_{k-1} and x_k. Inspection of figure 3.2 shows that

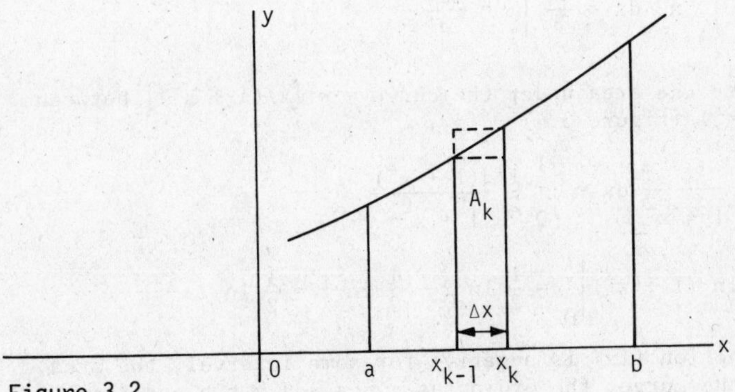

Figure 3.2

$$f(x_{k-1})\Delta x < A_k < f(x_k)\Delta x$$

and we can see that as Δx becomes smaller, $f(x_{k-1})\Delta x$ and $f(x_k)\Delta x$ will approach A_k. We can write

$$A \approx \sum_{k=1}^{n} f(C_k)\Delta x$$

where C_k is some number in the sub-interval between x_{k-1} and x_k. Using the theorem of the previous section gives

$$A = \lim_{n\to\infty} \sum_{k=1}^{n} f(C_k)\Delta x = \int_a^b f(x)\, dx \qquad (3.95)$$

Thus, for curves lying above the x-axis, the area under the curve between two points is given by a definite integral. We illustrate with examples.

(i) Calculate the area under the curve $y = x^2$ (figure 3.3) between $x = 1$ and $x = 5$.

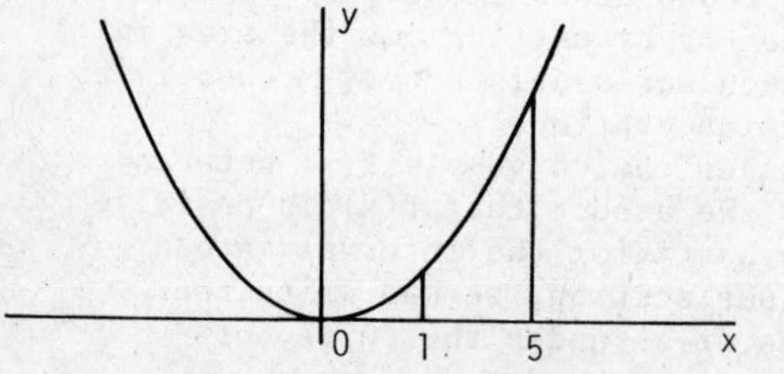

Figure 3.3

One should, in general, sketch the curve in question to check that there are no discontinuities and to find out where it crosses the x-axis. In this case

$$\text{area} = \int_1^5 x^2\, dx = \frac{x^3}{3}\Big|_1^5 = \frac{124}{3}$$

(ii) Calculate the area under the curve $y = [x/(1 + x^2)]$ between $x = 0$ and $x = 1$ (figure 3.4)

$$A = \int_0^1 \frac{x}{1 + x^2}\, dx = \int_0^1 \frac{1}{2}\,\frac{d(1 + x^2)}{1 + x^2}$$

$$= \frac{1}{2}\ln(1 + x^2)\Big|_0^1 = \frac{1}{2}\ln 2 - \frac{1}{2}\ln 1 = \frac{1}{2}\ln 2$$

If the function $f(x)$ is negative for some interval, the area enclosed by the curve, the ordinates $x = a$ and $x = b$ and the

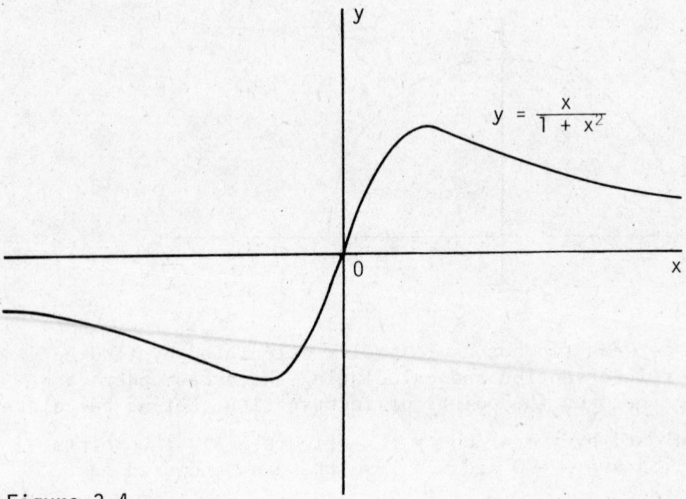

Figure 3.4

x-axis is calculated by the same method but must be given a negative sign. Taking the same example $y = [x/(1+x^2)]$ but calculating the area between x = -1 and x = 0 gives

$$A = -\left[\int_{-1}^{0} \frac{x\,dx}{1+x^2}\right] = -\frac{1}{2}(\ln 1 - \ln 2) = \frac{1}{2}\ln 2$$

If the curve crosses the x-axis in the interval of interest, the area must be subdivided into regions in which f(x) is positive or negative and the appropriate sign included. The area enclosed by $y = x/(1 + x^2)$, the x-axis, x = 1 and x = -1 is given by

$$A = -\left[\int_{-1}^{0} \frac{x\,dx}{1+x^2}\right] + \int_{0}^{1} \frac{x\,dx}{1+x^2} = \ln 2$$

Note that trying to calculate the area by simply taking the integral from -1 to 1 will give zero as we would expect because we are integrating an odd function from x = -1 to x = 1.

The area of a semi-circle can be calculated by integration. The equation of a circle of radius a having its centre at the origin is $x^2 + y^2 = a^2$, so we have to calculate the integral $\int_{-a}^{a} +\sqrt{(a^2 - x^2)}\,dx$ (figure 3.5).

By equations 3.85, 3.28 and 3.29 we can write

$$A = \int_{-a}^{a} +\sqrt{(a^2 - x^2)}\,dx = 2\int_{0}^{a} +\sqrt{(a^2 - x^2)}\,dx$$

$$= 2\left[\frac{a^2}{4}\sin 2u + a^2\frac{u}{2}\right]_0^{\pi/2} = \pi\frac{a^2}{2}$$

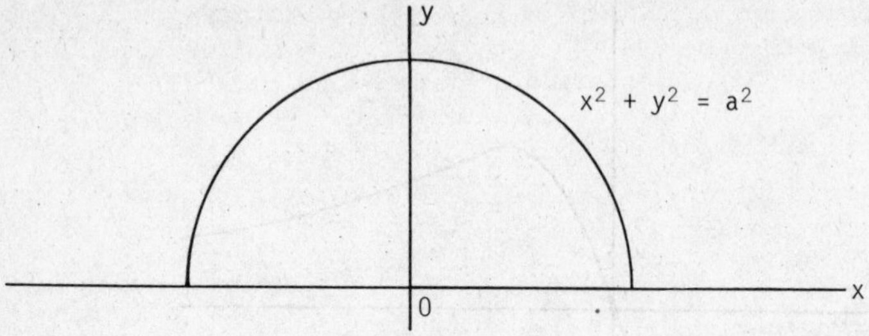

Figure 3.5

The area between two curves is easily calculated by finding the points of intersection and calculating the areas under each of the curves between the points of intersection. Let us calculate the area enclosed by $y = x^2$ and $y = x$ (figure 3.6). The points of intersection are $x = 0$ and $x = 1$ so the area enclosed is given by

$$A = \int_0^1 x\,dx - \int_0^1 x^2\,dx = \left.\frac{x^2}{2}\right|_0^1 - \left.\frac{x^3}{3}\right|_0^1 = \frac{1}{6}$$

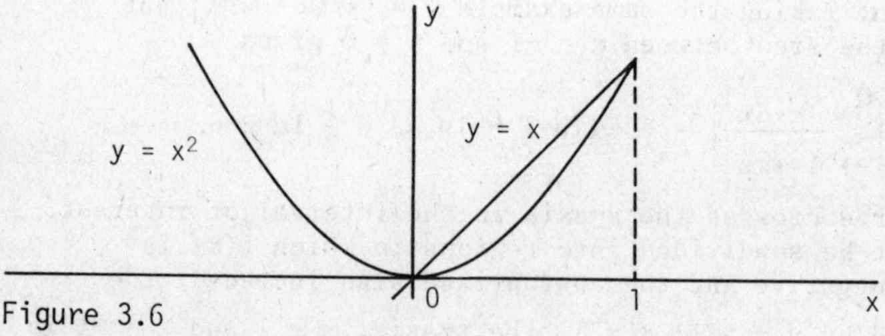

Figure 3.6

3.6.2 Work done by a force

If a force is constant, the work done when the force acts over a length is simply force × distance. If the force F is a function of position x we have to divide the distance between a and b over which the force acts into n sub-intervals of length Δx. If we consider the element between x_{k-1} and x_k, the force at some point C_k in this interval will be $F(C_k)$. Assuming that the force is essentially constant over the interval, the work done is approximately $F(C_k)\Delta x$ and the total work done W in going from a to b will be approximately

$$W \approx \sum_{k=1}^{n} F(C_k)\Delta x$$

The work done will be given exactly by

$$W = \lim_{n\to\infty} \sum_{k=1}^{n} F(C_k)\Delta x = \int_a^b F(x)\,dx \qquad (3.96)$$

A common application of this in thermodynamics is the calculation of work done by pressure. In section 2.7 we considered a cylinder containing gas at pressure P with a piston of area A. The force acting is PA and the work done by the gas when the piston moves from x = a to x = b is $\int_a^b PA\,dx$. Since A dx is a volume, this is more conveniently written as $\int_{V1}^{V2} P\,dV$. The precise dependence of P on V depends on the conditions under which the compression or expansion takes place.

We can use a similar approach to calculate the electrostatic potential resulting from bringing a unit positive charge to a distance r_1 from a charge Z_1. By *Coulomb's law* the force F between two charges Z_1 and Z_2 separated by a distance r is

$$F = \frac{Z_1 Z_2}{4\pi\varepsilon_0 r^2} \tag{3.97}$$

where ε_0 is the permittivity of free space. Thus the work done against the field of a charge Z_1 in bringing up a unit charge from infinity to r_1 is

$$W = -\int_{\infty}^{r_1} \frac{Z_1}{4\pi\varepsilon_0 r^2}\,dr = \frac{Z_1}{4\pi\varepsilon_0 r_1}$$

But this work done against the field of Z_1 is the *potential* V at the point r_1; that is

$$V = \frac{Z_1}{4\pi\varepsilon_0 r_1} \tag{3.98}$$

Equations 3.97 and 3.98 illustrate the relationship between force and potential energy

$$F = -\frac{dV}{dr} \tag{3.99}$$

3.6.3 Volumes of solids of revolution

If we rotate the semicircle of figure 3.5 through 2π radians about the x-axis we generate a sphere. This is known as a *solid of revolution*. In general, the rotation of any continuous function f(x) about a particular axis (say the x-axis) will generate a solid of revolution (figure 3.7). The volume of such a solid can be readily calculated by dividing it into n thin discs of thickness Δx perpendicular to the axis of revolution. For the sub-interval between x_{k-1} and x_k along the x-axis, the corresponding disc has a volume of $\pi[f(C_k)]^2\Delta x$ where C_k is some number between x_{k-1} and x_k. The

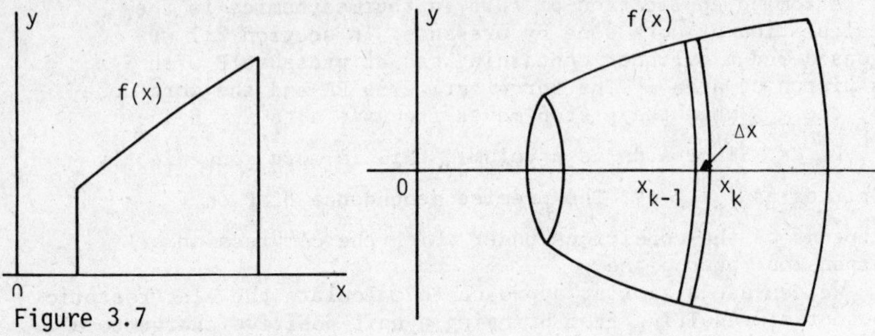

Figure 3.7

total volume is thus approximately equal to the sum of these individual volumes $\sum_{k=1}^{n} \pi[f(C_k)]^2 \Delta x$ and the exact volume is given by the definite integral $\int_a^b \pi[f(x)]^2 \, dx$. Let us apply this to the sphere and the right circular cone.

(i) The sphere

Rotating the semicircle $y = \sqrt{(a^2 - x^2)}$ about the x-axis gives a sphere whose volume is approximately $\sum_{k=1}^{n} \pi (a^2 - x^2)\Delta x$ (figure 3.8). In the limit of an infinite number of discs we get

$$V = \lim_{n\to\infty} \sum_{k=1}^{n} \pi (a^2 - x^2)\Delta x = \int_{-a}^{a} \pi (a^2 - x^2) \, dx$$

$$= 2 \left(\pi a^2 x - \pi \frac{x^3}{3}\right)\Bigg|_0^a = \frac{4}{3} \pi a^3 \qquad (3.100)$$

(ii) The right circular cone

A right circular cone with base of radius r and height h is obtained by rotating the line $y = (r/h)x$ between $x = 0$ and $x = h$ through 2π radians about the x-axis. The volume V is given by

$$V = \int_0^h \pi y^2 \, dx = \int_0^h \pi \frac{r^2}{h^2} x^2 \, dx = \frac{1}{3} \pi r^2 h \qquad (3.101)$$

In some cases, although the rotation may be about the x-axis, it may be more convenient to express the integral in terms of y.

3.6.4 Length of arc

We can also calculate the length of an arc of the curve $y = f(x)$ by integration (figure 3.9).

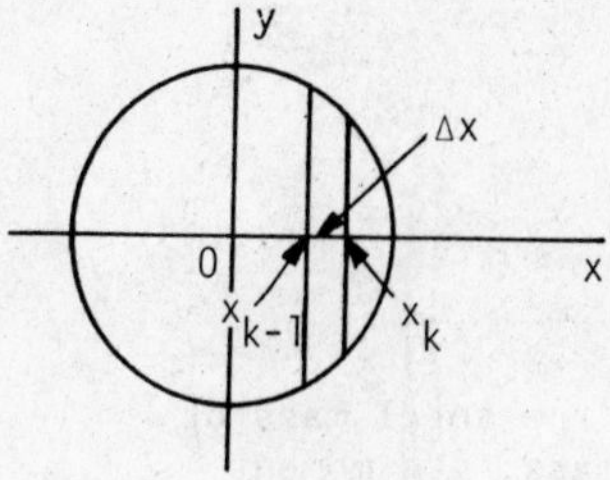

Figure 3.8

Consider the section in the subinterval x_{k-1} to x_k. By Pythagoras's theorem, the chord AB is of length $\sqrt{[(\Delta x)^2 + (\Delta y_k)]^2}$, which is equal to $\Delta x\sqrt{[1 + (\Delta y_k/\Delta x)^2]}$. But $\Delta y_k/\Delta x$ is the slope of the chord AB. There is a point C_k in the interval for which the slope of the curve $f'(C_k)$ is equal to the slope of AB. Thus the length of the chord is $\Delta x\sqrt{\{1 + [f'(C_k)]^2\}}$. As Δx decreases, the length of the chord approaches the length of the arc AB, so in the limit, the total length of arc S between $x = a$ and $x = b$ is given by

$$S = \lim_{n\to\infty} \sum_{k=1}^{n} \Delta x\sqrt{\{1 + [f'(C_k)]^2\}} = \int_a^b \sqrt{\{1 + [f'(x)]^2\}}\, dx \tag{3.102}$$

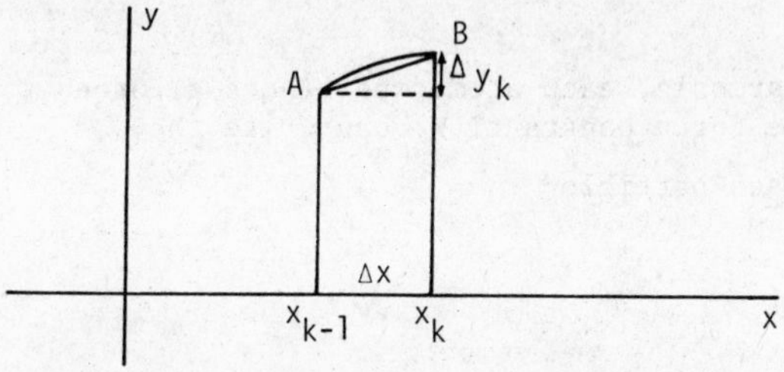

Figure 3.9

3.6.5 Centre of mass

The centre of mass is an important property of a body or a system of particles. If we consider a system of n point masses m_i whose positions are given by co-ordinates (x_i, y_i), the co-ordinates $(\bar{x}, \bar{y})$ of the centre of mass are given by

$$\bar{x}\,(m_1 + m_2 + \ldots + m_n) = x_1m_1 + x_2m_2 + \ldots + x_nm_n$$

$$\bar{y}\,(m_1 + m_2 + \ldots + m_n) = y_1m_1 + y_2m_2 + \ldots + y_nm_n$$

that is

$$\bar{x} = \frac{\sum_{i=1}^{n} x_i m_i}{\sum_i m_i}; \qquad \bar{y} = \frac{\sum_{i=1}^{n} y_i m_i}{\sum_i m_i} \tag{3.103}$$

The centre of mass is the point such that if the total mass of the system is concentrated at the centre of mass, its moment about any axis is equal to the sum of the moments of all the individual masses about that axis. An alternative definition is that the sum of all the individual moments with respect to the centre of mass is zero.

In two-body problems, important simplifications result from considering the motion of the two particles relative to the centre of mass of the system. Examples of this are: the vibration or rotation of a diatomic molecule; the solution of the Schrödinger equation for the hydrogen atom; or the scattering of one particle by the potential due to another particle. In the absence of external fields, the motion of the centre of mass is of no particular interest because the centre of mass moves through space with constant velocity. Consider a diatomic molecule with atoms of mass m_1 and m_2 separated by a distance r (figure 3.10). If the equilibrium separation is r_e and we

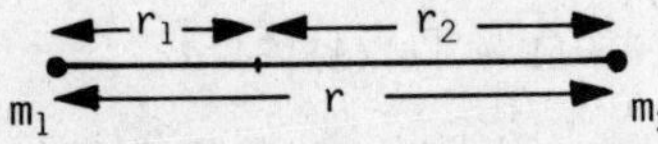

Figure 3.10

assume the potential is harmonic, each atom experiences a force $-k(r - r_e)$, where k is the force constant. We can write the equations of motion for each particle

$$m_1 \frac{d^2 r_1}{dt^2} = -k(r - r_e)$$

$$m_2 \frac{d^2 r_2}{dt^2} = -k(r - r_e) \tag{3.104}$$

where r_1 and r_2 are the distances of m_1 and m_2 from the centre of mass. Taking each atom in turn as the origin and using equations 3.103, we obtain for the positions r_1 and r_2 of m_1 and m_2 relative to the centre of mass

$$r_1 = \frac{m_2}{m_1 + m_2} r, \qquad r_2 = \frac{m_1}{m_1 + m_2} r \tag{3.105}$$

and equations 3.104 can be rewritten as the single equation

$$\frac{m_1 m_2}{m_1 + m_2} \frac{d^2 r}{dt^2} = -k(r - r_e)$$

or, since r_e is a constant

$$\frac{m_1 m_2}{m_1 + m_2} \frac{d^2(r - r_e)}{dt^2} = -k(r - r_e) \qquad (3.106)$$

Thus we have replaced the two equations 3.104 for the motions of particles 1 and 2 by the single equation 3.106 for the motion of a single mass $[m_1 m_2/(m_1 + m_2)]$ vibrating with an amplitude given by the change in the internuclear distance $(r - r_e)$. The quantity $[m_1 m_2/(m_1 + m_2)]$ is called the *reduced mass* μ. We shall use this further in the next section when we discuss rotational motion.

When we consider the centre of mass of a lamina or a solid, we shall require the definite integral to effect the summation. Consider the semi-circular lamina bounded by the curve $y = +\surd(a^2 - x^2)$ and the x-axis (figure 3.11).

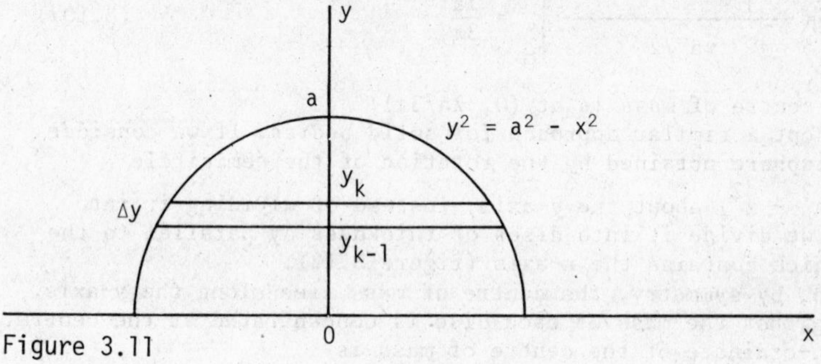

Figure 3.11

The y-axis is an axis of symmetry and the centre of mass will lie along it. We determine its position along the y-axis by dividing the interval between y = 0 and y = a into n subintervals of width Δy. Consider the subinterval between y_{k-1} and y_k. The area of this thin strip parallel to the x-axis is approximately $\Delta y \surd(a^2 - y_k^2)$. If the density of the material is ρ, the mass is $\rho \Delta y \surd(a^2 - y_k^2)$ and, assuming that its mass is concentrated at the mid-point, its moment about the y-axis is $y \rho \Delta y \surd(a^2 - y_k^2)$. To evaluate the summations in equation 3.103, we replace them by definite integrals

$$\bar{y} = \frac{\int_0^a \rho \surd(a^2 - y^2) y \, dy}{\int_0^a \rho \surd(a^2 - y^2) dy} = \frac{\int_0^a \surd(a^2 - y^2) y \, dy}{\int_0^a \surd(a^2 - y^2) \, dy}$$

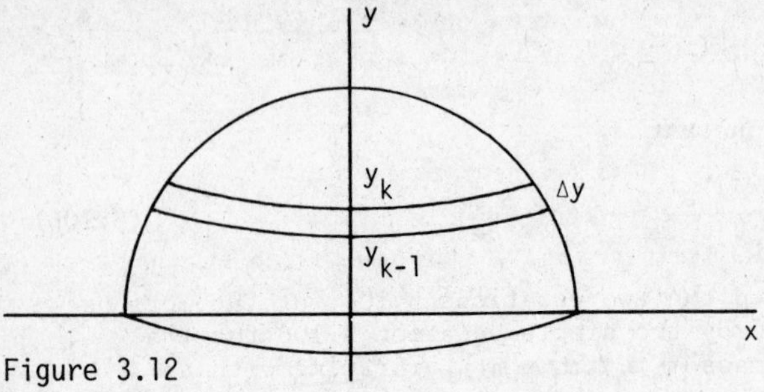

Figure 3.12

The denominator is simply the area of the semi-circle $\pi a^2/2$. Thus

$$\bar{y} = \frac{-\frac{1}{2}\int_0^a (a^2 - y^2)^{1/2}\, d(a^2 - y^2)}{\pi a^2/2}$$

$$= \left. \frac{-\frac{1}{3}(a^2 - y^2)^{3/2}}{\pi a^2/2} \right|_0^a = \frac{2a}{3\pi} \qquad (3.107)$$

and the centre of mass is at $(0, 2a/3\pi)$.

We adopt a similar approach for solid bodies. If we consider the hemisphere obtained by the rotation of the semicircle $y = +\sqrt{(a^2 - x^2)}$ about the y-axis, instead of dividing it into strips, we divide it into discs of thickness Δy parallel to the base, which contains the x-axis (figure 3.12).

Again, by symmetry, the centre of mass lies along the y-axis. Assuming that the mass of each disc is concentrated at the centre, the y-co-ordinate of the centre of mass is

$$\bar{y} = \frac{\int_0^a \rho\pi x^2 y\, dy}{\int_0^a \rho\pi x^2\, dy} = \frac{\int_0^a (a^2 - y^2) y\, dy}{\int_0^a (a^2 - y^2)\, dy} = \frac{a^4/4}{2a^3/3} = \frac{3a}{8} \qquad (3.108)$$

The centre of mass of the hemisphere is at the point $(0, 3a/8)$.

The calculation of the dipole moment of a molecule from a molecular wavefunction uses an approach that is very similar to that used in the calculation of centres of mass.

If we have a set of point charges q_i located at the points (x_i, y_i, z_i) the x-component μ_x of the dipole moment is given by

$$\mu_x = \sum_i q_i x_i \qquad (3.109)$$

This is applicable to the calculation of the nuclear contribution. The electronic-charge distribution, however, is continuous, and for a continuous three-dimensional distribution with density ρ (x,y,z) the summation in equation 3.109 is replaced by the definite integral

$$\mu_x = \iiint_{-\infty}^{\infty} x\rho(x,y,z)\ dx\ dy\ dz \tag{3.110}$$

This is a *triple integral*, which will be discussed further in section 3.7. The electronic-charge density at the point (x,y,z) is given by $-e\psi^*(x,y,z)\psi(x,y,z)$, where $-e$ is the charge of the electron and $\psi(x,y,z)$ is the molecular wavefunction. Thus the electronic contribution to the x-component of the dipole moment is given by

$$\mu_x = -e\iiint_{-\infty}^{\infty} x\psi^*(x,y,z)\psi(x,y,z)\ dx\ dy\ dz \tag{3.111}$$

Since for a normalised wavefunction

$$\iiint_{-\infty}^{\infty} \psi^*(x,y,z)\psi(x,y,z)\ dx\ dy\ dz = 1$$

equation 3.111 essentially gives $-e\bar{x}$ where $\bar{x}$ is the x-co-ordinate of the centre of mass of the charge density. In the dipole moment calculation one is interested in the distance between the centre of mass of the positive charge of the nuclei and that of the electrons.

3.6.6 Moment of Inertia

This is an important quantity for the description of a rotating body. If a body with moment of inertia I is rotating with an angular velocity ω about some axis, the kinetic energy is $1/2I\omega^2$ and the angular momentum is $I\omega$. For a mass M rotating about an axis at a perpendicular distance r from it, the moment of inertia is defined by $I = Mr^2$. This is readily generalised to a system of n point masses M_i at distances r_i from the rotation axis to give

$$I = \sum_{i=1}^{n} M_i r_i^2 \tag{3.112}$$

Using the notation of the previous section, the moment of inertia of a diatomic molecule rotating about an axis through the centre of mass is given by

$$I = m_1 r_1^2 + m_2 r_2^2$$

$$= m_1\left(\frac{m_2 r}{m_1 + m_2}\right)^2 + m_2\left(\frac{m_1 r}{m_1 + m_2}\right)^2 = \left(\frac{m_1 m_2}{m_1 + m_2}\right) r^2 = \mu\ r^2 \tag{3.113}$$

Thus we can consider the rotating molecule as being equivalent to a single mass equal to the reduced mass moving in a circle of radius r about the centre of mass. The further generalisation to solid bodies involves the replacement of the sum by a definite integral. Let us consider again the semicircular lamina and the hemisphere.

To calculate the moment of inertia of a semi-circular lamina rotating about the x-axis, we divide it into strips of width Δy parallel to the x-axis as in figure 3.11. Using arguments similar to those used in the previous section, we see that the moment of inertia of the strip is approximately

$\rho\Delta y\sqrt{(a^2 - y_k^2)}y_k^2$ and the total moment of inertia is therefore approximately given by

$$I \approx \sum_{k=1}^{n} \rho\Delta y\sqrt{(a^2 - y_k^2)}\, y_k^2$$

which can be calculated exactly by the definite integral

$$I = \int_0^a \rho\sqrt{(a^2 - y^2)}y^2\, dy$$

This can be integrated by making the substitution $y = a \sin u$ and changing the limits to 0 and $\pi/2$

$$I = \rho\int_0^{\pi/2} a^4 \sin^2 u \cos^2 u\, du = \rho\frac{a^4}{4}\int_0^{\pi/2} \sin^2 2u\, du$$

$$= \rho\frac{a^4}{8}\int_0^{\pi/2} (1 - \cos 4u)du = \frac{\pi\rho a^4}{16} \tag{3.114}$$

However, the mass M of the semicircle is $\pi\rho a^2/2$ so we can write $I = Ma^2/4$. We divide the hemisphere into circular discs of thickness Δy as in the centre of mass calculation in order to obtain the moment of inertia for rotation about the x-axis, which lies in the base. The mass of the disc between y_{k-1} and y_k is approximately $\rho\Delta y\pi(a^2 - y_k^2)$ and its moment of inertia about the x-axis is therefore $[\rho\Delta y\pi(a^2 - y_k^2)]y_k^2$. The total moment of inertia is given by the sum of these individual moments of inertia

$$I \approx \sum_{k=1}^{n} \rho\Delta y\pi(a^2 - y_k^2)y_k^2$$

which is given exactly by the definite integral

$$I = \int_0^a \rho\pi(a^2 - y^2)y^2 dy = \rho\pi\left(a^2\frac{y^3}{3} - \frac{y^5}{5}\right)\Bigg|_0^a = \frac{2\rho\pi a^5}{15} \tag{3.115}$$

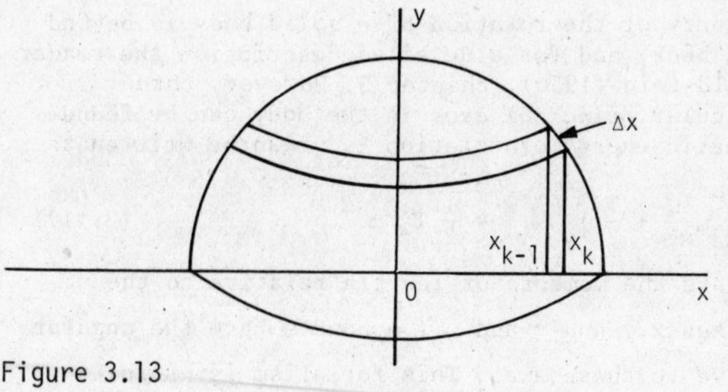

Figure 3.13

Recalling that the volume of a hemisphere is $2\pi a^3/3$, we can rewrite the moment of inertia in terms of the mass M as

$$I = \frac{Ma^2}{5}$$

It is very important to note that the moment of inertia depends on the axis of rotation and is *not* a constant of the body. To illustrate this we shall calculate the moment of inertia of the hemisphere for rotation about the y-axis (figure 3.13).

To do this we divide it into n hollow cylinders of thickness Δx. The volume of the cylinder defined by x_{k-1} and x_k is given by the height $\surd(a^2 - x_{k-1}^2)$ multiplied by the area of the end, which is $[\pi(x_{k-1} + \Delta x)^2 - \pi x_{k-1}^2]$. Neglecting terms in $(\Delta x)^2$ gives the volume of the cylinder as $2\pi x_{k-1}\Delta x\surd(a^2 - x_{k-1}^2)$ and the mass is therefore $2\pi\rho x_{k-1}\Delta x\surd(a^2 - x_{k-1}^2)$. The approximate moment of inertia about the y-axis is thus $[2\pi\rho x_{k-1}\Delta x\surd(a^2 - x_{k-1}^2)]x_{k-1}^2$ and the total moment of inertia is given by the definite integral

$$I = \int_0^a 2\pi\rho x^3\surd(a^2 - x^2)\,dx$$

This can also be integrated by making the substitution x = a sin u with the appropriate change of limits

$$I = \int_0^{\pi/2} 2\pi\rho a^5 \sin^3 u \cos^2 u\,du$$

$$= 2\pi\rho a^5\int_0^{\pi/2} (\cos^2 u - 1)\cos^2 u\,d(\cos u)$$

$$= 2\pi\rho a^5 \left(\frac{\cos^5 u}{5} - \frac{\cos^3 u}{3}\right)\Bigg|_0^{\pi/2} = \frac{4\pi\rho a^5}{15} = \frac{2Ma^2}{5} \qquad (3.116)$$

The general theory of the rotation of a solid body is beyond the scope of this book, and for a detailed description the reader should consult Goldstein (1950), chapter 5. However, three mutually perpendicular *principal axes* in the body can be found such that the kinetic energy of rotation E_{rot} can be written as

$$E_{rot} = \frac{1}{2} I_x \omega_x^2 + \frac{1}{2} I_y \omega_y^2 + \frac{1}{2} I_z \omega_z^2 \qquad (3.117)$$

where I_x, I_y, I_z are the moments of inertia relative to the three principal axes x,y and z and ω_x, ω_y and ω_z are the angular velocities relative to these axes. This formalism is useful in the discussion of the rotation of a polyatomic molecule. If a molecule has axes of symmetry, one principal axis (usually labelled the z-axis) is the axis of highest symmetry.
A second axis can be chosen perpendicular to the first and to a plane of symmetry, if there is one, and the third axis is simply perpendicular to the other two. For a linear molecule, the molecular axis is the axis of highest symmetry so $I_z = 0$ and $I_x = I_y$. Nonlinear molecules can be classified by the components of the moment of inertia as follows. If $I_x = I_y = I_z$ the molecule is a *spherical top*. For a *symmetric top* $I_x = I_y \neq I_z$. Here, there are two cases. If $I_x > I_z$ the symmetric top is *prolate* whereas if $I_x < I_z$ it is *oblate*. If all three components of the moment of inertia are different, the molecule is an *asymmetric top*.

3.6.7 Mean values

If we have a series of n distinct values y_i of some quantity y, the *mean value* or *average* $\bar{y}$ of y is given by

$$\bar{y} = \frac{\sum_{i=1}^{n} y_i}{n} \qquad (3.118)$$

The values y_i may be successive measurements in an experiment or a series of measurements made on different samples. We shall discuss in chapter 14 the use of the mean in estimating the value of a measured quantity. Here we are interested in the case where y is varying systematically with respect to some variable x. In that case we determine y_i for n equally spaced values x_i of x. If the interval between successive values x_i and x_{i+1} is Δx, then the number n is given by $n = (x_n - x_1)/\Delta x$ and we can rewrite equation 3.118 as

$$\bar{y} = \frac{\sum_{i=1}^{n} y_i \, \Delta x}{x_n - x_1} \tag{3.119}$$

Suppose, however, instead of a set of discrete values of y for particular values of x, we are interested in the average value of the function y = f(x) between x_1 and x_n. We can use equation 3.119 to define an approximate mean value by

$$\bar{y} \approx \frac{\sum_{k=1}^{n} f(c_k)\Delta x}{x_n - x_1} \tag{3.120}$$

where c_k is a number in the sub-interval of length Δx between x_{k-1} and x_k. We shall get a better estimate for the mean value $\bar{y}$ by letting n increase. In the limit, as n tends to infinity, the mean value of y will be given by the definite integral

$$\bar{y} = \frac{\int_a^b f(x)\, dx}{b - a} \tag{3.121}$$

The mean values of trigonometric functions are useful in many contexts. Using equation 3.121 we obtain the mean values of $\sin\theta$ and $\sin^2\theta$ as follows

$$\overline{\sin\theta} = \frac{\int_0^\pi \sin\theta \, d\theta}{\pi - 0} = -\frac{1}{\pi}\cos\theta\Big|_0^\pi = \frac{2}{\pi} \tag{3.122}$$

$$\overline{\sin^2\theta} = \frac{\int_0^\pi \sin^2\theta \, d\theta}{\pi - 0} = \frac{1}{\pi}\int_0^\pi \frac{1}{2}(1 - \cos 2\theta)\, d\theta$$

$$= \frac{1}{\pi}\left[\frac{\theta}{2} - \frac{\sin 2\theta}{4}\right]_0^\pi = \frac{1}{2} \tag{3.123}$$

The average lifetime of a radioactive atom or molecule undergoing first-order decomposition is given by integration as follows. If we have n particles at time t, the rate of decay is given by

$$\frac{dn}{dt} = -\lambda n = -\lambda n_0 \exp(-\lambda t)$$

where λ is the decay constant (or rate constant) and n_0 is the initial number of particles. If dn particles disintegrate in the time between t and t + dt, the mean lifetime τ is given by

$$\tau = \frac{\int_0^{n_0} t \, dn}{n_0 - 0} = \frac{1}{n_0}\int_0^\infty t\lambda \, n_0 \exp(-\lambda t)\, dt \tag{3.124}$$

which on integration by parts gives $1/\lambda$.

The dipolar coupling between two parallel magnetic dipoles in an external field is proportional to the term $(3\cos^2\theta - 1)$, where θ is the angle between the internuclear line and the applied field. In a solid this is nonzero but in a liquid, where all orientations are possible, the average value is given by $\int_0^{\pi} (3\cos^2\theta - 1)\sin\theta\, d\theta$ (the factor of $\sin\theta$ appears because the expression is in terms of spherical polar co-ordinates and we have to allow for cylindrical symmetry), which is zero.

The calculation of average values is of great importance in quantum mechanics but first we have to discuss the concepts of probability and weighting.

3.6.8 Probability and weighted means

In the case of n discrete readings y_i, a particular value y_i may occur n_i times. We can replace the summation in equation 3.118 by a summation over the k distinct values thus

$$\bar{y} = \frac{\sum_{i=1}^{k} n_i y_i}{\sum_{i=1}^{k} n_i} = \sum_{i=1}^{k} \frac{n_i}{n} y_i \qquad (3.125)$$

In the language of chapter 14, n_i is the *frequency* of the occurrence of the value y_i and n_i/n is the *relative frequency* or *probability* p_i of its occurrence. Thus we can rewrite equation 3.125 as

$$\bar{y} = \sum_{i=1}^{n} p_i y_i \qquad (3.126)$$

In the continuous case the discrete probabilities p_i are replaced by the *probability distribution function* $p(x)$, so we obtain the integral

$$\bar{y} = \int_a^b p(x) f(x)\, dx \qquad (3.127)$$

for the mean value of $f(x)$ for the interval $a \leqslant x \leqslant b$. Here it is assumed that the function $p(x)$ is *normalised* so that $\int_a^b p(x)\, dx$ is unity. Two examples of probability distribution functions were given in problems 2.9 and 2.10.

Let us consider the average molecular speed $\bar{c}$ of molecules for which the speeds obey the Maxwell-Boltzmann distribution. If we have N_0 molecules, the number dn having speeds between c and c + dc is given by

$$\frac{dn}{N_0} = 4\pi \left(\frac{m}{2\pi kT}\right)^{3/2} \exp\left(-\frac{mc^2}{2kT}\right) c^2\, dc \qquad (3.128)$$

where m is the mass of the molecule, k is the Boltzmann constant and T is the temperature. The mean molecular speed $\bar{c}$ is given by

$$\bar{c} = \int_0^\infty f(c)c\ dc = 4\pi\left(\frac{m}{2\pi kT}\right)^{3/2}\int_0^\infty \exp\left(-\frac{mc^2}{2kT}\right)c^3\ dc \qquad (3.129)$$

where f(c) is the probability distribution function dn/dc for molecular speeds.

Another example is the calculation of the average component of the dipole moment in the direction of the applied field when an assembly of molecules each having a permanent dipole moment μ is subjected to an electric field F along the z-axis. If all orientations were equally probable, the average component along the z-axis would be $\int \mu \cos\theta\ d\omega$, where θ is the angle between the dipole moment and the z-axis and $d\omega$ is an element of solid angle, which is $\sin\theta\ d\theta\ d\phi$ in spherical polar co-ordinates (see section 4.4.3). In the absence of an applied field the average dipole moment will be proportional to $2\pi\int_0^\pi \mu\cos\theta\sin\theta\ d\theta$, which is zero. In the presence of an external field F the potential energy of a dipole oriented at θ to the z-axis is $-\mu F\cos\theta$ and the probability of this orientation is given by the Boltzmann factor $\exp(\mu F\cos\theta/kT)$. The average value $\bar{\mu}$ of the dipole moment in the direction of the field is then given by

$$\bar{\mu} = \frac{2\pi\int_0^\pi \exp(\mu F\cos\theta/kT)\mu\cos\theta\sin\theta\ d\theta}{2\pi\int_0^\pi \exp(\mu F\cos\theta/kT)\sin\theta\ d\theta} \qquad (3.130)$$

In quantum mechanics many observables such as the position and momentum of an electron do not have well-defined values and we have to calculate average or *expectation values*. Let us consider a one-dimensional problem for which the wavefunction is $\psi(x)$. The probability of the particle being between x and x + dx is given by $\psi^*(x)\psi(x)$, where $\psi^*(x)$ is the complex conjugate (see section 7.2.4) of $\psi(x)$. Thus the average value or expectation value $\bar{x}$ of the position of the particle is given by the integral

$$\bar{x} = \frac{\int_{-\infty}^{\infty} \psi^*(x)\psi(x)x\ dx}{\int_{-\infty}^{\infty} \psi^*(x)\psi(x)\ dx} \qquad (3.131)$$

In general the calculation of expectation values for other observables is more complicated because in quantum mechanics observables are represented by operators. For example, the expectation value $\bar{p}_x$ for the momentum of a particle in one dimension is given by

$$\overline{p_x} = \frac{\int_{-\infty}^{\infty} \psi^*(x)\left[-(h/2\pi i)(d/dx)\right]\psi(x)\ dx}{\int_{-\infty}^{\infty} \psi^*(x)\psi(x)\ dx} \tag{3.132}$$

where $[(-h/2\pi i)\ (d/dx)]$ is the *operator* for the x-component of the momentum. In this expression the average of the value of the momentum at each point in space, weighted by the probability of the particle being at that point, has been taken.

In general, if an observable is described by an operator O, the expectation value is given by the integral

$$\frac{\int \psi^* O \psi\ d\tau}{\int \psi^* \psi\ d\tau} \tag{3.133}$$

where the integration is over all space and $d\tau$ is a volume element.

3.7 MULTIPLE INTEGRALS

The integrals in equations 3.110 and 3.111 are examples of *multiple integrals*. Such integrals occur frequently in quantum mechanics, and in this section we discuss briefly the definition, properties and evaluation of multiple integrals. The reader is referred to Stephenson (1973) for a more thorough discussion.

We define a *double integral* by extending our definition of the definite integral in equation 3.94 from the section of the line $y = 0$ lying between $x = a$ and $x = b$ $(a < b)$ to a rectangular area R bounded by the lines $x = a$, $x = b$, $y = c$, $y = d$. Let $f(x,y)$ be a function which is single valued and continuous both within the rectangular region R and on its boundary. As in the case of the fundamental theorem of integral calculus, we divide the interval $a \leqslant x \leqslant b$ into m parts of length Δx by $(m - 1)$ numbers x_i and the interval $c \leqslant y \leqslant d$ into n parts of length Δy by $(n - 1)$ numbers y_i, such that

$$a < x_1 < x_2 < \ldots < x_{m-1} < b$$

and

$$c < y_1 < y_2 < \ldots < y_{n-1} < d$$

Thus the region R is divided into mn rectangular elements of area $\Delta R_s = \Delta x \Delta y$. Let p_k and q_ℓ be sets of numbers such that

$$x_{k-1} \leqslant p_k \leqslant x_k; \qquad y_{\ell-1} \leqslant q_\ell \leqslant y_\ell$$

The double integral

$$I = \int_R f(x,y)\ dR = \iint_R f(x,y)\ dx\ dy \tag{3.134}$$

is given by

$$I = \lim_{\substack{m\to\infty \\ n\to\infty}} \sum_{k=1}^{m} \sum_{\ell=1}^{n} f(p_k, q_\ell)\Delta R_s \tag{3.135}$$

Provided that this limit exists, its value is independent of the order in which m and n tend to infinity. We can thus write the double integral in terms of *repeated* integrals

$$\iint_R f(x,y)\ dx\ dy = \int_{x=a}^{x=b}\left[\int_{y=c}^{y=d} f(x,y)\ dy\right] dx$$

$$= \int_{y=c}^{y=d}\left[\int_{x=a}^{x=b} f(x,y)\ dx\right] dy \tag{3.136}$$

Thus we first of all integrate f(x,y) with respect to y between the limits y = c and y = d and then integrate with respect to x between the limits x = a, x = b, or we perform the integrations in the reverse order.

For example, the integral $\iint_R (1 + 2x^2 + y^2)\ dx\ dy$ for the region bounded by the lines x = −3, x = 3, y = −4, y = 4 is given by

$$\int_{x=-3}^{x=3} dx \int_{y=-4}^{y=4} (1 + 2x^2 + y^2)\ dy = \int_{x=-3}^{x=3} dx\ (y + 2x^2y + y^3/3)\Big|_{y=-4}^{y=4}$$

$$= \int_{-3}^{3} \left(8 + 16x^2 + \frac{128}{3}\right) dx = 592 \tag{3.137}$$

Here we have adopted a notation that avoids the use of the square brackets in equation 3.136. Alternatively, we obtain

$$\int_{y=-4}^{y=4} dy \int_{x=-3}^{x=3} (1 + 2x^2 + y^2)\ dx = \int_{y=-4}^{y=4} dy(x + 2x^3/3 + xy^2)\Big|_{x=-3}^{x=3}$$

$$= \int_{-4}^{4} (6 + 36 + 6y^2)\ dy = 592 \tag{3.138}$$

In equation 3.137, keeping x constant, we summed along a vertical strip AB and then summed over all vertical strips making up R, whereas in equation 3.138 we first of all summed along a horizontal strip CD with y kept constant and then summed over all such horizontal strips (see figure 3.14).

In fact the region of integration can be any bounded region and does not necessarily have to be rectangular. Thus it can be defined by the equations

$$\left.\begin{aligned} y_1(x) \leqslant y < y_2(x), \text{ for } a \leqslant x \leqslant b \\ x_1(y) \leqslant x \leqslant x_2(y), \text{ for } c \leqslant y \leqslant d \end{aligned}\right\} \tag{3.139}$$

provided that f(x,y) is continuous everywhere in the region R.

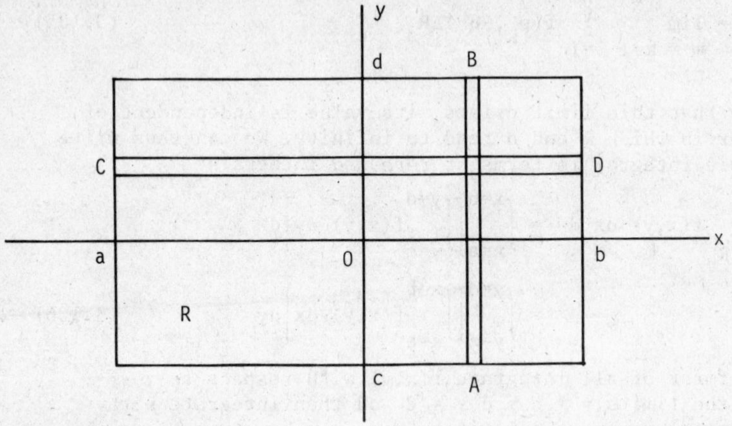

Figure 3.14

The double integral can then be written as follows

$$\int_{x=a}^{x=b} dx \int_{y=y_1(x)}^{y=y_2(x)} f(x,y)\ dy = \int_{y=c}^{y=d} dy \int_{x=x_1(y)}^{x=x_2(y)} f(x,y)\ dx \tag{3.140}$$

The order in which the integrations are performed depends on the relative ease of the integrations.

Let us consider the evaluation of the integral $\int_0^1 dx \int_x^{\sqrt{x}} xy^2\ dy$ over the region R lying between the line y = x and the curve $y = \sqrt{x}$ between x = 0 and x = 1 (figure 3.15). Summing first over a vertical strip AB, keeping x constant, and then integrating with respect to x gives

$$I = \int_0^1 dx \int_{y=x}^{y=\sqrt{x}} xy^2\ dy = \int_0^1 dx \left(\frac{1}{3} xy^3\right)\Bigg|_x^{\sqrt{x}}$$

$$= \int_0^1 \frac{1}{3} (x^{5/2} - x^4)\ dx = \frac{1}{35} \tag{3.141}$$

Alternatively, summing first over a horizontal strip CD gives

$$I = \int_0^1 dy \int_{x=y^2}^{x=y} xy^2\ dx = \int_0^1 dy \left(\frac{1}{2} x^2 y^2\right)\Bigg|_{y^2}^{y}$$

$$= \int_0^1 \frac{1}{2}(y^4 - y^6)\ dy = \frac{1}{35} \tag{3.142}$$

These ideas are readily generalised to *triple integrals* over a volume V

$$I = \iiint_V f(x,y,z)\ dx\ dy\ dz \tag{3.143}$$

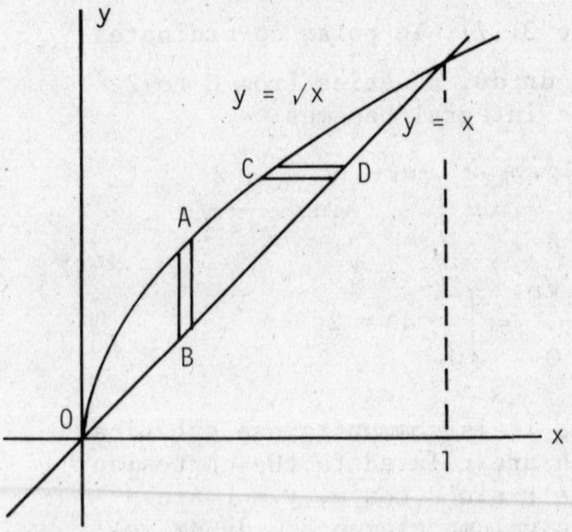

Figure 3.15

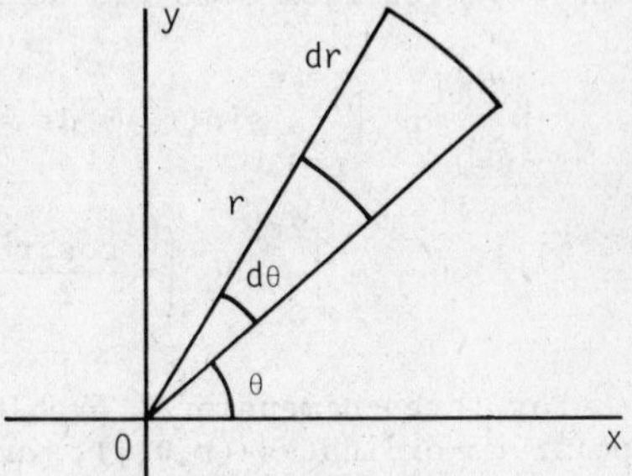

Figure 3.16

Problems in quantum mechanics are usually more easily handled in terms of polar co-ordinates (see section 4.4.1 for a full discussion) than in cartesian co-ordinates. In two dimensions, the polar co-ordinates (r,θ) of a point are related to the cartesian coordinates (x,y) by the transformation $x = r \cos \theta$, $y = r \sin \theta$. Before transforming an integral to polar co-ordinates it is necessary to express the element of area dx dy in terms of the new co-ordinates. Consider the element of area generated by increasing r by dr and θ by dθ. The area is nonrectangular but for small dr and dθ it is given approximately by dr (r dθ) (figure 3.16). Thus on transforming to polar co-ordinates we replace dx dy by r dr dθ.

As an example we consider the integral

$$\int_{-\sqrt{\pi}}^{\sqrt{\pi}} \int_{\sqrt{(\pi - y^2)}}^{\sqrt{(\pi - y^2)}} \sin(x^2 + y^2)\, dx\, dy$$

Here the region over which the integration is to be performed

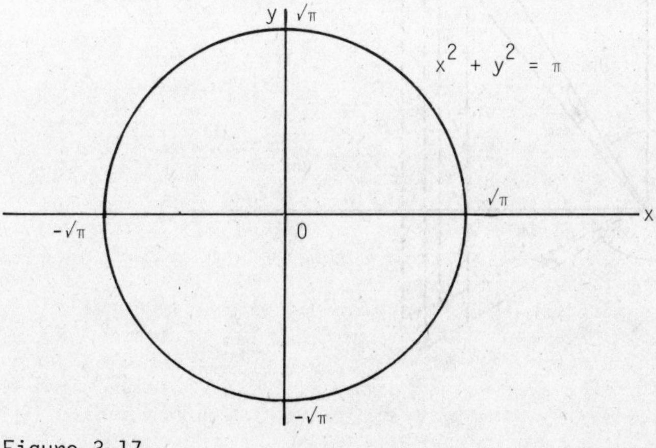

Figure 3.17

is the circle $x^2 + y^2 = \pi$ (figure 3.17). In polar co-ordinates $\sin(x^2 + y^2) = \sin r^2$, $dx\,dy = r\,dr\,d\theta$, θ varies from 0 to 2π and r varies from 0 to $\sqrt{\pi}$, so the integral becomes

$$\int_{\theta=0}^{\theta=2\pi} d\theta \int_{r=0}^{r=\sqrt{\pi}} \sin(r^2) r\,dr = \int_{\theta=0}^{\theta=2\pi} d\theta \int_{r=0}^{r=\sqrt{\pi}} \sin r^2 \frac{dr^2}{2}$$
$$= \int_0^{2\pi} d\theta \left(-\frac{\cos r^2}{2}\right)\Bigg|_0^{\sqrt{\pi}} = \int_0^{2\pi} d\theta = 2\pi \tag{3.144}$$

For three-dimensional problems it is common to use spherical polar co-ordinates (r,θ,ϕ), which are related to the cartesian co-ordinates by the relations $x = r \sin\theta \cos\phi$, $y = r \sin\theta \sin\phi$, $z = r\cos\theta$. The cartesian volume element dx dy dz is replaced by the volume obtained by increasing r, θ, ϕ by dr, $d\theta$, $d\phi$, respectively. Inspection of figure 3.18 shows that this is given approximately by $(dr)\ (r\,d\theta)\ (r \sin\theta\, d\phi)$, that is by $r^2 \sin\theta\, dr\, d\theta\, d\phi$.

As we shall see in chapter 12, molecular wavefunctions such as $\psi(x,y,z)$ in equation 3.111 are usually written as a product of functions of a single variable, for example $\psi(x,y,z) = R(r)\Theta(\theta)\Phi(\phi)$. Thus the integral in equation 3.111 can be expressed as the product of three definite integrals

$$\iiint_{-\infty}^{\infty} x\psi^*(x,y,z)\psi(x,y,z)\,dx\,dy\,dz = \int_0^{2\pi} \cos\phi\,\Phi^*(\phi)\Phi(\phi)\,d\phi \times$$
$$\int_0^{\pi} \sin\theta\,\Theta^*(\theta)\Theta(\theta)\sin\theta\,d\theta \int_0^{\infty} r\,R^*(r)\,R(r)\,r^2\,dr \tag{3.145}$$

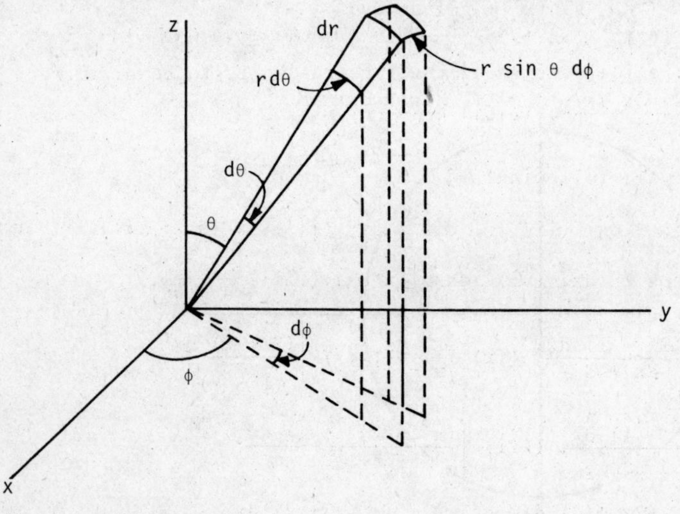

Figure 3.18

The limits $-\infty$, $+\infty$ for cartesian co-ordinates are replaced by $0 \leqslant \phi \leqslant 2\pi$, $0 \leqslant \theta \leqslant \pi$, $0 \leqslant r < \infty$ for spherical polar co-ordinates. In this case we have considered an unbounded integration volume. For wavefunctions such integrals are usually well behaved.

Whenever a function of many variables can be written as a product of functions of single variables and the various limits of integration are independent of each other, the evaluation of multiple integrals is straightforward provided that it is possible to perform each of the individual integrations.

3.8 PROBLEMS FOR SOLUTION

1. Integrate with respect to x:

(i) $\int 0.4x^4\, dx$; (ii) $\int (4x^2 - 5x + 1)dx$; (iii) $\int \frac{dx}{x^{1.4}}$; (iv) $\int \frac{dx}{x + 3}$;

(v) $\int \frac{2x\, dx}{x^2 + 4}$; (vi) $\int \sqrt{(ax + b)}\, dx$; (vii) $e^{(3x - 1)}\, dx$;

(viii) $\int x(x^2 + 1)^7\, dx$; (ix) $\int x \exp(x^2)\, dx$; (x) $\int (\cos 3x - \sin x/3)dx$;

(xi) $\int \sin^3 x \cos x\, dx$; (xii) $\int \frac{\sec^2 x\, dx}{1 + \tan x}$; (xiii) $\int \cos^2(ax + b)\, dx$;

(xiv) $\int \cos^3 x\, dx$; (xv) $\int \sin^2 x \cos^2 x\, dx$; (xvi) $\int \frac{dx}{\sin^2 x \cos^2 x}$;

(xvii) $\int \sin 4x \cos \frac{3x}{2}\, dx$.

2. Integrate the following using the method of substitution:

(i) $\int \sqrt{(1 - 4x^2)}\, dx$; (ii) $\int \sec x \operatorname{cosec} x\, dx$; (iii) $\int \frac{dx}{5 - 3\cos x}$;

(iv) $\int x^2 \cos x^3\, dx$; (v) $\int \frac{x^2\, dx}{1 - 2x^3}$; (vi) $\int \frac{1}{\sqrt{x}} \sin \sqrt{x}\, dx$;

(vii) $\int \frac{\sin x\, dx}{1 + 2\cos x}$; (viii) $\int \frac{\ln x\, dx}{x}$.

3. Integrate the following:

(i) $\int x \sin x\, dx$; (ii) $\int x^3 \cos x\, dx$; (iii) $\int x \ln x$; (iv) $\int x^3 \ln x$;

(v) $\int e^x \cos 2x\, dx$; (vi) $\int \tan^{-1} x\, dx$; (vii) $\int \frac{x\, dx}{a + bx}$;

(viii) $\int \frac{(2x - 1)\, dx}{2x + 3}$; (ix) $\int \frac{x^3\, dx}{x - 1}$; (x) $\int \frac{(2 + x)\, dx}{(1 - x)^2}$;

(xi) $\int \frac{(x^2 + 1)\, dx}{x^2 - x - 2}$; (xii) $\int \frac{(x^3 - 2x^2 - 1)\, dx}{x^2 - 1}$;

(xiii) $\int \frac{(2x + 3)\, dx}{x(x - 1)(x + 2)}$; (xiv) $\int \frac{(x + 2)\, dx}{(x^2 + 4)(1 - x)}$;

(xv) $\int \frac{dx}{x^2 + 6x + 17}$; (xvi) $\int \frac{dx}{2x^2 + 2x + 7}$;

(xvii) $\int \frac{dx}{\sqrt{(x^2 - 4x + 2)}}$; (xviii) $\int \frac{(x + 2)\,dx}{\sqrt{(x^2 + 2x - 1)}}$;

(xix) $\int \sqrt{\left(\frac{2 - x}{2 + x}\right)}\,dx$; (xx) $\int \frac{dx}{x\sqrt{(3x^2 + 4x + 1)}}$;

(xxi) $\int \frac{x^2\,dx}{\sqrt{(1 - x^2)}}$; (xxii) $\int \frac{x\,dx}{\sqrt{(1 - x)}}$.

4. Evaluate the definite integrals:

(i) $\int_0^{\pi/2} \sin^4 x \cos^3 x\,dx$; (ii) $\int_0^{\pi/2} \sin 4x \cos(3/2)x\,dx$;

(iii) $\int_0^{\pi/4} \frac{\sin^3 \theta}{1 - \cos \theta}\,d\theta$; (iv) $\int_3^4 \frac{x^2 + 4}{x^2 - 4}\,dx$.

5. Show by integration that $\int_{-1}^{1} \cos^{-1} x\,dx = \pi$.

6. Evaluate the orthogonality integral for 1s and 2s atomic orbitals

$$\int_0^\infty \exp(-r/a)(1 - r/2a)\exp(-r/2a)r^2\,dr$$

where a is a constant.

7. Evaluate the following integrals which are useful in Fourier series (chapter 8).

(i) $\int_{-\pi}^{\pi} \sin m\theta \sin n\theta\,d\theta$, for $m = n$ and $m \neq n$

(ii) $\int_{-\pi}^{\pi} \sin m\theta \cos n\theta\,d\theta$, for $m = n$ and $m \neq n$

(iii) $\int_{-\pi}^{\pi} \cos m\theta \cos n\theta\,d\theta$, for $m = n$ and $m \neq n$

8. Find the area included between the curve $y = 2x - 3x^2$ and the x-axis.

9. Show that the area of the region bounded by the three lines $y = 0$, $x = 1$, $x = 4$ and the curve $y = (4 + x^2)/x$ is $8 \ln 2 + 15/2$. Calculate the volume of the solid generated by the revolution of this area through 2π radians about the x-axis.

10. Find the area bounded by the lines $x = 1$, $x = 2$ and the curve $y^2 = 4x^2(x^2 + 1)^3$.

11. The ellipse $x^2/a^2 + y^2/b^2 = 1$ is rotated through 2π radians about the x-axis. Prove that the solid so formed has a volume $4\pi ab^2/3$. What is the volume of the solid formed by rotating the ellipse about the y-axis?

12. The portion of the curve $y = \sin x$ between $x = 0$ and $x = \pi$ is rotated through 2π radians about the x-axis. Calculate the volume of the solid thus generated.

13. A force $m \cos (pt)$ acts on a particle of mass m in the positive direction of 0_x. t is the time and p is a constant. The particle starts at $x = 0$ at $t = 0$. What is the velocity? Show that

$$x = \frac{1}{p^2} (1 - \cos pt)$$

Let $x = a$ at time T. What is the work done up to this moment?

14. Calculate the co-ordinates of the centre of mass of the area under the curve $y = 2 \sin 3x$ between $x = 0$ and $x = \pi/3$.

15. Calculate the work done when a gas is compressed from V_1 to V_2 under the following conditions:

(a) isothermally ($P_1V_1 = P_2V_2 = RT$); (b) adiabatically ($P_1V_1^\gamma = P_2V_2^\gamma$ = constant).

16. Find the centre of gravity of the solid formed by the rotation of $y = x^2$ about the x-axis between the origin and $x = 3$.

17. Find the moment of inertia of the body defined in problem 16 for rotation:

(a) about the x-axis; (b) about the y-axis.

18. Calculate the mean values of:

(a) $\sin x$; (b) $\sin^2 x$

for the interval $0 \leqslant x \leqslant \pi$.

19. Calculate the mean molecular speed $\bar{c}$ for molecules in a gas at temperature T given by

$$\bar{c} = 4\pi \left(\frac{m}{2\pi kT}\right)^{3/2} \int_0^\infty \exp \left(\frac{-mc^2}{2kT}\right) c^3 \, dc$$

20. The range of a projectile fired with initial velocity V_0 and an elevation θ is $(V_0^2/g) \sin 2\theta$. Find the mean range as θ varies from 0 to $\pi/2$.

4
Functions of Many Variables - Partial Differentiation

In chapter 2 we discussed in detail the differentiation of functions of a single variable and associated the derivative dy/dx of the function y = f(x) with the rate of change of y with respect to x. However, we saw in section 1.1.2 that in the physical world some property of the system of interest may depend on several variables. For example, the pressure P of a gas depends on the volume V, temperature T and the number of moles of gas n; that is

$$P = f(T,V,n)$$

In this chapter we discuss how we might define derivatives of functions of many variables, how the differentiation of functions of many variables differs from the differentiation of functions of a single variable and some important applications to chemistry.

4.1 DEFINITION OF PARTIAL DERIVATIVES

If we consider the ideal-gas law

$$P = \frac{nRT}{V} \tag{4.1}$$

and ask what is the rate of change of P as T changes, we could imagine keeping n and V constant and differentiating with respect to T

$$\frac{dP}{dT} = \frac{nR}{V} \tag{4.2}$$

We could define two other derivatives in this way

$$\frac{dP}{dV} = -\frac{nRT}{V^2}; \qquad \frac{dP}{dn} = \frac{RT}{V} \tag{4.3}$$

for which n,T and T,V, respectively, are kept constant.

These three derivatives are, in fact, *partial derivatives* and are given the special symbols $(\partial P/\partial T)_{n,V}$, $(\partial P/\partial V)_{n,T}$ and

$(\partial P/\partial n)_{T,V}$, where the variables outside the parentheses are those that are being kept constant.

The formal definitions of the partial derivatives of the function $z = f(x,y)$ are given by

$$\left(\frac{\partial f}{\partial x}\right)_y = \lim_{h \to 0} \left[\frac{f(x + h,\ y) - f(x,y)}{h}\right]$$
$$\left(\frac{\partial f}{\partial y}\right)_x = \lim_{k \to 0} \left[\frac{f(x,\ y + k) - f(x,y)}{k}\right] \qquad (4.4)$$

Alternative symbols for $(\partial f/\partial x)_y$ are $(\partial z/\partial x)_y$, f_x or z_x. Where there is no scope for ambiguity, the parentheses and the variables outside may be omitted. Parentheses and subscripts should be retained in thermodynamic notation. In the f_x or z_x notation, the subscript indicates the variable with respect to which the derivative is being taken.

We have to be clear that the independent variables x and y in the function $z = f(x,y)$ really are independent. Suppose we have an equilateral triangle of side x and a square of side y on a line AB of length 1 (figure 4.1). The total area A of the square and the triangle is

$$A = \frac{\sqrt{3}}{4} x^2 + y^2$$

However, x and y are not independent because $x + y = 1$.

Given the basic definitions (equations 4.4) of the partial derivative, we can use all the rules and methods we developed in chapter 2 in order to obtain partial derivatives. For example if

$$z = 4x^2 + 2xy + y^2$$

then

$$\left(\frac{\partial z}{\partial x}\right) = 4 \times 2x + 2y$$
$$\left(\frac{\partial z}{\partial y}\right) = 2x + 2y$$

If $z = \ln (x/y)$, spotting that

$$\ln \left(\frac{x}{y}\right) = \ln x - \ln y$$

we see that

$$\left(\frac{\partial z}{\partial x}\right) = \frac{1}{x}; \quad \left(\frac{\partial z}{\partial y}\right) = -\frac{1}{y}$$

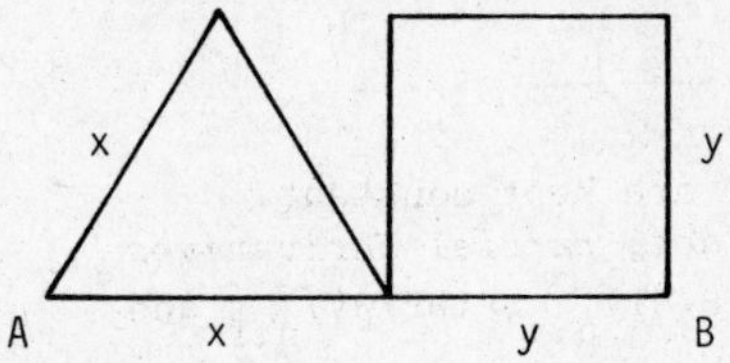

Figure 4.1

If

$$w = \sin ax \sin by \sin [kt\surd(a^2 + b^2)]$$

then

$$\frac{\partial w}{\partial x} = (a \cos ax) \sin by \sin [kt\surd(a^2 + b^2)]$$

$$\frac{\partial w}{\partial y} = \sin ax \,(b \cos by) \sin [kt\surd(a^2 + b^2)]$$

$$\frac{\partial w}{\partial t} = \sin ax \sin by \,[k\surd(a^2 + b^2)] \cos [kt\surd(a^2 + b^2)]$$

We may have a case in which $z = f(u)$ but u is a function of the two variables x and y; that is, $u = g(x,y)$. We apply the chain rule of section 2.4.5 in a straightforward manner to give

$$\frac{\partial z}{\partial x} = \frac{dz}{du} \times \frac{\partial u}{\partial x}$$

$$\frac{\partial z}{\partial y} = \frac{dz}{du} \times \frac{\partial u}{\partial y}$$

For example, $z = \cos (x/y)$. Here $u = x/y$, so

$$\frac{\partial z}{\partial x} = -\sin \left(\frac{x}{y}\right)\left(\frac{1}{y}\right)$$

$$\frac{\partial z}{\partial y} = -\sin \left(\frac{x}{y}\right)\left(-\frac{x}{y^2}\right)$$

4.2 GEOMETRICAL INTERPRETATION OF THE PARTIAL DERIVATIVE

We interpreted the derivative dy/dx of $y = f(x)$ as being the slope of the tangent to the curve at the point (x,y). The geometrical interpretation of the partial derivatives $\partial z/\partial x$ and $\partial z/\partial y$ of the function $z = f(x,y)$ is not so simple because we require a surface in three dimensions to portray the function z (see figure 4.2). At any point on the surface

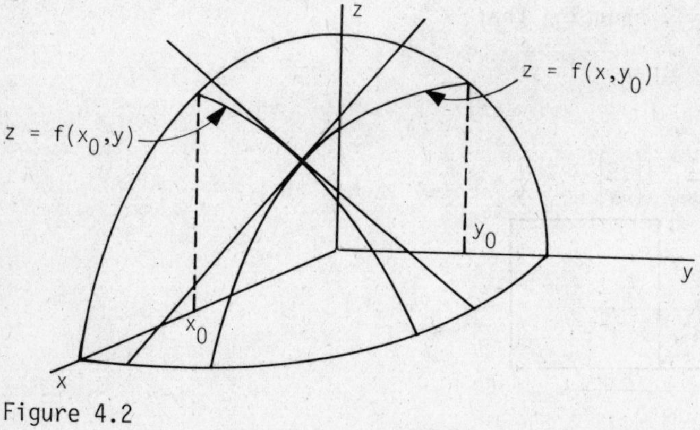

Figure 4.2

there will be an infinite number of ways of drawing the tangent. If we take a point on the surface (x_0, y_0, z_0), the value of $\partial f/\partial x$ at this point is the gradient of the tangent lying in a plane parallel to the xz plane at a distance y_0 along the y-axis; that is, it is the gradient in the plane for which y_0 is constant. Similarly the value of $\partial f/\partial y$ is the gradient in the plane parallel to the yz plane and passing through the point (x_0, y_0, z_0).

It is not possible to give a geometrical interpretation of the derivatives of a function $w = f(x,y,z)$ because we cannot represent w in three dimensions.

4.3 HIGHER DERIVATIVES

As in the case of functions of a single variable, partial derivatives are still functions of the independent variables. If $z = f(x,y)$

$$\frac{\partial z}{\partial x} = f_x(x,y), \quad \frac{\partial z}{\partial y} = f_y(x,y) \tag{4.5}$$

and these derivatives can be differentiated further provided that they are differentiable at the point in question. However, the situation is rather more complicated than the case of $y = f(x)$, because we can differentiate $f_x(x,y)$ with respect to x or y to give two second derivatives

$$\begin{aligned} \frac{\partial}{\partial x} f_x(x,y) &= \frac{\partial^2 z}{\partial x^2} = f_{xx}(x,y) \\ \frac{\partial}{\partial y} f_x(x,y) &= \frac{\partial^2 z}{\partial y\, \partial x} = f_{yx}(x,y) \end{aligned} \tag{4.6}$$

Similarly, there are two second derivatives derived from $f_y(x,y)$

$$\begin{aligned} \frac{\partial}{\partial x} f_y(x,y) &= \frac{\partial^2 z}{\partial x\, \partial y} = f_{xy}(x,y) \\ \frac{\partial}{\partial y} f_y(x,y) &= \frac{\partial^2 z}{\partial y^2} = f_{yy}(x,y) \end{aligned} \tag{4.7}$$

Provided that the derivatives f_{xy} and f_{yx} are continuous at the point of differentiation, it can be shown that $\partial^2 z/\partial x\partial y = \partial^2 z/\partial y\partial x$, so in general there are three distinct second derivatives. If $z = x/(x^2 + y^2)$, the first derivatives are

$$\frac{\partial z}{\partial x} = \frac{x^2 + y^2 - 2x^2}{(x^2 + y^2)^2} = \frac{y^2 - x^2}{(x^2 + y^2)^2}$$

$$\frac{\partial z}{\partial y} = -\frac{2xy}{(x^2 + y^2)^2}$$

and the second derivatives are

$$\frac{\partial^2 z}{\partial x^2} = \frac{(x^2 + y^2)^2(-2x) - (y^2 - x^2)4x(x^2 + y^2)}{(x^2 + y^2)^4}$$

$$= \frac{4x^3 - 6xy^2}{(x^2 + y^2)^3}$$

$$\frac{\partial^2 z}{\partial y^2} = \frac{(x^2 + y^2)^2(-2x) - (-2xy)4y(x^2 + y^2)}{(x^2 + y^2)^4}$$

$$= \frac{6xy^2 - 2x^3}{(x^2 + y^2)^3}$$

$$\frac{\partial^2 z}{\partial x \partial y} = \frac{(x^2 + y^2)^2(-2y) - (-2xy)4x(x^2 + y^2)}{(x^2 + y^2)^4}$$

$$= \frac{6x^2y - 2y^3}{(x^2 + y^2)^3}$$

$$\frac{\partial^2 z}{\partial y \partial x} = \frac{(x^2 + y^2)^2 2y - (y^2 - x^2)4y(x^2 + y^2)}{(x^2 + y^2)^4}$$

$$= \frac{6x^2y - 2y^3}{(x^2 + y^2)^3}$$

In this example, we see that the two mixed second derivatives $\partial^2 z/\partial y\partial x$ and $\partial^2 z/\partial x\partial y$ are equal. This, however, is not a proof of their equality in general. Thus it doesn't matter whether we differentiate with respect to x and then with respect to y or whether we do it the other way round. We say that the operations of differentiation with respect to x and y *commute* or that the operators $\partial/\partial x$ and $\partial/\partial y$ commute; that is

$$\frac{\partial}{\partial x} \times \frac{\partial}{\partial y} f(x,y) = \frac{\partial}{\partial y} \times \frac{\partial}{\partial x} f(x,y) \tag{4.9}$$

There will be four distinct third derivatives, namely

$$\frac{\partial^3 z}{\partial x^3}, \ \frac{\partial^3 z}{\partial x^2 \partial y}, \ \frac{\partial^3 z}{\partial x \partial y^2} \quad \text{and} \quad \frac{\partial^3 z}{\partial y^3}$$

4.4 CHANGE OF VARIABLE

4.4.1 First derivative

A particularly important result in partial differentiation concerns the change of variable. Suppose we have $z = F(u,v)$ but u and v are in turn functions of two other variables x and y

$$u = f(x,y) \text{ and } v = g(x,y)$$

and we wish to calculate the derivatives of z with respect to x and y. They are given by the formulae

$$\frac{\partial z}{\partial x} = \frac{\partial z}{\partial u} \times \frac{\partial u}{\partial x} + \frac{\partial z}{\partial v} \times \frac{\partial v}{\partial x}$$
$$\frac{\partial z}{\partial y} = \frac{\partial z}{\partial u} \times \frac{\partial u}{\partial y} + \frac{\partial z}{\partial v} \times \frac{\partial v}{\partial y} \qquad (4.10)$$

where it is assumed that z, u and v are differentiable functions.

A common application of this is in the change from cartesian to polar co-ordinates. We discussed cartesian co-ordinates in section 1.1. For many problems a more convenient co-ordinate system is that of *polar co-ordinates*, in which we specify the position of a point P on a plane in terms of its distance r from the origin O and the direction θ of the line OP with respect to some defined direction (usually the x-axis) (figure 4.3). If the point P has cartesian co-ordinates (x,y), its polar co-ordinates (r, θ) are given by the relations

$$x = r \cos \theta, \; y = r \sin \theta \qquad (4.11)$$

that is

$$r = +\sqrt{(x^2 + y^2)}, \; \theta = \tan^{-1}\left(\frac{y}{x}\right) \qquad (4.12)$$

If z = f(x,y) then the derivatives of z with respect to r and θ are

$$\frac{\partial z}{\partial r} = \frac{\partial z}{\partial x} \times \frac{\partial x}{\partial r} + \frac{\partial z}{\partial y} \times \frac{\partial y}{\partial r} = \cos\theta \frac{\partial z}{\partial x} + \sin\theta \frac{\partial z}{\partial y}$$
$$\frac{\partial z}{\partial \theta} = \frac{\partial z}{\partial x} \times \frac{\partial x}{\partial \theta} + \frac{\partial z}{\partial y} \times \frac{\partial y}{\partial \theta} = -r\sin\theta \frac{\partial z}{\partial x} + r\cos\theta \frac{\partial z}{\partial y} \qquad (4.13)$$

We may require the reverse transformation to obtain $\partial z/\partial x$ and $\partial z/\partial y$ in terms of derivatives with respect to r and θ. We could regard equations 4.13 as simultaneous equations and solve for $\partial z/\partial x$ and $\partial z/\partial y$ or we can proceed directly as follows

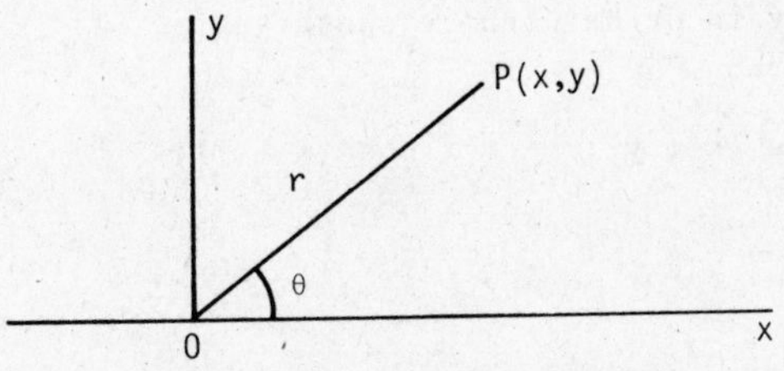

Figure 4.3

$$\frac{\partial r}{\partial x} = \frac{x}{\sqrt{(x^2 + y^2)}} = \cos\theta; \quad \frac{\partial r}{\partial y} = \frac{y}{\sqrt{(x^2 + y^2)}} = \sin\theta$$

$$\frac{\partial\theta}{\partial x} = -\frac{y}{x^2 + y^2} = -\frac{\sin\theta}{r}; \quad \frac{\partial\theta}{\partial y} = \frac{x}{x^2 + y^2} = \frac{\cos\theta}{r}$$

so

$$\frac{\partial z}{\partial x} = \frac{\partial z}{\partial r} \times \frac{\partial r}{\partial x} + \frac{\partial z}{\partial\theta} \times \frac{\partial\theta}{\partial x} = \cos\theta\,\frac{\partial z}{\partial r} - \frac{\sin\theta}{r}\,\frac{\partial z}{\partial\theta}$$

$$\frac{\partial z}{\partial y} = \frac{\partial z}{\partial r} \times \frac{\partial r}{\partial y} + \frac{\partial z}{\partial\theta} \times \frac{\partial\theta}{\partial y} = \sin\theta\,\frac{\partial z}{\partial r} + \frac{\cos\theta}{r}\,\frac{\partial z}{\partial\theta} \qquad (4.14)$$

It is very important to note that

$$\frac{\partial r}{\partial x} \neq \frac{1}{\partial x/\partial r}$$

here. This is because $\partial r/\partial x$ is really $(\partial r(x,y)/\partial x)_y$, whereas $\partial x/\partial r$ is $(\partial x(r,\theta)/\partial r)_\theta$, so we are discussing derivatives of completely different functions. One has to be very careful in these transformations to ensure that variables of different types are not being mixed.

If $z = f(u, v)$, where $u = 2\sqrt{(x\,y)}$ and $v = 2/\sqrt{(xy)}$, then

$$\frac{\partial z}{\partial x} = \frac{\partial z}{\partial u} \times \frac{\partial u}{\partial x} + \frac{\partial z}{\partial v} \times \frac{\partial v}{\partial x} = \sqrt{\left(\frac{y}{x}\right)}\,\frac{\partial z}{\partial u} - \frac{1}{x\sqrt{(xy)}}\,\frac{\partial z}{\partial v}$$

$$\frac{\partial z}{\partial y} = \frac{\partial z}{\partial u} \times \frac{\partial u}{\partial y} + \frac{\partial z}{\partial v} \times \frac{\partial v}{\partial y} = \sqrt{\left(\frac{x}{y}\right)}\,\frac{\partial z}{\partial u} - \frac{1}{y\sqrt{(xy)}}\,\frac{\partial z}{\partial v} \qquad (4.15)$$

A less general problem is the case in which $z = F(u,v)$, where u and v are functions of a single variable t, $u = f(t)$, $v = g(t)$. The expression for the ordinary derivative of z with respect to t, dz/dt is

$$\frac{dz}{dt} = \frac{\partial z}{\partial u} \times \frac{du}{dt} + \frac{\partial z}{\partial v} \times \frac{dv}{dt} \qquad (4.16)$$

This approach can also be applied to a function of the type $z = F(x,y)$, where y is some function $k(x)$ of x. In our previous notation $x \equiv u = t$ and $y \equiv v = k(x)$, so

$$\frac{dz}{dx} = \left(\frac{\partial z}{\partial x}\right)_y + \left(\frac{\partial z}{\partial y}\right)_x \frac{dy}{dx} \qquad (4.17)$$

A simple example is $z = x \sin(x + y)$, where $y = \sin x$, where this method enables us to obtain dz/dx without substituting for y

$$\frac{\partial z}{\partial x} = \sin(x + y) + x\cos(x + y); \quad \frac{\partial z}{\partial y} = x\cos(x + y);$$

$$\frac{dy}{dx} = \cos x$$

Therefore

$$\frac{dz}{dx} = \sin(x + y) + x\cos(x + y) + x\cos(x + y)\cos x$$

This formula occurs in thermodynamics when we wish to express, for example, the derivative with respect to temperature of the internal energy U, expressed as a function of temperature T and pressure P, $U = f_1(T,P)$, in terms of derivatives of the function $U = f_2(T,V)$. These two functions for U are related because T, P and V are related by an equation of state $V = g(T,P)$. Hence

$$\left(\frac{\partial U(T,P)}{\partial T}\right)_P = \left(\frac{\partial U(T,V)}{\partial T}\right)_V + \left(\frac{\partial U(T,V)}{\partial V}\right)_T \left(\frac{\partial V}{\partial T}\right)_P \qquad (4.18)$$

We can use this relationship to derive an expression for the specific heat of a gas at constant pressure C_p, in terms of its specific heat at constant volume C_v. C_p and C_v are defined in terms of the enthalpy H and internal energy by

$$C_p = \left(\frac{\partial H}{\partial T}\right)_P ; \; C_v = \left(\frac{\partial U}{\partial T}\right)_V$$

The enthalpy $H = U + PV$ so

$$C_p = \frac{\partial}{\partial T}(U + PV) = \left(\frac{\partial U}{\partial T}\right)_P + P\left(\frac{\partial V}{\partial T}\right)_P$$

Thus substituting into equation 4.18 gives

$$C_p - P\left(\frac{\partial V}{\partial T}\right)_P = C_v + \left(\frac{\partial U}{\partial V}\right)_T \left(\frac{\partial V}{\partial T}\right)_P \qquad (4.19)$$

that is

$$C_p = C_v + \left[\left(\frac{\partial U}{\partial V}\right)_T + P\right]\left(\frac{\partial V}{\partial T}\right)_P$$

The equation of state for one mole of an ideal gas is

$$PV = RT$$

and because the forces between the molecules are neglected, the internal energy is independent of the volume; that is $(\partial U/\partial V)_T$ is zero. Thus for an ideal gas

$$C_p = C_v + R \qquad (4.20)$$

4.4.2 Second derivative

The transformation of the first derivative discussed in the section above is fairly straightforward but the second derivative is more complicated. If $z = F(u,v)$, where $u = f(x,y)$ and $v = g(x,y)$, the first derivative is given by

$$\frac{\partial z}{\partial x} = \frac{\partial z}{\partial u} \times \frac{\partial u}{\partial x} + \frac{\partial z}{\partial v} \times \frac{\partial v}{\partial x} \qquad (4.21)$$

We obtain the second derivative by differentiating $\partial z/\partial x$ with respect to x. Formally

$$\frac{\partial^2 z}{\partial x^2} = \frac{\partial}{\partial x}\left(\frac{\partial z}{\partial x}\right) = \frac{\partial}{\partial x}\left(\frac{\partial z}{\partial u} \times \frac{\partial u}{\partial x} + \frac{\partial z}{\partial v} \times \frac{\partial v}{\partial x}\right) \quad (4.22)$$

We have to differentiate each term on the right-hand side of equation 4.22 by the product rule

$$\frac{\partial^2 z}{\partial x^2} = \left[\frac{\partial}{\partial x}\left(\frac{\partial z}{\partial u}\right)\right]\frac{\partial u}{\partial x} + \frac{\partial z}{\partial u} \times \frac{\partial^2 u}{\partial x^2} + \left[\frac{\partial}{\partial x}\left(\frac{\partial z}{\partial v}\right)\right]\frac{\partial v}{\partial x} + \frac{\partial z}{\partial v} \times \frac{\partial^2 v}{\partial x^2} \quad (4.23)$$

In order to evaluate $(\partial/\partial x)(\partial z/\partial u)$ and $(\partial/\partial x)(\partial z/\partial v)$ we have to realise that $\partial z/\partial u$ and $\partial z/\partial v$ are functions of u and v, and in order to obtain their derivatives with respect to x (and y) we have to use the basic formulae (equations 4.10) again

$$\begin{aligned}\frac{\partial}{\partial x}\left(\frac{\partial z}{\partial u}\right) &= \left[\frac{\partial}{\partial u}\left(\frac{\partial z}{\partial u}\right)\right]\frac{\partial u}{\partial x} + \left[\frac{\partial}{\partial v}\left(\frac{\partial z}{\partial u}\right)\right]\frac{\partial v}{\partial x}\\ \frac{\partial}{\partial x}\left(\frac{\partial z}{\partial v}\right) &= \left[\frac{\partial}{\partial u}\left(\frac{\partial z}{\partial v}\right)\right]\frac{\partial u}{\partial x} + \left[\frac{\partial}{\partial v}\left(\frac{\partial z}{\partial v}\right)\right]\frac{\partial v}{\partial x}\end{aligned} \quad (4.24)$$

so we obtain for $\partial^2 z/\partial x^2$

$$\frac{\partial^2 z}{\partial x^2} = \frac{\partial^2 z}{\partial u^2}\left(\frac{\partial u}{\partial x}\right)^2 + 2\frac{\partial^2 z}{\partial u \partial v}\left(\frac{\partial u}{\partial x}\right)\left(\frac{\partial v}{\partial x}\right) + \frac{\partial^2 z}{\partial v^2}\left(\frac{\partial v}{\partial x}\right)^2 + \left(\frac{\partial z}{\partial u}\right)\left(\frac{\partial^2 u}{\partial x^2}\right) + \left(\frac{\partial z}{\partial v}\right)\left(\frac{\partial^2 v}{\partial x^2}\right) \quad (4.25)$$

The other second derivatives $\partial^2 z/\partial x\partial y$ and $\partial^2 z/\partial y^2$ can be obtained similarly.

Often it is not necessary to work from first principles in order to obtain the second derivatives. If we wish to transform the derivatives $\partial^2\psi/\partial x^2 + \partial^2\psi/\partial y^2$ in the two-dimensional Schrödinger equation into polar co-ordinates, we can do this using the results for the first derivatives $\partial\psi/\partial x$ and $\partial\psi/\partial y$ from equation 4.14. If $\psi = f(x,y)$, where $x = r\cos\theta$ and $y = r\sin\theta$, we have shown that

$$\frac{\partial\psi}{\partial x} = \cos\theta\,\frac{\partial\psi}{\partial r} - \frac{\sin\theta}{r}\frac{\partial\psi}{\partial\theta}$$

$$\frac{\partial\psi}{\partial y} = \sin\theta\,\frac{\partial\psi}{\partial r} + \frac{\cos\theta}{r}\frac{\partial\psi}{\partial\theta}$$

We can use these relations to write down the *operators* for differentiation with respect to x and y in terms of r and θ only

$$\begin{aligned}\frac{\partial}{\partial x} &= \cos\theta\,\frac{\partial}{\partial r} - \frac{\sin\theta}{r}\frac{\partial}{\partial\theta}\\ \frac{\partial}{\partial y} &= \sin\theta\,\frac{\partial}{\partial r} + \frac{\cos\theta}{r}\frac{\partial}{\partial\theta}\end{aligned} \quad (4.26)$$

Here we are saying that if ψ is transformed to a function of r and θ, expressions for $\partial\psi/\partial x$ and $\partial\psi/\partial y$ in terms of r and θ can be obtained by allowing the expressions on the right-hand side of equation 4.26 to operate on $\psi(r,\theta)$.

We require $\partial^2\psi/\partial x^2 + \partial^2\psi/\partial y^2$. $\partial^2\psi/\partial x^2$ is obtained by differentiating $\partial\psi/\partial x$ with respect to x, thus

$$\frac{\partial^2\psi}{\partial x^2} = \frac{\partial}{\partial x}\left(\frac{\partial\psi}{\partial x}\right) = \left(\cos\theta\frac{\partial}{\partial r} - \frac{\sin\theta}{r}\frac{\partial}{\partial\theta}\right)\left(\cos\theta\frac{\partial\psi}{\partial r} - \frac{\sin\theta}{r}\frac{\partial\psi}{\partial\theta}\right) \quad (4.27)$$

In manipulating the expression on the right-hand side of equation 4.27, we have to remember that the first bracket contains differential operators and that we shall have to use the rule for differentiating products where appropriate

$$\frac{\partial^2\psi}{\partial x^2} = \cos\theta\frac{\partial}{\partial r}\left(\cos\theta\frac{\partial\psi}{\partial r}\right) - \cos\theta\frac{\partial}{\partial r}\left(\frac{\sin\theta}{r}\frac{\partial\psi}{\partial\theta}\right) - \frac{\sin\theta}{r}\frac{\partial}{\partial\theta}\left(\cos\theta\frac{\partial\psi}{\partial r}\right) + \frac{\sin\theta}{r}\frac{\partial}{\partial\theta}\left(\frac{\sin\theta}{r}\frac{\partial\psi}{\partial\theta}\right) \quad (4.28)$$

$$= \cos^2\theta\frac{\partial^2\psi}{\partial r^2} + \frac{\cos\theta\sin\theta}{r^2}\frac{\partial\psi}{\partial\theta} - \frac{\cos\theta\sin\theta}{r}\frac{\partial^2\psi}{\partial r\partial\theta} + \frac{\sin^2\theta}{r}\frac{\partial\psi}{\partial r} - \frac{\sin\theta\cos\theta}{r}\frac{\partial^2\psi}{\partial r\partial\theta} + \frac{\sin\theta\cos\theta}{r^2}\frac{\partial\psi}{\partial\theta} + \frac{\sin^2\theta}{r^2}\frac{\partial^2\psi}{\partial\theta^2}$$

$$= \cos^2\theta\frac{\partial^2\psi}{\partial r^2} + \frac{2\cos\theta\sin\theta}{r}\frac{\partial\psi}{\partial\theta} - \frac{2\cos\theta\sin\theta}{r}\frac{\partial^2\psi}{\partial r\partial\theta} + \frac{\sin^2\theta}{r}\frac{\partial\psi}{\partial r} + \frac{\sin^2\theta}{r^2}\frac{\partial^2\psi}{\partial\theta^2}$$

By a similar method we obtain

$$\frac{\partial^2\psi}{\partial y^2} = \left(\sin\theta\frac{\partial}{\partial r} + \frac{\cos\theta}{r}\frac{\partial}{\partial\theta}\right)\left(\sin\theta\frac{\partial\psi}{\partial r} + \frac{\cos\theta}{r}\frac{\partial\psi}{\partial\theta}\right)$$

$$= \sin^2\theta\frac{\partial^2\psi}{\partial r^2} - \frac{2\cos\theta\sin\theta}{r^2}\frac{\partial\psi}{\partial\theta} + \frac{2\sin\theta\cos\theta}{r}\frac{\partial^2\psi}{\partial r\partial\theta} + \frac{\cos^2\theta}{r}\frac{\partial\psi}{\partial r} + \frac{\cos^2\theta}{r^2}\frac{\partial^2\psi}{\partial\theta^2} \quad (4.29)$$

so

$$\frac{\partial^2\psi}{\partial x^2} + \frac{\partial^2\psi}{\partial y^2} = \frac{\partial^2\psi}{\partial r^2} + \frac{1}{r}\frac{\partial\psi}{\partial r} + \frac{1}{r^2}\frac{\partial^2\psi}{\partial\theta^2} \tag{4.30}$$

We can apply similar techniques to other problems. Earlier we discussed the example of $z = f(u,v)$, where $u = 2\sqrt{(xy)}$ and $v = 2/\sqrt{(xy)}$ and showed that

$$\frac{\partial z}{\partial x} = \sqrt{\left(\frac{y}{x}\right)}\frac{\partial z}{\partial u} - \frac{1}{x\sqrt{(xy)}}\frac{\partial z}{\partial v}$$

and

$$\frac{\partial z}{\partial y} = \sqrt{\left(\frac{x}{y}\right)}\frac{\partial z}{\partial u} - \frac{1}{y\sqrt{(xy)}}\frac{\partial z}{\partial v}$$

We cannot conveniently express the right-hand side entirely in terms of u and v at this stage. However, if we consider $2x\,\partial z/\partial x$ and $2y\,\partial z/\partial y$, we obtain

$$2x\frac{\partial z}{\partial x} = 2\sqrt{(xy)}\frac{\partial z}{\partial u} - \frac{2}{\sqrt{(xy)}}\frac{\partial z}{\partial v} = u\frac{\partial z}{\partial u} - v\frac{\partial z}{\partial v} \tag{4.31}$$

and

$$2y\frac{\partial z}{\partial y} = 2\sqrt{(xy)}\frac{\partial z}{\partial u} - \frac{2}{\sqrt{(xy)}}\frac{\partial z}{\partial v} = u\frac{\partial z}{\partial u} - v\frac{\partial z}{\partial v}$$

We can now readily obtain second derivatives from these expressions because

$$\begin{aligned} 2x\frac{\partial}{\partial x}\left(2y\frac{\partial z}{\partial y}\right) &= 4xy\frac{\partial^2 z}{\partial x\partial y} \\ 2x\frac{\partial}{\partial x}\left(2x\frac{\partial z}{\partial x}\right) &= 4x\frac{\partial z}{\partial x} + 4x^2\frac{\partial^2 z}{\partial x^2} \\ 2y\frac{\partial}{\partial y}\left(2y\frac{\partial z}{\partial y}\right) &= 4y\frac{\partial z}{\partial y} + 4y^2\frac{\partial^2 z}{\partial y^2} \end{aligned} \tag{4.32}$$

Thus

$$\begin{aligned} 4xy\frac{\partial^2 z}{\partial x\partial y} &= \left(u\frac{\partial}{\partial u} - v\frac{\partial}{\partial v}\right)\left(u\frac{\partial z}{\partial u} - v\frac{\partial z}{\partial v}\right) \\ &= u\frac{\partial}{\partial u}\left(u\frac{\partial z}{\partial u}\right) - u\frac{\partial}{\partial u}\left(v\frac{\partial z}{\partial v}\right) - v\frac{\partial}{\partial v}\left(u\frac{\partial z}{\partial u}\right) \\ &\quad + v\frac{\partial}{\partial v}\left(v\frac{\partial z}{\partial v}\right) \qquad (4.33) \\ &= u^2\frac{\partial^2 z}{\partial u^2} + u\frac{\partial z}{\partial u} - uv\frac{\partial^2 z}{\partial u\partial v} - vu\frac{\partial^2 z}{\partial v\partial u} + v^2\frac{\partial^2 z}{\partial v^2} \\ &\quad + v\frac{\partial z}{\partial v} \\ &= u^2\frac{\partial^2 z}{\partial u^2} + v^2\frac{\partial^2 z}{\partial v^2} - 2uv\frac{\partial^2 z}{\partial u\partial v} + u\frac{\partial z}{\partial u} + v\frac{\partial z}{\partial v} \end{aligned}$$

4.4.3 Spherical polar co-ordinates

The transformations of equation 4.11 are appropriate for two-dimensional problems. In general we are interested in three dimensional problems. For example, in quantum mechanics the Schrödinger equation is

$$\frac{\partial^2\psi}{\partial x^2} + \frac{\partial^2\psi}{\partial y^2} + \frac{\partial^2\psi}{\partial z^2} + \frac{8\pi^2 m}{h^2}\left[E - V\right]\psi = 0$$

where ψ is the wavefunction, m is the mass of the particle, h is Planck's constant, E is the total energy and V is the potential energy. In the hydrogen atom, V is of the form $1/r$, where r is the distance of the electron from the centre of mass. In terms of rectangular cartesian co-ordinates, V is proportional to $1/\sqrt{(x^2 + y^2 + z^2)}$ which is a very awkward expression to work with. The equation is much easier to solve when it is transformed to *spherical polar co-ordinates*. Let the cartesian co-ordinates of P be (x,y,z). OP (figure 4.4) makes an angle θ with the z-axis. However, we have to define the plane in which OP lies and this is done by dropping a perpendicular PR on to the xy plane and defining the angle between OR and the x-axis as ϕ. Elementary trigonometry then gives the relations

$$\begin{aligned} x &= r \sin\theta \cos\phi \\ y &= r \sin\theta \sin\phi \\ z &= r \cos\theta \end{aligned} \qquad (4.34)$$

We shall, therefore, wish to obtain expressions for $\partial^2\psi/\partial x^2$, $\partial^2\psi/\partial y^2$ and $\partial^2\psi/\partial z^2$ in terms of r, θ and ϕ. The basic equations are an extension of equations 4.10 and are

$$\begin{aligned} \frac{\partial\psi}{\partial x} &= \frac{\partial\psi}{\partial r}\times\frac{\partial r}{\partial x} + \frac{\partial\psi}{\partial\theta}\times\frac{\partial\theta}{\partial x} + \frac{\partial\psi}{\partial\phi}\times\frac{\partial\phi}{\partial x} \\ \frac{\partial\psi}{\partial y} &= \frac{\partial\psi}{\partial r}\times\frac{\partial r}{\partial y} + \frac{\partial\psi}{\partial\theta}\times\frac{\partial\theta}{\partial y} + \frac{\partial\psi}{\partial\phi}\times\frac{\partial\phi}{\partial y} \\ \frac{\partial\psi}{\partial z} &= \frac{\partial\psi}{\partial r}\times\frac{\partial r}{\partial z} + \frac{\partial\psi}{\partial\theta}\times\frac{\partial\theta}{\partial z} + \frac{\partial\psi}{\partial\phi}\times\frac{\partial\phi}{\partial z} \end{aligned} \qquad (4.35)$$

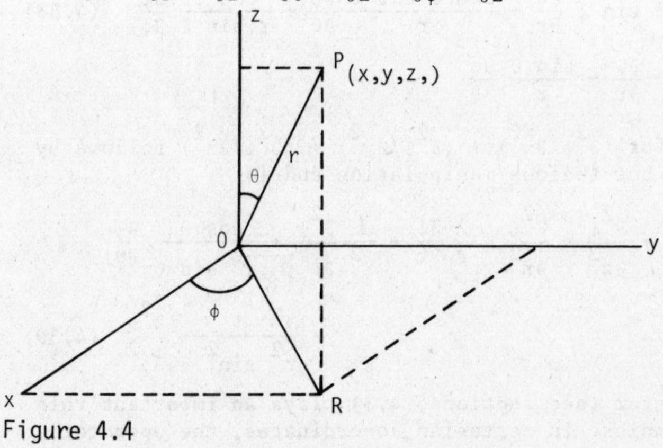

Figure 4.4

Thus we require the derivatives of r, θ and ϕ with respect to x, y and z, and therefore we first have to obtain r, θ and ϕ as functions of x, y and z

$$r = \sqrt{(x^2 + y^2 + z^2)} \qquad \theta = \cos^{-1}\left(\frac{z}{\sqrt{(x^2 + y^2 + z^2)}}\right)$$

$$\phi = \tan^{-1}\left(\frac{y}{x}\right) \tag{4.36}$$

The calculation of the derivatives is excellent practice in partial differentiation and the results are

$$\frac{\partial r}{\partial x} = \frac{x}{\sqrt{(x^2 + y^2 + z^2)}} = \sin\theta\cos\phi; \quad \frac{\partial r}{\partial y} = \frac{y}{\sqrt{(x^2 + y^2 + z^2)}} = \sin\theta\sin\phi$$

$$\frac{\partial r}{\partial z} = \frac{z}{\sqrt{(x^2 + y^2 + z^2)}} = \cos\theta; \quad \frac{\partial \theta}{\partial x} = \frac{xz}{(x^2 + y^2 + z^2)\sqrt{(x^2 + y^2)}} = \frac{\cos\phi\cos\theta}{r} \tag{4.37}$$

$$\frac{\partial \theta}{\partial y} = \frac{yz}{(x^2 + y^2 + z^2)\sqrt{(x^2 + y^2)}} = \frac{\sin\phi\cos\theta}{r};$$

$$\frac{\partial \theta}{\partial z} = -\sqrt{\left(\frac{x^2 + y^2}{x^2 + y^2 + z^2}\right)} = -\frac{\sin\theta}{r}$$

$$\frac{\partial \phi}{\partial x} = -\frac{y}{x^2 + y^2} = -\frac{\sin\phi}{r\sin\theta}; \quad \frac{\partial \phi}{\partial y} = \frac{x}{x^2 + y^2} = \frac{\cos\phi}{r\sin\theta};$$

$$\frac{\partial \phi}{\partial z} = 0$$

Thus

$$\frac{\partial \psi}{\partial x} = \sin\theta\cos\phi\frac{\partial \psi}{\partial r} + \frac{\cos\theta\cos\phi}{r}\frac{\partial \psi}{\partial \theta} - \frac{\sin\phi}{r\sin\theta}\frac{\partial \psi}{\partial \phi}$$

$$\frac{\partial \psi}{\partial y} = \sin\theta\sin\phi\frac{\partial \psi}{\partial r} + \frac{\sin\phi\cos\theta}{r}\frac{\partial \psi}{\partial \theta} + \frac{\cos\phi}{r\sin\theta}\frac{\partial \psi}{\partial \phi} \tag{4.38}$$

$$\frac{\partial \psi}{\partial z} = \cos\theta\frac{\partial \psi}{\partial r} - \frac{\sin\theta}{r}\frac{\partial \psi}{\partial \theta}$$

The expression for $(\partial^2\psi/\partial x^2) + (\partial^2\psi/\partial y^2) + (\partial^2\psi/\partial z^2)$ follows by straightforward but tedious manipulation and is

$$\frac{\partial^2\psi}{\partial x^2} + \frac{\partial^2\psi}{\partial y^2} + \frac{\partial^2\psi}{\partial z^2} = \frac{\partial^2\psi}{\partial r^2} + \frac{2}{r}\frac{\partial \psi}{\partial r} + \frac{1}{r^2}\frac{\partial^2\psi}{\partial \theta^2} + \frac{\cos\theta}{r^2\sin\theta}\frac{\partial \psi}{\partial \theta} + \frac{1}{r^2\sin^2\theta}\frac{\partial^2\psi}{\partial \phi^2} \tag{4.39}$$

Angular momentum (see section 5.4.3) plays an important role in quantum mechanics. In cartesian co-ordinates, the operator for the z component is given by

$$M_z = \frac{h}{2\pi i}\left[x\frac{\partial}{\partial y} - y\frac{\partial}{\partial x}\right] \tag{4.40}$$

where h is Planck's constant and i is the square root of -1 (see chapter 7). Using the relations we have just derived, in spherical polar co-ordinates this becomes

$$\frac{h}{2\pi i}\left[r \sin\theta \cos\phi \left(\sin\theta \sin\phi \frac{\partial}{\partial r} + \frac{\cos\theta \sin\phi}{r}\frac{\partial}{\partial\theta} + \frac{\cos\phi}{r\sin\theta}\frac{\partial}{\partial\phi}\right) - r\sin\theta\sin\phi\left(\sin\theta\cos\phi\frac{\partial}{\partial r} + \frac{\cos\theta\cos\phi}{r}\frac{\partial}{\partial\theta} - \frac{\sin\phi}{r\sin\theta}\frac{\partial}{\partial\phi}\right)\right] \tag{4.41}$$

$$= \frac{h}{2\pi i}\left[\cos^2\phi\frac{\partial}{\partial\phi} + \sin^2\phi\frac{\partial}{\partial\phi}\right] = \frac{h}{2\pi i}\frac{\partial}{\partial\phi}$$

4.5 THE TOTAL DIFFERENTIAL

In section 2.7, we discussed an approximate formula for the change Δy in y for the function $y = f(x)$ as x changes by a small amount Δx and saw that

$$\Delta y \approx f'(x)\,\Delta x \tag{4.42}$$

We derived this by rearranging the definition of the derivative to give

$$f(x + \Delta x) - f(x) = \Delta x\left[f'(x) + \phi(\Delta x)\right] \tag{4.43}$$

There is an analagous expression for the case of $z = f(x,y)$. If we increase x and y by amounts Δx and Δy from the values x_0, y_0, z changes by

$$\Delta z = f_x(x_0, y_0)\,\Delta x + f_y(x_0, y_0)\Delta y + \varepsilon_1\Delta x + \varepsilon_2\Delta y \tag{4.44}$$

where ε_1 and ε_2 are functions that approach zero as Δx and Δy approach zero. This leads to an approximate expression for the change in z

$$\Delta z \approx f_x(x_0, y_0)\Delta x + f_y(x_0, y_0)\Delta y \tag{4.45}$$

This is often a useful method for calculating the change in z resulting from small changes Δx and Δy in x and y, respectively.

By analogy with the single-variable case, we can define for $z = f(x,y)$ the differential of z, dz in terms of the differentials dx and dy

$$dz = \left(\frac{\partial z}{\partial x}\right)_y dx + \left(\frac{\partial z}{\partial y}\right)_x dy \tag{4.46}$$

dz is known as the *total differential*. In contrast with equation 4.45, this is an exact expression. Thus if

$$z = 4x^2 + 2xy + y^2$$

using the derivatives obtained on page 91, we get the total differential

$$dz = (8x + 2y)\,dx + (2x + 2y)\,dy \tag{4.47}$$

If $z = \cos(x/y)$, we obtain

$$dz = \left[-\frac{1}{y}\sin\left(\frac{x}{y}\right)\right]dx + \left[\frac{x}{y^2}\sin\left(\frac{x}{y}\right)\right]dy \tag{4.48}$$

The total differential for a function of more than two variables is the logical extension of equation 4.46. If $z = f(u,v,w,x,y\ \ldots)$ then

$$dz = \frac{\partial f}{\partial u}du + \frac{\partial f}{\partial v}dv + \frac{\partial f}{\partial w}dw + \ldots \tag{4.49}$$

In thermodynamics we shall often deduce a relation of the form

$$dz = M(x,y)dx + N(x,y)dy \tag{4.50}$$

where $M(x,y)$ and $N(x,y)$ are functions of x and y. It is a matter of considerable interest and importance to decide whether we can deduce from this relation a function $z = f(x,y)$ such that

$$\left(\frac{\partial z}{\partial x}\right)_y = M(x,y) \quad \text{and} \quad \left(\frac{\partial z}{\partial y}\right)_x = N(x,y) \tag{4.51}$$

If we return to the definition of the total differential

$$dz = \left(\frac{dz}{\partial x}\right)dx + \left(\frac{\partial z}{\partial y}\right)dy$$

we know from the commutative property of partial differentiation that

$$\frac{\partial}{\partial y}\left(\frac{\partial z}{\partial x}\right) = \frac{\partial}{\partial x}\left(\frac{\partial z}{\partial y}\right) \tag{4.52}$$

provided, of course, that the second derivatives are continuous at the point of differentiation. We can easily check that the total differentials 4.47 and 4.48 satisfy this criterion.

$$\frac{\partial}{\partial y}(8x + 2y) = 2; \quad \frac{\partial}{\partial x}(2x + 2y) = 2 \tag{4.53}$$

$$\frac{\partial}{\partial y}\left[-\frac{1}{y}\sin\left(\frac{x}{y}\right)\right] = \left(\frac{1}{y^2}\right)\sin\left(\frac{x}{y}\right) + \left(\frac{x}{y^3}\right)\cos\left(\frac{x}{y}\right)$$

$$\frac{\partial}{\partial x}\left[\frac{x}{y^2}\sin\left(\frac{x}{y}\right)\right] = \left(\frac{1}{y^2}\right)\sin\left(\frac{x}{y}\right) + \left(\frac{x}{y^3}\right)\cos\left(\frac{x}{y}\right) \tag{4.54}$$

We can use this property as a criterion for the existence of a function $z = f(x,y)$ such that, for

$$dz = M(x,y)dx + N(x,y)dy$$

$$\left(\frac{\partial z}{\partial x}\right) = M(x,y) \quad \text{and} \quad \left(\frac{\partial z}{\partial y}\right) = N(x,y) \tag{4.55}$$

This condition is the *Euler reciprocity relation* that

$$\frac{\partial}{\partial y}M(x,y) = \frac{\partial}{\partial x}N(x,y) \tag{4.56}$$

If this relation is obeyed, then there is a function $z = f(x,y)$ satisfying equation 4.55, and dz is said to be an *exact differential*. An important property of z is that if x and y change from (x_1,y_1) to (x_2,y_2), then the change in z, $\Delta z = f(x_2,y_2) - f(x_1,y_1)$ is *independent* of the way in which x and y vary in going from one set of values to the other. We shall discuss this further in section 4.8.

The differential

$$y\,dx + 2\ln x\,dy \tag{4.57}$$

is not exact because

$$\frac{\partial}{\partial y}(y) \neq \frac{\partial}{\partial x}(2\ln x)$$

However, the differential

$$\frac{y^2}{x}\,dx + 2y\ln x\,dy \tag{4.58}$$

is exact since $\partial/\partial y(y^2/x)$ is equal to $\partial/\partial x(2y\ln x)$.

Examples of functions in thermodynamics that have exact differentials are volume, internal energy U, enthalpy H, entropy S, Helmholtz free energy A, Gibbs free energy G, and these functions are known as *state functions*. The differentials of work and heat change are not exact.

If we consider one mole of an ideal gas obeying the law

$$PV = RT$$

$$dV = \left(\frac{\partial V}{\partial T}\right)dT + \left(\frac{\partial V}{\partial P}\right)dP = \frac{R}{P}\,dT - \frac{RT}{P^2}\,dP \tag{4.59}$$

is obviously an exact differential because we have derived it from $V = f(P,T)$ and condition 4.56 is satisfied. The work done dW on such a gas in expansion, from section 2.7, is -PdV; that is

$$dW = -PdV = -RdT + \frac{RT}{P}\,dP \tag{4.60}$$

This is not an exact differential because $\partial/\partial P(-R) = 0$, but $\partial/\partial T(RT/P) = R/P$ and criterion 4.56 is not satisfied. Thus the work done on the gas depends on the precise way in which the expansion from P_1, V_1 to P_2, V_2 is carried out, whereas the volume change depends only on the initial and final values.

The heat change dQ in a process is given by

$$dQ = dU - dW$$

where dU is the change in internal energy. U is a function of T and V so

$$\begin{aligned} dQ &= \left(\frac{\partial U}{\partial T}\right)_V dT + \left(\frac{\partial U}{\partial V}\right)_T dV + PdV \\ &= \left(\frac{\partial U}{\partial T}\right)_V dT + \left[\left(\frac{\partial U}{\partial V}\right)_T + P\right]dV \end{aligned} \tag{4.61}$$

For an ideal gas we said in section 4.4.1 that the internal energy is independent of the volume; that is $(\partial U/\partial V)_T = 0$.

$(\partial U/\partial T)_V$ is the specific heat at constant volume, C_v and is a function of temperature so

$$dQ = C_v\, dT + PdV$$
$$= C_v\, dT + \frac{RT}{V}\, dV \qquad (4.62)$$

$$\frac{\partial}{\partial V}(C_v) = \frac{\partial}{\partial V}\left(\frac{\partial U}{\partial T}\right)_V = \frac{\partial}{\partial T}\left(\frac{\partial U}{\partial V}\right)_T = 0$$

and

$$\frac{\partial}{\partial T}\left(\frac{RT}{V}\right) = \frac{R}{V}$$

so the differential is not exact.

However, if we divide by T

$$\frac{dQ}{T} = \frac{C_v}{T}\, dT + \frac{R}{V}\, dV \qquad (4.63)$$

we see that the right-hand side is an exact differential because

$$\frac{\partial}{\partial V}\left(\frac{C_v}{T}\right) = \frac{\partial}{\partial T}\left(\frac{R}{V}\right) = 0.$$

Thus dQ/T is an exact differential and is therefore the differential of a state function, which is in fact the entropy S. Here we have converted an inexact differential into an exact differential by multiplying by an *integrating factor*.

4.6 IMPLICIT FUNCTIONS

4.6.1 Functions of a single variable

We can use the total differential to obtain an alternative method for the differentiation of implicit functions of the type $f(x,y) = 0$, for example $x \cos y - y \cos x = c$. Even though $f(x,y) = 0$, we can write down the total differential

$$df = \left(\frac{\partial f}{\partial x}\right) dx + \left(\frac{\partial f}{\partial y}\right) dy \qquad (4.64)$$

but since $f(x,y)$ is equal to zero, df is zero and we can rearrange equation 4.64 to give

$$\frac{dy}{dx} = -\frac{(\partial f/\partial x)}{(\partial f/\partial y)} = -\frac{f_x}{f_y} \qquad (4.65)$$

So, in our example

$$\frac{dy}{dx} = -\frac{(\cos y + y \sin x)}{(-x \sin y - \cos x)}$$

If exp(x sin y) - 2 exp(x cos y) - exp(x) = 0, then

$$\frac{dy}{dx} = - \frac{[\sin y \exp(x \sin y) - 2 \cos y \exp(x \cos y) - \exp(x)]}{[x \cos y \exp(x \sin y) + 2x \sin y \exp(x \cos y)]}$$

4.6.2 Functions of two variables

The above section merely gives us an alternative to the method of section 2.8. However, if we have an implicit function of two variables, F(x,y,z) = 0, we can use a similar approach to obtain, for example, the partial derivative of z with respect to x or y. Writing down the total differential

$$dF = \left(\frac{\partial F}{\partial x}\right) dx + \left(\frac{\partial F}{\partial y}\right) dy + \left(\frac{\partial F}{\partial z}\right) dz = 0 \qquad (4.66)$$

we can rearrange to obtain

$$dz = - \frac{(\partial F/\partial x)\,dx}{(\partial F/\partial z)} - \frac{(\partial F/\partial y)\,dy}{(\partial F/\partial z)} \qquad (4.67)$$

If y is constant, dy is zero and we obtain (dz/dx) which is really the partial derivative of z with respect to x because we have kept y constant; that is

$$\left(\frac{\partial z}{\partial x}\right)_y = - \frac{(\partial F/\partial x)}{(\partial F/\partial z)} \qquad (4.68)$$

Similarly

$$\left(\frac{\partial z}{\partial y}\right)_x = - \frac{(\partial F/\partial y)}{(\partial F/\partial z)} \qquad (4.69)$$

Suppose we wish to calculate the coefficient of expansion for a gas obeying Dieterici's equation of state

$$P(V - b)\exp(a/RTV) = RT \qquad (4.70)$$

where a and b are constants. We require the derivative $(\partial V/\partial T)_P$, which we cannot obtain by direct means. However, using equation 4.68 we see that

$$\left(\frac{\partial V}{\partial T}\right)_P = - \frac{(\partial F/\partial T)_{V,P}}{(\partial F/\partial V)_{T,P}}$$

where F(P,V,T) = P(V - b)exp(a/RTV) - RT = 0

$$\left(\frac{\partial F}{\partial T}\right)_{V,P} = - \frac{a}{TV} - R; \quad \left(\frac{\partial F}{\partial V}\right)_{T,P} = \frac{RT}{V - b} - \frac{a}{V^2}$$

so

$$\left(\frac{\partial V}{\partial T}\right)_P = \frac{(a/TV) + R}{[RT/(V - b)] - (a/V^2)} \qquad (4.71)$$

4.6.3 A useful relation between partial derivatives

If $z = f(x,y)$, we can use the above ideas to relate $(\partial z/\partial x)_y$, $(\partial z/\partial y)_x$ and $(\partial y/\partial x)_z$ as follows. The total differential dz is

$$dz = \left(\frac{\partial z}{\partial x}\right)_y dx + \left(\frac{\partial z}{\partial y}\right)_x dy \qquad (4.72)$$

If z is a constant, dz is zero and we obtain $(\partial y/\partial x)_z$ by rearranging equation 4.72 to give

$$\left(\frac{\partial y}{\partial x}\right)_z = -\frac{(\partial z/\partial x)_y}{(\partial z/\partial y)_x} \qquad (4.73)$$

For example, we can relate the rate of change of the pressure of a gas with temperature T, the thermal expansivity $\alpha = (1/V_0)(\partial V/\partial T)_P$ and the compressibility $\beta = -(1/V_0)(\partial V/\partial P)_T$ because

$$\left(\frac{\partial P}{\partial T}\right)_V = -\frac{(\partial V/\partial T)_P}{(\partial V/\partial P)_T} = \frac{\alpha}{\beta} \qquad (4.74)$$

An alternative form of equation 4.73 is

$$\left(\frac{\partial y}{\partial x}\right)_z \left(\frac{\partial x}{\partial z}\right)_y \left(\frac{\partial z}{\partial y}\right)_x = -1 \qquad (4.75)$$

Here it is in order to write

$$\left(\frac{\partial x}{\partial z}\right)_y = \frac{1}{(\partial z/\partial x)_y}$$

because no change of variable is involved.

4.7 THE LEGENDRE TRANSFORMATION AND MAXWELL'S RELATIONS

The differential of the internal energy can be written as

$$dU = TdS - PdV \qquad (4.76)$$

where S is the entropy. But if $U = f(S,V)$

$$dU = \left(\frac{\partial U}{\partial S}\right)_V dS + \left(\frac{\partial U}{\partial V}\right)_S dV$$

we can write $T = (\partial U/\partial S)_V$ and $P = -(\partial U/\partial V)_S$. We can obtain similar total differentials for the other state functions A, H and G from their definitions in terms of U, S, P, V and T, that is

$$H = U + PV; \quad A = U - TS; \quad G = H - TS \qquad (4.77)$$

and the *Legendre transformation*. If f is a function of n variables $x_1, x_2 \ldots x_n$, then

$$df = \left(\frac{\partial f}{\partial x_1}\right)dx_1 + \left(\frac{\partial f}{\partial x_2}\right)dx_2 + \ldots + \left(\frac{\partial f}{\partial x_n}\right)dx_n \qquad (4.78)$$

Let us now consider the function

$$g = f - \left(\frac{\partial f}{\partial x_1}\right) x_1 \tag{4.79}$$

The total differential of g will be

$$dg = df - \left(\frac{\partial f}{\partial x_1}\right) dx_1 - d\left(\frac{\partial f}{\partial x_1}\right) x_1$$

$$= -d\left(\frac{\partial f}{\partial x_1}\right) x_1 + \left(\frac{\partial f}{\partial x_2}\right) dx_2 + \left(\frac{\partial f}{\partial x_3}\right) dx_3 + \ldots + \left(\frac{\partial f}{\partial x_n}\right) dx_n \tag{4.80}$$

This is the *Legendre transformation*. Now

$$H = U + PV = U - \left(\frac{\partial U}{\partial V}\right)_S V$$

which is of the form of equation 4.79. Therefore, using equation 4.80, we get

$$dH = V\,dP + T\,dS \tag{4.81}$$

Similarly

$$A = U - TS = U - S\left(\frac{\partial U}{\partial S}\right)_V$$

so

$$dA = -P\,dV - S\,dT \tag{4.82}$$

and

$$G = H - TS = H - S\left(\frac{\partial U}{\partial S}\right)_V$$

so

$$dG = V\,dP - S\,dT \tag{4.83}$$

Collecting these results together along with the usual total differentials we get

$$\begin{aligned}
dU &= T\,dS - P\,dV = \left(\frac{\partial U}{\partial S}\right)_V dS + \left(\frac{\partial U}{\partial V}\right)_S dV \\
dH &= T\,dS + V\,dP = \left(\frac{\partial H}{\partial S}\right)_P dS + \left(\frac{\partial H}{\partial P}\right)_S dP \\
dA &= -P\,dV - S\,dT = \left(\frac{\partial A}{\partial V}\right)_T dV + \left(\frac{\partial A}{\partial T}\right)_V dT \\
dG &= V\,dP - S\,dT = \left(\frac{\partial G}{\partial P}\right)_T dP + \left(\frac{\partial G}{\partial T}\right)_P dT
\end{aligned} \tag{4.84}$$

Comparing coefficients gives the set of relations

$$
\begin{aligned}
T &= \left(\frac{\partial U}{\partial S}\right)_V & P &= -\left(\frac{\partial U}{\partial V}\right)_S \\
V &= \left(\frac{\partial H}{\partial P}\right)_S & T &= \left(\frac{\partial H}{\partial S}\right)_P \\
P &= -\left(\frac{\partial A}{\partial V}\right)_T & S &= -\left(\frac{\partial A}{\partial T}\right)_V \\
V &= \left(\frac{\partial G}{\partial P}\right)_T & S &= -\left(\frac{\partial G}{\partial T}\right)_P
\end{aligned}
\qquad (4.85)
$$

Because of the expressions in equation 4.84, we can apply the Euler reciprocity relation; for example

$$\frac{\partial}{\partial V}\left(\frac{\partial U}{\partial S}\right)_V = \frac{\partial}{\partial S}\left(\frac{\partial U}{\partial V}\right)_S$$

to give *Maxwell's relations*, which are

$$
\begin{aligned}
\left(\frac{\partial T}{\partial V}\right)_S &= -\left(\frac{\partial P}{\partial S}\right)_V \\
\left(\frac{\partial V}{\partial S}\right)_P &= \left(\frac{\partial T}{\partial P}\right)_S \\
\left(\frac{\partial P}{\partial T}\right)_V &= \left(\frac{\partial S}{\partial V}\right)_T \\
\left(\frac{\partial V}{\partial T}\right)_P &= -\left(\frac{\partial S}{\partial P}\right)_T
\end{aligned}
\qquad (4.86)
$$

4.8 LINE INTEGRALS

In section 4.5 we referred to the calculation of the change in z, $z(x_2,y_2) - z(x_1,y_1)$ from the differential expression

$$dz = M(x,y)\ dx + N(x,y)\ dy \qquad (4.87)$$

Unless we can write y as a function of x or x as a function of y, we cannot integrate this expression. If we write down formally the integral

$$z_1 - z_2 = \int_{z_1}^{z_2} dz = \int_{y_1}^{y_2}\int_{x_1}^{x_2} [M(x,y)\ dx + N(x,y)\ dy] \qquad (4.88)$$

the expression is meaningless unless we can eliminate x or y from the integral. Such integrals are *line integrals* because we have to specify the path C, y = f(x) or x = g(y) in the xy plane, along which the integration is to be performed. Making the substitution reduces the integral to a straightforward integral with respect to x or y.

Consider, for example, the integral

$$\int(x^2 + 2xy + y^2)dx + \int(x^3 + 3x^2y + 3xy^2 + y^3)dy$$

along the path $y = x^2$ from $x = 0$ to $x = 4$. Making the appropriate substitution gives

$$\int_0^4(x^2 + 2x^3 + x^4)dx + \int_0^4(x^3 + 3x^4 + 3x^5 + x^6)x\,dx \qquad (4.89)$$

which can easily be integrated.

A simple example of a line integral is the expression for the work W done on a gas on expansion

$$W = -\int_{V_1}^{V_2} P\,dV \qquad (4.90)$$

We cannot evaluate this unless we know how P varies with V. If for an ideal gas, the process is isothermal (that is, it is performed at constant temperature), PV is a constant C and

$$W = -\int_{V_1}^{V_2} C\,\frac{dV}{V} = -C\ln\frac{V_2}{V_1} \qquad (4.91)$$

whereas for an adiabatic process PV^γ = a constant k and

$$W = -\int_{V_1}^{V_2} k\,\frac{dV}{V^\gamma} = +\frac{k}{\gamma - 1}\left[\frac{1}{V_2^{\gamma-1}} - \frac{1}{V_1^{\gamma-1}}\right] \qquad (4.92)$$

Thus, in general, the line integral depends on the path taken.

However, we said in section 4.5 that if

$$dz = M(x,y)\,dx + N(x,y)\,dy$$

is an exact differential, the change in z in going from (x_1,y_1) to (x_2,y_2) depends only on (x_1,y_1) and (x_2,y_2) and not on the path taken. Thus the line integral of an exact differential is path independent.

An important case is integration round a closed plane curve. The direction of integration matters and we define a positive and negative sense as in figure 4.5, and the line integrals are

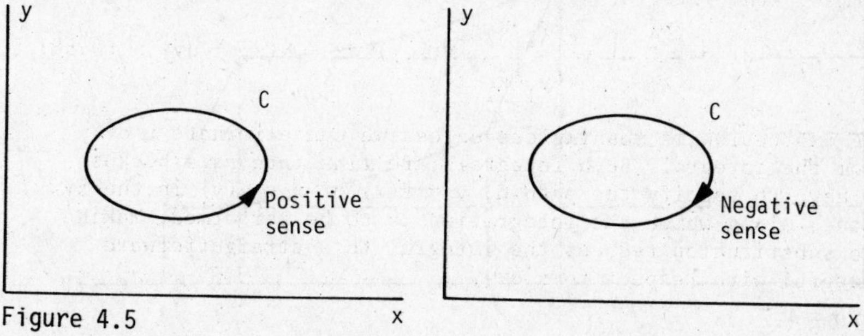

Figure 4.5

designated thus

$$\text{Positive sense} \qquad \oint [M(x,y)\,dx + N(x,y)\,dy]$$

$$\text{Negative sense} \qquad \oint [M(x,y)\,dx + N(x,y)\,dy] \tag{4.93}$$

The integration has to be performed in sections as shown in figure 4.6.

$$I = \int_{A\to M\to B} [M(x,y)\,dx + N(x,y)\,dy] + \int_{B\to N\to A} [M(x,y)\,dx + N(x,y)\,dy)] \tag{4.94}$$

An example of this is the Carnot cycle (figure 4.7) in which we calculate the work done in expanding a gas isothermally from P_1V_1 to P_2V_2, expanding it adiabatically to P_3V_3, compressing it isothermally to P_4V_4 and finally compressing it back to P_1V_1 adiabatically.

If we integrate an exact differential around a closed plane curve, the line integral will be zero because the starting and finishing points are identical.

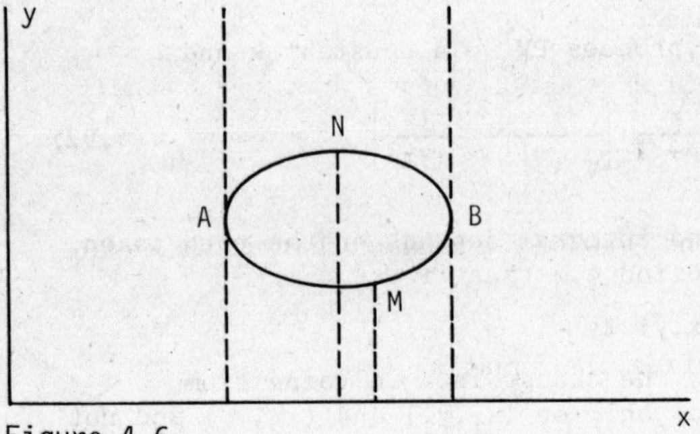

Figure 4.6

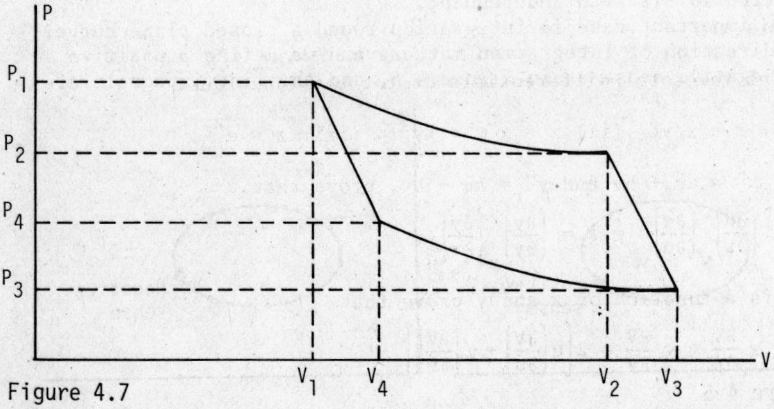

Figure 4.7

4.9 PROBLEMS FOR SOLUTION

1. Find the partial derivatives $\partial z/\partial x$ and $\partial z/\partial y$ for the functions

(i) $z = \cos(x^2 + y^2)$; (ii) $z = \dfrac{xy}{x^2 + y^2}$ $[(x,y) \neq 0]$;

(iii) $z = \dfrac{ax}{y^2}$

2. If $f(x,y) = \sin(x - y)e^{x+y}$, find:

(i) $\dfrac{\partial f}{\partial x}$; (ii) $\dfrac{\partial f}{\partial y}$; (iii) $\dfrac{\partial^2 f}{\partial x^2}$; (iv) $\dfrac{\partial^2 f}{\partial x \partial y}$; (v) $\dfrac{\partial^2 f}{\partial y^2}$.

3. The temperature θ in a homogeneous body, at the point (x,y) at time t is given by the function

$$\theta = \frac{1}{t} \exp \frac{-(x^2 + y^2)}{4t}$$

Show that θ satisfies the diffusion equation

$$\frac{\partial^2 \theta}{\partial x^2} + \frac{\partial^2 \theta}{\partial y^2} = \frac{\partial \theta}{\partial t}$$

4. If $f(x,y,z) = \left[\left(\frac{x}{y}\right) + \left(\frac{y}{z}\right) + \left(\frac{z}{x}\right)\right] \log\left[\left(\frac{x}{y}\right) + \left(\frac{y}{z}\right) + \left(\frac{z}{x}\right)\right]$, find:

(i) f_x; (ii) f_y; (iii) f_z.

5. If $u = x^5 y - \sin y$, find $\partial^2 u/\partial x \partial y$ and show that it is equal to $\partial^2 u/\partial y \partial x$.

6. If $V = x^3 + axy^2$ satisfies the equation

$$\frac{\partial^2 V}{\partial x^2} + \frac{\partial^2 V}{\partial y^2} = 0$$

what is a?

7. Find the total differentials dz for the functions:

(i) $z = x/y$; (ii) $z = x^2 y + xy^3$; (iii) $z = e^{xy}$.

8. If $x^2 = au + bv$ and $y^2 = au - bv$, prove that

$$\left(\frac{\partial u}{\partial x}\right)_y \left(\frac{\partial x}{\partial u}\right)_v = \tfrac{1}{2} = \left(\frac{\partial v}{\partial y}\right)_x \left(\frac{\partial y}{\partial v}\right)_u$$

If V is a function of x and y prove that

$$x\frac{\partial V}{\partial x} + y\frac{\partial V}{\partial y} = 2\left[u\left(\frac{\partial V}{\partial u}\right) + v\left(\frac{\partial V}{\partial v}\right)\right]$$

9. If f is a function of x and y that can, using the substitution $x = re^{\theta}$ and $y = re^{-\theta}$, be transformed into a function of r and θ, prove that:

(i) $$2x\left(\frac{\partial f}{\partial x}\right) = r\left(\frac{\partial f}{\partial r}\right) + \frac{\partial f}{\partial \theta}$$

$$2y\left(\frac{\partial f}{\partial y}\right) = r\left(\frac{\partial f}{\partial r}\right) - \frac{\partial f}{\partial \theta}$$

(ii) $$2x^2\left(\frac{\partial^2 f}{\partial x^2}\right) + 2y^2\left(\frac{\partial^2 f}{\partial y^2}\right) = r^2\left(\frac{\partial^2 f}{\partial r^2}\right) + \frac{\partial^2 f}{\partial \theta^2} - r\left(\frac{\partial f}{\partial r}\right)$$

10. If $u = x - y$ and $v = xy$ and $f(x,y)$ is a function of x and y, express (i) $\partial f/\partial x$ and (ii) $\partial f/\partial y$ in terms of $\partial f/\partial u$ and $\partial f/\partial v$, and hence prove that

$$\frac{\partial^2 f}{\partial x \partial y} = \frac{\partial f}{\partial v} - \frac{\partial^2 f}{\partial u^2} + u\frac{\partial^2 f}{\partial u \partial v} + v\frac{\partial^2 f}{\partial v^2}$$

(U.W.)

11. If $w = f(x,y)$, where $x = u + v$ and $y = u - v$, show that

$$\frac{\partial^2 w}{\partial u \partial v} = \frac{\partial^2 w}{\partial x^2} - \frac{\partial^2 w}{\partial y^2}$$

(U.W.)

12. Given that ψ is a function of r, ψ(r), where $r^2 = x^2 + y^2 + z^2$ prove that

$$\frac{\partial^2 \psi}{\partial x^2} + \frac{\partial^2 \psi}{\partial y^2} + \frac{\partial^2 \psi}{\partial z^2} = \frac{1}{r^2}\frac{\partial}{\partial r}\left[r^2\left(\frac{\partial \psi}{\partial r}\right)\right]$$

13. If $z = f(x,y)$, where $x = \exp(s)\cos t$ and $y = \exp(s)\sin t$, show that

$$\left(\frac{\partial z}{\partial s}\right)^2 + \left(\frac{\partial z}{\partial t}\right)^2 = \exp(2s)\left[\left(\frac{\partial z}{\partial x}\right)^2 + \left(\frac{\partial z}{\partial y}\right)^2\right]$$

14. Derive expressions in spherical polar co-ordinates for the quantum mechanical operators for the x and y components of angular momentum given that the cartesian expressions are

$$M_x = \frac{h}{2\pi i}\left[y\left(\frac{\partial}{\partial z}\right) - z\left(\frac{\partial}{\partial y}\right)\right]$$

$$M_y = \frac{h}{2\pi i}\left[z\left(\frac{\partial}{\partial x}\right) - x\left(\frac{\partial}{\partial z}\right)\right]$$

15. Given that $E = f(P,V,T)$ and $g(P,V,T) = 0$, show that

$$C_p = C_v + \left[V - \left(\frac{\partial H}{\partial P}\right)_T\right]\left(\frac{\partial P}{\partial T}\right)_V$$

where $H = PV + E$, $C_P = (\partial H/\partial T)_P$ and $C_V = (\partial E/\partial T)_V$.

16. Find dy/dx for the following functions, using the formula involving partial derivatives:

(i) $3x^2 + 7xy + 9y^2 = 6$; (ii) $(x^2 + y^2)^2 - (x^2 - y^2) = 0$;
(iii) $x^3 + y^3 = 3xy$; (iv) $\sin x \cos y = c$; (v) $x^m y^n = a^{x+y}$.

17. Derive an expression for the coefficient of thermal expansion $\alpha = (1/V_0)(\partial V/\partial T)_P$ for a gas that follows:

(i) the ideal-gas law $PV = RT$; (ii) the van der Waals equation $[P + (a/V^2)](V - b) = RT$.

18. Test the following differentials for exactness:

(i) $(e^y + 1)\cos x\, dx + e^y \sin x\, dy$;
(ii) $y(x^2 + \ln y)dx + x\, dy$; (iii) $2xy\, dx + (y^2 - x^2)dy$;
(iv) $(x^3 - 3x^2y + 5xy^2 - 7y^3)dx + (y^4 + 2y^2 - x^3 + 5x^2y - 21xy^2)dy$.

19. Evaluate the line integrals:

(i) $\int[2xy\, dx + (y^2 - x^2)dy]$ along the curve $y = x^2$ from $x = 0$ to $x = 4$;
(ii) $\int[2xy\, dx + (y^2 - x^2)dy]$ along the curve $y = x$ from $x = 0$ to $x = 4$;
(iii) $\int[y(x^2 \ln y)dx + x\, dy]$ along the curve $y = e^x$ from $x = 1$ to $x = 3$;
(iv) $\int[2xy\, dx + (x^2 + y^2)dy]$ along the curves $y = x$ and $y = x^2$ from $x = 0$ to $x = 1$.

5

Vectors

Many of the quantities we consider in physical and chemical problems are pure numbers and do not have any directional properties. Examples are mass, temperature and energy. Such quantities are *scalars*. However, other properties such as force, velocity, electric field and angular momentum have both magnitude and direction and are called *vectors*. Vector quantities are of great importance in many molecular problems such as the discussion of angular momentum in atomic and molecular structure, the interaction of electromagnetic fields with matter and in diffusion problems, so it is essential that we learn how to work with such quantities.

A vector can be represented diagrammatically by a line PQ. The length of the line is a measure of its *magnitude* and its orientation indicates the direction of the vector (figure 5.1). The way in which the arrow points is important. In this case P is the *origin* and Q is the *terminus* of the vector $\vec{PQ}$. Vectors are usually represented by a single bold face character $\mathbf{a}$. A *unit vector* is a vector of unit length and the vector $\mathbf{a}$ can be written as the product of the magnitude of $\mathbf{a}$, $|\mathbf{a}|$ and a unit vector $\hat{\mathbf{a}}$ having the same direction

$$\mathbf{a} = |\mathbf{a}|\hat{\mathbf{a}} \tag{5.1}$$

We shall make very frequent use of unit vectors.

5.1 VECTOR ALGEBRA

Since vectors are very different from scalars, we have to consider their manipulation in some detail.

(i) Two vectors are equal only when they have the same magnitude and the same direction.
(ii) If $\mathbf{b}$ has the same magnitude as $\mathbf{a}$ but is opposite in direction, then it is the vector $-\mathbf{a}$ (figure 5.2).
(iii) We can have a *null vector* $\mathbf{0}$ which has zero magnitude and no directional properties.
(iv) Vector addition. You have probably already met the idea of vector addition in the *parallelogram of forces* in which the *resultant* $\mathbf{C}$ of two forces $\mathbf{A}$ and $\mathbf{B}$ acting at a point O is given by the diagonal of a parallelogram obtained from $\mathbf{A}$ and $\mathbf{B}$ (figure 5.3). Since forces are vectors, this method is perfectly general and can be applied to all vectors. In vector notation we write

Figure 5.1

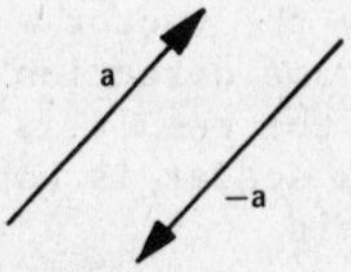

Figure 5.2

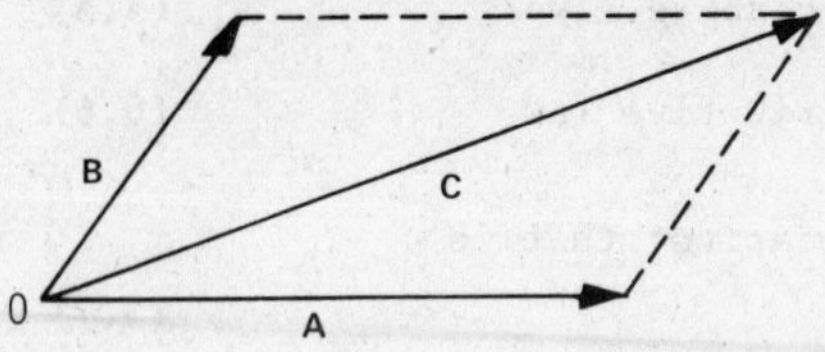

Figure 5.3

$$\mathbf{C} = \mathbf{A} + \mathbf{B} \tag{5.2}$$

This is the *parallelogram law for vector addition*. It is clearly immaterial whether we take **A** first and then add **B** or whether we add **A** to **B**.

We say that vector addition is *commutative* (see figure 5.4), that is

$$\mathbf{C} = \mathbf{A} + \mathbf{B} = \mathbf{B} + \mathbf{A} \tag{5.3}$$

(v) Vector subtraction. We can obtain the difference between two vectors, **A** − **B** by rewriting this as **A** + (−**B**) and recalling that (−**B**) is a vector of the same magnitude as **B** but having the opposite direction. Applying the parallelogram law gives for **C** = **A** − **B** the result shown in figure 5.5. This can be obtained from a triangle (figure 5.6). Clearly **A** − **A** = **0**.

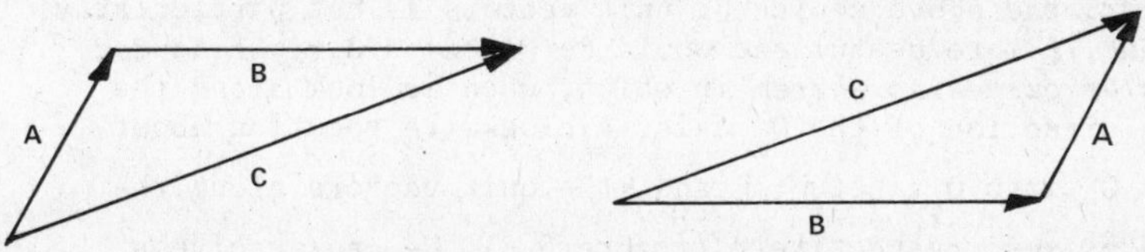

Figure 5.4

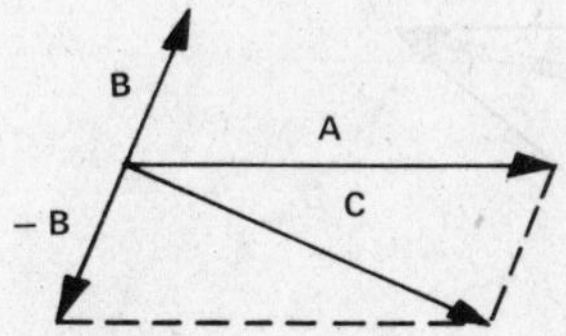

Figure 5.5

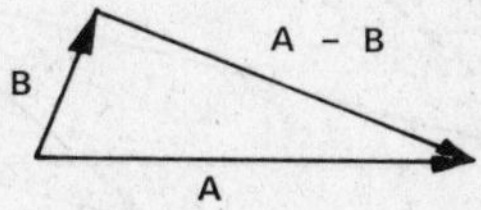

Figure 5.6

(vi) If we multiply the vector $\mathbf{a}$ by a scalar m, we obtain a vector having the same direction as $\mathbf{a}$ but with magnitude $m|\mathbf{a}|$. If m is zero the result is the null vector. Multiplication by a scalar is *commutative, associative* and *distributive*, that is

$$m\mathbf{a} = \mathbf{a}m \qquad \text{commutative law} \qquad (5.4)$$

$$m(n\mathbf{a}) = n(m\mathbf{a}) \qquad \text{associative law} \qquad (5.5)$$

$$\left.\begin{array}{l}(m+n)\mathbf{a} = m\mathbf{a} + n\mathbf{a}\\ m(\mathbf{a}+\mathbf{b}) = m\mathbf{a} + m\mathbf{b}\end{array}\right\} \qquad \text{distributive law} \qquad (5.6)$$

(vii) Vector addition is *associative*; that is

$$\mathbf{a} + (\mathbf{b} + \mathbf{c}) = (\mathbf{a} + \mathbf{b}) + \mathbf{c} \qquad (5.7)$$

This means that it doesn't matter whether we first add $\mathbf{b}$ and $\mathbf{c}$ and then add $\mathbf{a}$ or whether we add $\mathbf{a}$ and $\mathbf{b}$ and then $\mathbf{c}$.

5.2 RESOLUTION OF A VECTOR

Consider the vector

$$\mathbf{r} = \mathbf{a} + \mathbf{b} + \mathbf{c} \qquad (5.8)$$

where $\mathbf{a}$, $\mathbf{b}$ and $\mathbf{c}$ are three vectors in three dimensions. We can represent these geometrically by the three edges of a parallelepiped (figure 5.7). Let the magnitudes of $\mathbf{a}$, $\mathbf{b}$ and $\mathbf{c}$ be a, b and c, respectively, and let us define three *unit vectors* $\hat{\mathbf{a}}$, $\hat{\mathbf{b}}$ and $\hat{\mathbf{c}}$ having the same directions as $\mathbf{a}$, $\mathbf{b}$ and $\mathbf{c}$. Thus we can write

$$\mathbf{r} = a\hat{\mathbf{a}} + b\hat{\mathbf{b}} + c\hat{\mathbf{c}} \qquad (5.9)$$

We say that a, b and c are the *components* of the vector $\mathbf{r}$ in the directions of $\hat{\mathbf{a}}$, $\hat{\mathbf{b}}$ and $\hat{\mathbf{c}}$, and that we have resolved the vector into its components. This is unique.

However, the above choice of unit vectors is not particularly convenient. A more useful set would be based on a *right-handed rectangular cartesian system* in which, when we look along the positive direction of the O_z axis, a clockwise rotation about O_z takes O_x into O_y. Let $\hat{\mathbf{i}}$, $\hat{\mathbf{j}}$ and $\hat{\mathbf{k}}$ be unit vectors along the x, y and z axes, respectively (figure 5.8). We can resolve a vector $\mathbf{r}$ into its components $r_x\hat{\mathbf{i}}$, $r_y\hat{\mathbf{j}}$, $r_z\hat{\mathbf{k}}$, thus

$$\mathbf{r} = r_x\hat{\mathbf{i}} + r_y\hat{\mathbf{j}} + r_z\hat{\mathbf{k}} \qquad (5.10)$$

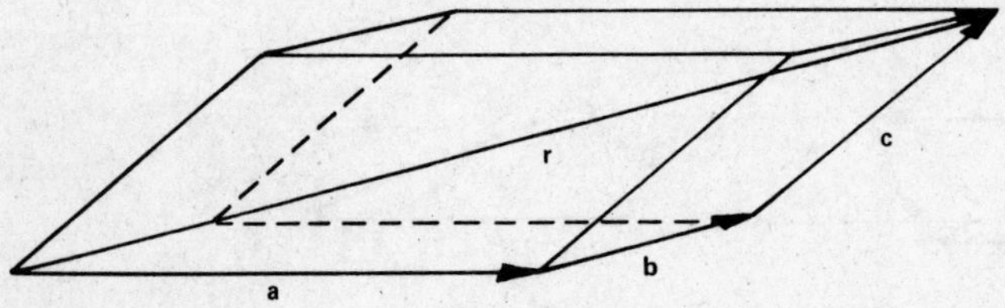

Figure 5.7

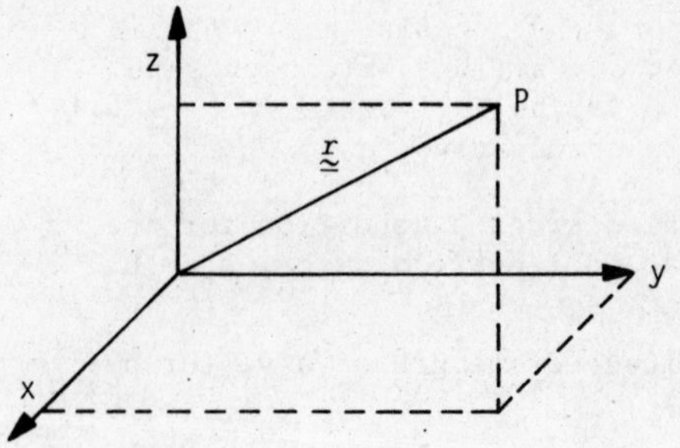

Figure 5.8

Any arbitrary vector **a** can be resolved in this way

$$\mathbf{a} = a_x\hat{\mathbf{i}} + a_y\hat{\mathbf{j}} + a_z\hat{\mathbf{k}} \tag{5.11}$$

If **r** makes the angles α, β, γ with the x-, y- and z-axes, we can write

$$\frac{\mathbf{r}}{|\mathbf{r}|} = \hat{\mathbf{r}} = \hat{\mathbf{i}} \cos\alpha + \hat{\mathbf{j}} \cos\beta + \hat{\mathbf{k}} \cos\gamma \tag{5.12}$$

where $\cos\alpha$, $\cos\beta$, $\cos\gamma$ are the *direction cosines* of the position vector $\hat{\mathbf{r}}$ and can be denoted by l, m and n. They are useful in the discussion of crystal structures.

The addition and subtraction of vectors is particularly straightforward when we express the vectors in terms of components. Let us take the two-dimensional example of **a** + **b**, where $\mathbf{a} = a_x\hat{\mathbf{i}} + a_y\hat{\mathbf{j}}$ and $\mathbf{b} = b_x\hat{\mathbf{i}} + b_y\hat{\mathbf{j}}$ (figure 5.9). Performing the addition graphically using the parallelogram, we see that $c_x = a_x + b_x$ and $c_y = a_y + b_y$. Generalising this to three dimensions,

$$\mathbf{c} = \mathbf{a} + \mathbf{b} = (a_x + b_x)\hat{\mathbf{i}} + (a_y + b_y)\hat{\mathbf{j}} + (a_z + b_z)\hat{\mathbf{k}} \tag{5.13}$$

that is

$$c_x = a_x + b_x, \quad c_y = a_y + b_y, \quad c_z = a_z + b_z \tag{5.14}$$

If we have the vectors $\mathbf{a} = 2\hat{\mathbf{i}} + 3\hat{\mathbf{j}} - 6\hat{\mathbf{k}}$ and $b = 3\hat{\mathbf{i}} - 4\hat{\mathbf{j}} + 7\hat{\mathbf{k}}$, then

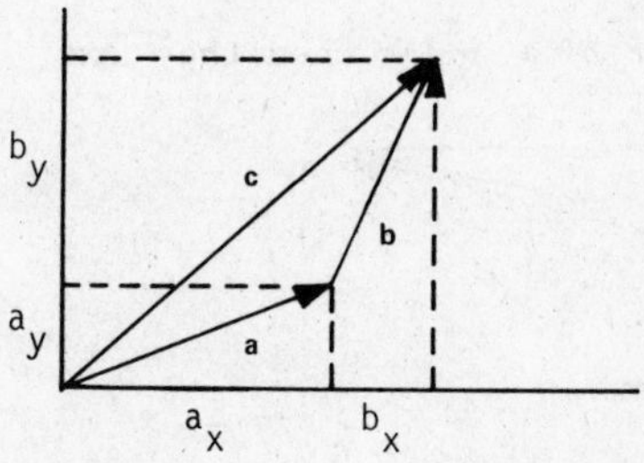

Figure 5.9

$$\mathbf{a} + \mathbf{b} = 5\hat{i} - \hat{j} + \hat{k}$$

and (5.15)

$$\mathbf{a} - \mathbf{b} = -\hat{i} + 7\hat{j} - 13\hat{k}$$

Resolution into components also gives a condition for the equality of **a** and **b**, namely that we require $a_x = b_x$, $a_y = b_y$ and $a_z = b_z$.

We can also define the magnitude or length of a vector by applying Pythagoras's theorem

$$r = |\mathbf{r}| = \sqrt{(r_x^2 + r_y^2 + r_z^2)} \tag{5.16}$$

for example the length of the vector $\mathbf{a} = 2\hat{i} + 3\hat{j} - 6\hat{k}$ is

$$|\mathbf{a}| = \sqrt{(4 + 9 + 36)} = 7 \tag{5.17}$$

5.3 PRODUCTS OF VECTORS

Two types of product can be defined for two vectors depending on whether the result is a scalar or a vector.

5.3.1 Scalar product

This is written $\mathbf{a}\cdot\mathbf{b}$ and is defined by

$$\mathbf{a}\cdot\mathbf{b} = |\mathbf{a}||\mathbf{b}| \cos\theta \tag{5.18}$$

where θ is the angle between **a** and **b** (figure 5.10). $|\mathbf{b}|\cos\theta$ is the projection of **b** on to **a** and $|\mathbf{a}|\cos\theta$ is the projection of **a** on to **b** so we can regard the *scalar product* or *dot product* $\mathbf{a}\cdot\mathbf{b}$ as equal to the projection of **b** on to **a** × the magnitude of **a** or equal to the projection of **a** on to **b** × the magnitude **b**.

Scalar multiplication is commutative

$$\mathbf{a}\cdot\mathbf{b} = \mathbf{b}\cdot\mathbf{a} \tag{5.19}$$

and obeys the distributive law

$$\mathbf{a}\cdot(\mathbf{b} + \mathbf{c}) = \mathbf{a}\cdot\mathbf{b} + \mathbf{a}\cdot\mathbf{c} \tag{5.20}$$

Scalar multiplying factors follow the rules of ordinary algebra

$$(s\mathbf{a})\cdot(t\mathbf{b}) = st(\mathbf{a}\cdot\mathbf{b}). \tag{5.21}$$

Let us now consider the scalar product of **a** and **b** when they are expressed in terms of components; that is

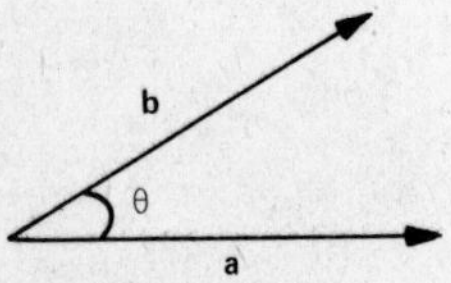

Figure 5.10

$$\mathbf{a} = a_x\hat{\mathbf{i}} + a_y\hat{\mathbf{j}} + a_z\hat{\mathbf{k}}$$
$$\mathbf{b} = b_x\hat{\mathbf{i}} + b_y\hat{\mathbf{j}} + b_z\hat{\mathbf{k}} \quad (5.22)$$

We require the individual scalar products $\hat{\mathbf{i}}.\hat{\mathbf{i}}$ and $\hat{\mathbf{i}}.\hat{\mathbf{j}}$, etc. The angle between $\hat{\mathbf{i}}$ and itself is 0 and therefore $\hat{\mathbf{i}}.\hat{\mathbf{i}} = 1.1 \cos 0 = 1$.

$$\hat{\mathbf{i}}.\hat{\mathbf{i}} = \hat{\mathbf{j}}.\hat{\mathbf{j}} = \hat{\mathbf{k}}.\hat{\mathbf{k}} = 1 \quad (5.23)$$

However, $\mathbf{i}$ and $\mathbf{j}$ are perpendicular and $\hat{\mathbf{i}}.\hat{\mathbf{j}} = 1.1 \cos(\pi/2) = 0$. Thus we have

$$\hat{\mathbf{i}}.\hat{\mathbf{j}} = \hat{\mathbf{i}}.\hat{\mathbf{k}} = \hat{\mathbf{j}}.\hat{\mathbf{k}} = 0 \quad (5.24)$$

We can now expand $\mathbf{a}.\mathbf{b}$ in terms of components

$$\mathbf{a}.\mathbf{b} = (a_x\hat{\mathbf{i}} + a_y\hat{\mathbf{j}} + a_z\hat{\mathbf{k}}).(b_x\hat{\mathbf{i}} + b_y\hat{\mathbf{j}} + b_z\hat{\mathbf{k}})$$
$$= a_xb_x\hat{\mathbf{i}}.\hat{\mathbf{i}} + a_xb_y\hat{\mathbf{i}}.\hat{\mathbf{j}} + a_xb_z\hat{\mathbf{i}}.\hat{\mathbf{k}}$$
$$+ a_yb_x\hat{\mathbf{j}}.\hat{\mathbf{i}} + a_yb_y\hat{\mathbf{j}}.\hat{\mathbf{j}} + a_yb_z\hat{\mathbf{j}}.\hat{\mathbf{k}}$$
$$+ a_zb_x\hat{\mathbf{k}}.\hat{\mathbf{i}} + a_zb_y\hat{\mathbf{k}}.\hat{\mathbf{j}} + a_zb_z\hat{\mathbf{k}}.\hat{\mathbf{k}} \quad (5.25)$$

Using equations 5.23 and 5.24, we have

$$\mathbf{a}.\mathbf{b} = a_xb_x + a_yb_y + a_zb_z \quad (5.26)$$

which is a very useful expression for the scalar product. For example, if

$$\mathbf{a} = 2\hat{\mathbf{i}} - 3\hat{\mathbf{j}} + 4\hat{\mathbf{k}}$$
$$\mathbf{b} = 4\hat{\mathbf{i}} + \hat{\mathbf{j}} - 2\hat{\mathbf{k}}$$

then

$$\mathbf{a}.\mathbf{b} = 4.2 + (-3).1 + 4(-2) = -3 \quad (5.27)$$

The scalar product of a vector with itself is equal to the square of its magnitude

$$\mathbf{a}.\mathbf{a} = |\mathbf{a}||\mathbf{a}|\cos 0 = a_x^2 + a_y^2 + a_z^2 \quad (5.28)$$

If $\mathbf{a}.\mathbf{b}$ is zero, this immediately tells us that $\mathbf{a}$ and $\mathbf{b}$ are *perpendicular* or *orthogonal*. For example, if $\mathbf{a} = \hat{\mathbf{i}} - 2\hat{\mathbf{j}} + \hat{\mathbf{k}}$ and $\mathbf{b} = \hat{\mathbf{i}} + \hat{\mathbf{j}} + \hat{\mathbf{k}}$, then $\mathbf{a}.\mathbf{b} = 1.1 - 2.1 + 1.1 = 0$ and $\mathbf{a}$ and $\mathbf{b}$ are perpendicular. We can also use the scalar product to obtain the angle between two vectors thus

$$\cos\theta = \frac{\mathbf{a}.\mathbf{b}}{|\mathbf{a}||\mathbf{b}|} \quad (5.29)$$

The cosine of the angle between the vectors

$$\mathbf{a} = \mathbf{i} + \mathbf{j} + \mathbf{k} \quad \text{and} \quad \mathbf{b} = 2\mathbf{i} + \mathbf{j} - \mathbf{k}$$

is

$$\cos\theta = \frac{2.1 + 1.1 - 1.1}{2\sqrt{3}} = \frac{1}{\sqrt{3}}$$

that is

$$\theta = \cos^{-1}\left(\frac{1}{\sqrt{3}}\right) \tag{5.30}$$

If we express a and b in terms of unit vectors and direction cosines

$$\mathbf{a} = |\mathbf{a}|[\hat{\mathbf{i}} \cos \alpha_1 + \hat{\mathbf{j}} \cos \beta_1 + \hat{\mathbf{k}} \cos \gamma_1]$$

$$\mathbf{b} = |\mathbf{b}|[\hat{\mathbf{i}} \cos \alpha_2 + \hat{\mathbf{j}} \cos \beta_2 + \hat{\mathbf{k}} \cos \gamma_2]$$

equation 5.29 gives

$$\cos \theta = \cos \alpha_1 \cos \alpha_2 + \cos \beta_1 \cos \beta_2 + \cos \gamma_1 \cos \gamma_2 \tag{5.31}$$

The vectors are parallel if $\cos \theta = +1$ and perpendicular if $\cos \theta = 0$. If we consider the scalar product **a.a**, this gives the important result

$$\cos^2 \alpha_1 + \cos^2 \beta_1 + \cos^2 \gamma_1 = 1 \tag{5.32}$$

Applications of the scalar product

A. The cosine formula

The scalar product has many geometrical applications but we shall restrict ourselves to the cosine formula. Consider the triangle ABC (figure 5.11). We see that by vector addition **c** = **a** + **b** and hence

$$\mathbf{c}.\mathbf{c} = (\mathbf{a} + \mathbf{b}).(\mathbf{a} + \mathbf{b}) = \mathbf{a}.\mathbf{a} + \mathbf{b}.\mathbf{b} + 2\mathbf{a}.\mathbf{b} = |\mathbf{a}|^2 + |\mathbf{b}|^2 + 2|\mathbf{a}||\mathbf{b}|\cos \theta$$

If the lengths of AB, BC and CA are a, b and c respectively, we get the familiar cosine formula

$$c^2 = a^2 + b^2 - 2ab \cos C \tag{5.33}$$

where $C = \pi - \theta$.

B. Work done by a force

If a force **F** acts at an angle θ to the displacement **d**, the work done over the displacement is given by the product of the component of the force along **d** and the displacement (figure 5.12)

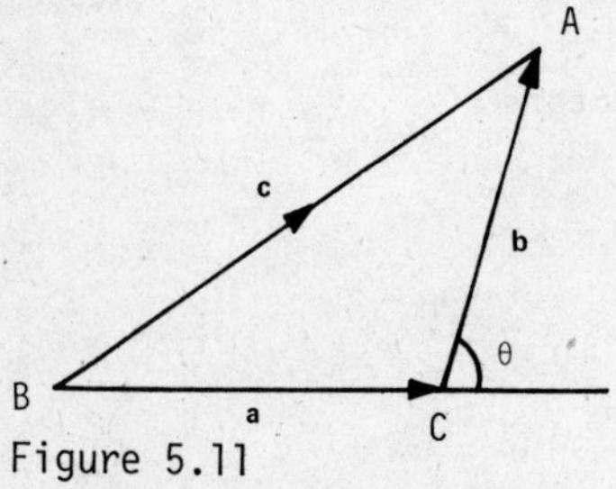

Figure 5.11

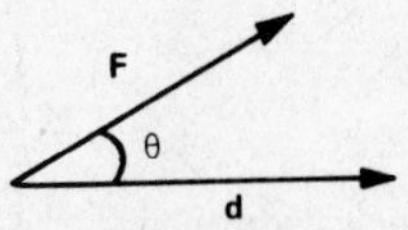

Figure 5.12

$$\text{work done} = |\mathbf{F}|\cos\theta|\mathbf{d}| = \mathbf{F}.\mathbf{d} \tag{5.34}$$

C. Potential of a dipole in a field

If a dipole μ is oriented at an angle θ to a field **E**, the potential W of the dipole is given by

$$W = -\mu.\mathbf{E} \tag{5.35}$$

D. Flux

Consider a fluid flowing with velocity **v** through a small area ds. The amount flowing through the area ds in unit time is the volume of the skew cylinder of base area ds and length $|\mathbf{v}|$. If the normal to ds makes an angle θ with **v**, the volume is given by $|\mathbf{v}|\cos\theta\ ds$. This is very much like a scalar product and we shall see in the next section that we can represent an area by a vector perpendicular to the area. So in this case we represent the area ds by a vector d**s** normal to the area and we can write the flux through ds as

$$\text{flux} = \mathbf{v}.d\mathbf{s} \tag{5.36}$$

This also applies to electric and magnetic fields.

5.3.2 Vector product

Let **a** and **b** be two vectors and let $\hat{\mathbf{n}}$ be a unit vector perpendicular to the plane defined by **a** and **b** (figure 5.14). The direction of $\hat{\mathbf{n}}$ is such that **a**, **b** and $\hat{\mathbf{n}}$ form a right-handed set of vectors; that is, if we look along $\hat{\mathbf{n}}$, a clockwise rotation transforms **a** into **b**. Let θ be the angle between **a** and **b**, defined in a positive sense in going from **a** to **b**. The *vector product* or *cross product* $\mathbf{a} \wedge \mathbf{b}$ or $\mathbf{a} \times \mathbf{b}$ is defined by

$$\mathbf{a} \wedge \mathbf{b} = |\mathbf{a}||\mathbf{b}|\sin\theta\ \hat{\mathbf{n}} \tag{5.37}$$

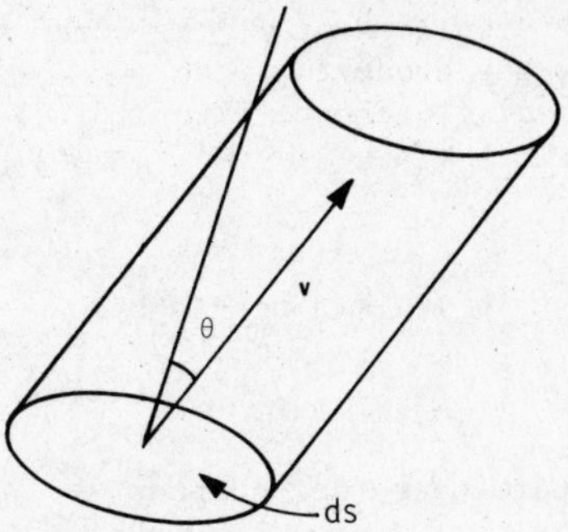

Figure 5.13

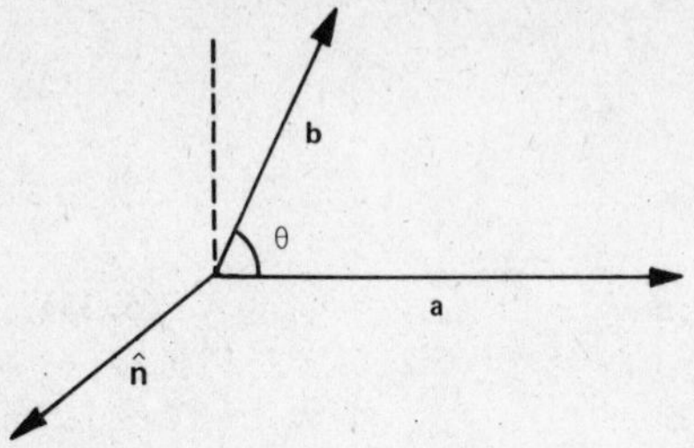

Figure 5.14

that is, it is a vector of magnitude $|\mathbf{a}||\mathbf{b}|\sin\theta$ in the direction of $\hat{\mathbf{n}}$, that is, perpendicular to the plane containing **a** and **b**.

Vector multiplication is *not* commutative because

$$\mathbf{b} \wedge \mathbf{a} = |\mathbf{b}||\mathbf{a}|\sin(-\theta)\hat{\mathbf{n}} = -|\mathbf{a}||\mathbf{b}|\sin\theta\,\hat{\mathbf{n}}$$

that is

$$\mathbf{b} \wedge \mathbf{a} = -\mathbf{a} \wedge \mathbf{b}$$

The distributive law holds

$$\mathbf{a} \wedge (\mathbf{b} + \mathbf{c}) = \mathbf{a} \wedge \mathbf{b} + \mathbf{a} \wedge \mathbf{c} \qquad (5.38)$$

and scalar factors obey the laws of ordinary algebra

$$(s\mathbf{a}) \wedge (t\mathbf{b}) = st(\mathbf{a} \wedge \mathbf{b})$$

If the vector product of two vectors is zero, the angle between them is zero; that is, they are parallel. It can be seen from the basic definition of the vector product that the following relationships hold for the unit vectors

$$\hat{\mathbf{i}} \wedge \hat{\mathbf{i}} = \hat{\mathbf{j}} \wedge \hat{\mathbf{j}} = \hat{\mathbf{k}} \wedge \hat{\mathbf{k}} = 0$$

$$\hat{\mathbf{i}} \wedge \hat{\mathbf{j}} = \hat{\mathbf{k}}; \quad \hat{\mathbf{j}} \wedge \hat{\mathbf{k}} = \hat{\mathbf{i}}; \quad \hat{\mathbf{k}} \wedge \hat{\mathbf{i}} = \hat{\mathbf{j}} \qquad (5.41)$$

$$\hat{\mathbf{j}} \wedge \hat{\mathbf{i}} = -\hat{\mathbf{k}}; \quad \hat{\mathbf{k}} \wedge \hat{\mathbf{j}} = -\hat{\mathbf{i}}; \quad \hat{\mathbf{i}} \wedge \hat{\mathbf{k}} = -\hat{\mathbf{j}}$$

Expanding the vector product of **a** and **b** in terms of components gives

$$\begin{aligned}\mathbf{a} \wedge \mathbf{b} &= (a_x\hat{\mathbf{i}} + a_y\hat{\mathbf{j}} + a_z\hat{\mathbf{k}}) \wedge (b_x\hat{\mathbf{i}} + b_y\hat{\mathbf{j}} + b_z\hat{\mathbf{k}}) \\ &= a_xb_x\hat{\mathbf{i}} \wedge \hat{\mathbf{i}} + a_xb_y\hat{\mathbf{i}} \wedge \hat{\mathbf{j}} + a_xb_z\hat{\mathbf{i}} \wedge \hat{\mathbf{k}} \\ &\quad + a_yb_x\hat{\mathbf{j}} \wedge \hat{\mathbf{i}} + a_yb_y\hat{\mathbf{j}} \wedge \hat{\mathbf{j}} + a_yb_z\hat{\mathbf{j}} \wedge \hat{\mathbf{k}} \\ &\quad + a_zb_x\hat{\mathbf{k}} \wedge \hat{\mathbf{i}} + a_zb_y\hat{\mathbf{k}} \wedge \hat{\mathbf{j}} + a_zb_z\hat{\mathbf{k}} \wedge \hat{\mathbf{k}}\end{aligned} \qquad (5.42)$$

Using equations 5.41 gives

$$\mathbf{a} \wedge \mathbf{b} = \hat{\mathbf{i}}(a_yb_z - a_zb_y) + \hat{\mathbf{j}}(a_zb_x - a_xb_z) + \hat{\mathbf{k}}(a_xb_y - a_yb_x) \qquad (5.43)$$

which can be written compactly as a determinant (see chapter 9)

$$\mathbf{a} \wedge \mathbf{b} = \begin{vmatrix} \mathbf{i} & \mathbf{j} & \mathbf{k} \\ a_x & a_y & a_z \\ b_x & b_y & b_z \end{vmatrix} \tag{5.44}$$

For example, if

$$\mathbf{a} = 2\hat{\mathbf{i}} + 3\hat{\mathbf{j}} - \hat{\mathbf{k}}$$

$$\mathbf{b} = \hat{\mathbf{i}} - 2\hat{\mathbf{j}} + 2\hat{\mathbf{k}}$$

then

$$\mathbf{a} \wedge \mathbf{b} = \begin{vmatrix} \hat{\mathbf{i}} & \hat{\mathbf{j}} & \hat{\mathbf{k}} \\ 2 & 3 & -1 \\ 1 & -2 & 2 \end{vmatrix} \tag{5.45}$$

$$= 4\hat{\mathbf{i}} - 5\hat{\mathbf{j}} - 7\hat{\mathbf{k}}$$

Two properties of the vector product are apparent from inspecting the determinantal form. If $\mathbf{a} = \mathbf{b}$ or $\mathbf{a} = m\mathbf{b}$, two rows of the determinant will be the same or a multiple of each other and the determinant will be zero. The determinant for $\mathbf{b} \wedge \mathbf{a}$ is obtained from equation 5.44 by interchanging the second and third rows, and $\mathbf{b} \wedge \mathbf{a}$ is thus seen to be equal to $-\mathbf{a} \wedge \mathbf{b}$.

Applications of the vector product

A. Areas

We mentioned earlier that an area can be represented by a vector. Let us now apply this to a parallelogram of sides $\mathbf{a}$ and $\mathbf{b}$ with an angle θ between them. The area of the parallelogram is $|\mathbf{a}||\mathbf{b}|\sin\theta$, which is the magnitude of the vector $\mathbf{a} \wedge \mathbf{b}$, so we can represent the area by a vector $|\mathbf{a} \wedge \mathbf{b}|.\hat{\mathbf{n}}$, where $\hat{\mathbf{n}}$ is a unit vector perpendicular to $\mathbf{a}$ and $\mathbf{b}$ (figure 5.15).

B. Moment of a force

If we have a force $\mathbf{F}$, whose line of action is defined with respect to an origin O by a vector $\mathbf{d}$, the moment of the force about O is given by the magnitude of the force $|\mathbf{F}|$ multiplied by the perpendicular distance of its line of action from O (figure 5.16). In this case this is $|\mathbf{d}|\sin\theta$. The moment of the force = $|\mathbf{d}|\sin\theta|\mathbf{F}|$, so we can represent the moment by a vector

$$\mathbf{M} = \mathbf{d} \wedge \mathbf{F} \tag{5.46}$$

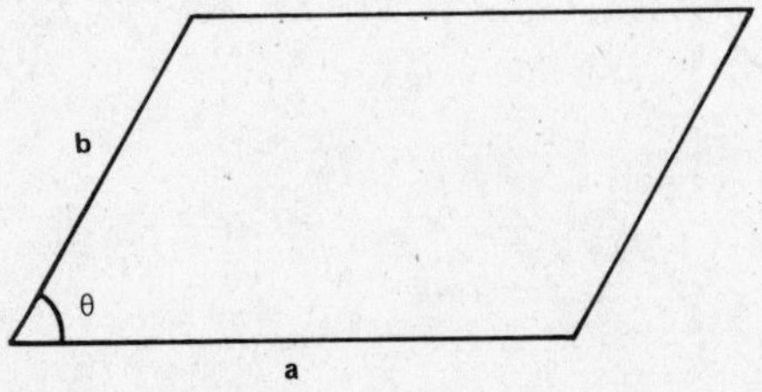

Figure 5.15

Figure 5.16

where **M** is a vector perpendicular to the plane of **d** and **F** and pointing out of the paper.

C. Moment of a couple

Two forces **F** and **−F** acting along different lines form a couple. Let $\mathbf{r}_1$ and $\mathbf{r}_2$ define points on **F** and **−F**, respectively (figure 5.17). Consider the moments of **F** and **−F** with respect to a point defined by a vector **a**

$$\text{moment of } \mathbf{F} = (\mathbf{r}_1 - \mathbf{a}) \wedge \mathbf{F}$$

$$\text{moment of } -\mathbf{F} = (\mathbf{r}_2 - \mathbf{a}) \wedge (-\mathbf{F}) = -(\mathbf{r}_2 - \mathbf{a}) \wedge \mathbf{F}$$

Thus

$$\begin{aligned}\text{moment of couple} &= (\mathbf{r}_1 - \mathbf{a}) \wedge \mathbf{F} - (\mathbf{r}_2 - \mathbf{a}) \wedge \mathbf{F} \\ &= (\mathbf{r}_1 - \mathbf{r}_2) \wedge \mathbf{F} \qquad (5.47)\end{aligned}$$

and is independent of **a**.

5.3.3 Triple products

Only two triple products are meaningful and of interest.

(i) The scalar triple product

This is the product $\mathbf{a}.(\mathbf{b} \wedge \mathbf{c})$, which is obtained by taking the vector product of **b** and **c**, which gives the vector

$$(\mathbf{b} \wedge \mathbf{c}) = \hat{\mathbf{i}}\,(b_y c_z - b_z c_y) + \hat{\mathbf{j}}\,(b_z c_x - b_x c_z) + \hat{\mathbf{k}}\,(b_x c_y - b_y c_x) \qquad (5.48)$$

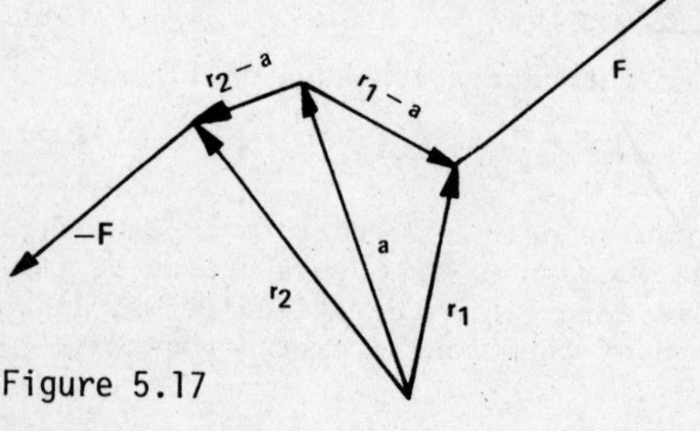

Figure 5.17

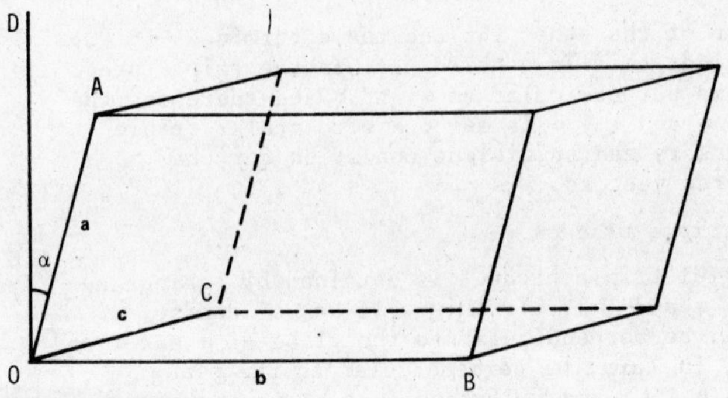

Figure 5.18

and then taking the scalar product of the result with **a**. Applying equation 5.26 gives

$$\mathbf{a}.(\mathbf{b} \wedge \mathbf{c}) = a_x(b_y c_z - b_z c_y) + a_y(b_z c_x - b_x c_z) + a_z(b_x c_y - b_y c_x) \quad (5.49)$$

which can be written as a determinant

$$\mathbf{a}.(\mathbf{b} \wedge \mathbf{c}) = \begin{vmatrix} a_x & a_y & a_z \\ b_x & b_y & b_z \\ c_x & c_y & c_z \end{vmatrix} \quad (5.50)$$

The scalar product represents the volume of a parallelepiped with edges represented by the vectors **a**, **b** and **c** (figure 5.18). The area of the base is given by the vector $\mathbf{b} \wedge \mathbf{c}$ and the volume of the solid is given by the area of the base multiplied by the vertical height. If OD is a line perpendicular to the base and **a** makes an angle α with OD, the vertical height is $|\mathbf{a}|\cos\alpha$. The volume is therefore $(|\mathbf{a}|\cos\alpha)(|\mathbf{b} \wedge \mathbf{c}|)$, where $|\mathbf{b} \wedge \mathbf{c}|$ is the magnitude of $\mathbf{b} \wedge \mathbf{c}$. But α is the angle between **a** and $\mathbf{b} \wedge \mathbf{c}$. Thus the expression for the volume is in the form of a scalar product and can be written

$$V = \mathbf{a}.(\mathbf{b} \wedge \mathbf{c}) \quad (5.51)$$

If we permute the vectors in cyclic order, the scalar triple product is unchanged

$$\mathbf{a}.(\mathbf{b} \wedge \mathbf{c}) = \mathbf{b}.(\mathbf{c} \wedge \mathbf{a}) = \mathbf{c}.(\mathbf{a} \wedge \mathbf{b}) \quad (5.52)$$

Departure from the cyclic order introduces a change of sign

$$\mathbf{a}.(\mathbf{c} \wedge \mathbf{b}) = -\mathbf{a}.(\mathbf{b} \wedge \mathbf{c}) \quad (5.53)$$

because $\mathbf{c} \wedge \mathbf{b} = -\mathbf{b} \wedge \mathbf{c}$.

The scalar triple product can be used as a test of coplanarity of three vectors. If the three vectors **a**, **b**, **c**, are coplanar, the volume of the parallelepiped is zero. In mathematical terms, if three vectors are coplanar, one of them can be expressed as a linear combination of the other two and the determinant (5.50) is zero. We can consider this in a third way. In the triple product $\mathbf{a}.(\mathbf{a} \wedge \mathbf{b})$, $\mathbf{a} \wedge \mathbf{b}$ is perpendicular to $\mathbf{a}$ and $\mathbf{b}$ and therefore the scalar product of $\mathbf{a}$ and $\mathbf{a} \wedge \mathbf{b}$ is zero. A zero scalar triple product is a necessary and sufficient condition for the coplanarity of three vectors.

(ii) The vector triple product

The other meaningful triple product is obtained by taking the vector product of $\mathbf{a}$ and $(\mathbf{b} \wedge \mathbf{c})$. This will be, of course, a vector. $\mathbf{b} \wedge \mathbf{c}$ will be perpendicular to the plane of $\mathbf{b}$ and $\mathbf{c}$ and $\mathbf{a} \wedge (\mathbf{b} \wedge \mathbf{c})$ will, in turn, be perpendicular to the plane containing $\mathbf{a}$ and $(\mathbf{b} \wedge \mathbf{c})$ and will therefore be in the plane of $\mathbf{b}$ and $\mathbf{c}$ (figure 5.19). The vector triple product is given by

$$\mathbf{a} \wedge (\mathbf{b} \wedge \mathbf{c}) = (\mathbf{a}.\mathbf{c})\mathbf{b} - (\mathbf{a}.\mathbf{b})\mathbf{c} \tag{5.54}$$

This can be derived by straightforward but rather tedious manipulation

$$\mathbf{b} \wedge \mathbf{c} = \hat{\imath}(b_y c_z - b_z c_y) + \hat{\jmath}(b_z c_x - b_x c_z) + \hat{k}(b_x c_y - b_y c_x)$$

Taking the vector product with $\mathbf{a}$ gives

$$\begin{aligned}
\mathbf{a} \wedge (\mathbf{b} \wedge \mathbf{c}) &= \hat{\imath}\left[a_y(b_x c_y - b_y c_x) - a_z(b_z c_x - b_x c_z)\right] \\
&\quad + \hat{\jmath}\left[a_z(b_y c_z - b_z c_y) - a_x(b_x c_y - b_y c_x)\right] \\
&\quad + \hat{k}\left[a_x(b_z c_x - b_x c_z) - a_y(b_y c_z - b_z c_y)\right] \\
&= \hat{\imath}\left[b_x(a_x c_x + a_y c_y + a_z c_z)\right. \\
&\quad \left. - c_x(a_x b_x + a_y b_y + a_z b_z)\right] \\
&\quad + \hat{\jmath}\left[b_y(a_x c_x + a_y c_y + a_z c_z)\right. \\
&\quad \left. - c_y(a_x b_x + a_y b_y + a_z b_z)\right] \\
&\quad + \hat{k}\left[b_z(a_x c_x + a_y c_y + a_z c_z)\right. \\
&\quad \left. - c_z(a_x b_x + a_y b_y + a_z b_z)\right] \\
&= \hat{\imath}\left[b_x \mathbf{a}.\mathbf{c} - c_x \mathbf{a}.\mathbf{b}\right] + \hat{\jmath}\left[b_y \mathbf{a}.\mathbf{c} - c_y \mathbf{a}.\mathbf{b}\right] \\
&\quad + \hat{k}\left[b_z \mathbf{a}.\mathbf{c} - c_z \mathbf{a}.\mathbf{b}\right] \\
&= (\mathbf{a}.\mathbf{c})\mathbf{b} - (\mathbf{a}.\mathbf{b})\mathbf{c}
\end{aligned} \tag{5.55}$$

The position of the brackets in $\mathbf{a} \wedge (\mathbf{b} \wedge \mathbf{c})$ is very important. Other vector triple products can be obtained from equation 5.55 by using the basic properties of vector products. For example

$$\begin{aligned}
(\mathbf{a} \wedge \mathbf{b}) \wedge \mathbf{c} &= -\mathbf{c} \wedge (\mathbf{a} \wedge \mathbf{b}) \\
&= -\left[(\mathbf{c}.\mathbf{b})\mathbf{a} - (\mathbf{c}.\mathbf{a})\mathbf{b}\right]
\end{aligned} \tag{5.56}$$

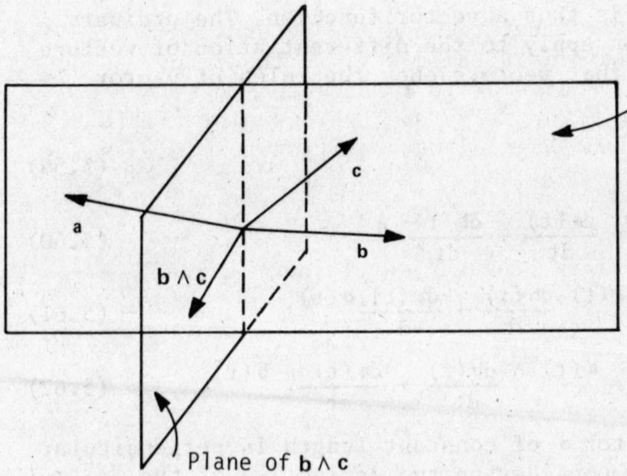

Figure 5.19

5.4 DERIVATIVES OF VECTORS

We have so far regarded vectors as being fixed. However, this is an unnecessary restriction since, for example, we can describe the position of a moving point by a vector function $\mathbf{a}(t)$, whose components are the co-ordinates of the point at time t, that is $(a_x(t), a_y(t), a_z(t))$, and functions of time

$$\mathbf{a}(t) = a_x(t)\hat{\imath} + a_y(t)\hat{\jmath} + a_z(t)\hat{k} \tag{5.57}$$

Can we define the derivative of $\mathbf{a}$? Applying the usual definition for a derivative from section 2.3, we obtain

$$\begin{aligned} \frac{d}{dt}\mathbf{a}(t) &= \lim_{\delta t \to 0}\left[\frac{\mathbf{a}(t+\delta t) - \mathbf{a}(t)}{\delta t}\right] \\ &= \lim_{\delta t \to 0}\left[\hat{\imath}\,(a_x(t+\delta t) - a_x(t)) + \hat{\jmath}\,(a_y(t+\delta t) - a_y(t)) \right. \\ &\qquad \left. + \hat{k}(a_z(t+\delta t) - a_z(t))\right]/\delta t \\ &= \hat{\imath}\lim_{\delta t \to 0}\left[\frac{a_x(t+\delta t) - a_x(t)}{\delta t}\right] \\ &\quad + \hat{\jmath}\lim_{\delta t \to 0}\left[\frac{a_y(t+\delta t) - a_y(t)}{\delta t}\right] \\ &\quad + \hat{k}\lim_{\delta t \to 0}\left[\frac{a_z(t+\delta t) - a_z(t)}{\delta t}\right] \end{aligned} \tag{5.58}$$

$$= \hat{\imath}\,\frac{da_x}{dt} + \hat{\jmath}\,\frac{da_y}{dt} + \hat{k}\,\frac{da_z}{dt}$$

The derivative of $\mathbf{a}(t)$ is thus a vector function. The ordinary rules of differentiation apply to the differentiation of vectors provided one remembers that vectors obey the rules of vector algebra. Thus

$$\frac{d}{dt}\left[c\,\mathbf{a}(t)\right] = c\,\frac{d\mathbf{a}}{dt} \tag{5.59}$$

$$\frac{d}{dt}\left[\mathbf{a}(t) + \mathbf{b}(t)\right] = \frac{d\mathbf{a}(t)}{dt} + \frac{d\mathbf{b}(t)}{dt} \tag{5.60}$$

$$\frac{d}{dt}(\mathbf{a}(t).\mathbf{b}(t)) = \mathbf{a}(t).\frac{d\mathbf{b}(t)}{dt} + \frac{d\mathbf{a}(t)}{dt}.\mathbf{b}(t) \tag{5.61}$$

$$\frac{d}{dt}(\mathbf{a}(t) \wedge \mathbf{b}(t)) = \mathbf{a}(t) \wedge \frac{d\mathbf{b}(t)}{dt} + \frac{d\mathbf{a}(t)}{dt} \wedge \mathbf{b}(t) \tag{5.62}$$

The derivative of a vector $\mathbf{a}$ of constant length is perpendicular to $\mathbf{a}$, as can be seen by considering the derivative of the scalar product of $\mathbf{a}(t)$ with itself

$$\mathbf{a}(t).\mathbf{a}(t) = |\mathbf{a}|^2 = \text{constant} \tag{5.63}$$

Therefore

$$\frac{d}{dt}(\mathbf{a}(t).\mathbf{a}(t)) = 0$$

and

$$\mathbf{a}(t).\frac{d}{dt}\mathbf{a}(t) + \frac{d\mathbf{a}(t)}{dt}.\mathbf{a}(t) = 0$$

that is

$$\mathbf{a}(t).\frac{d}{dt}\mathbf{a}(t) = 0 \tag{5.64}$$

and thus $\mathbf{a}(t)$ and $d\mathbf{a}(t)/dt$ are perpendicular.

Applications to mechanics

A. Vector derivatives

Vector derivatives are of great importance in mechanics, since they are vectors for velocity, acceleration, etc. The vector $[\mathbf{a}(t + \delta t) - \mathbf{a}(t)]$ represents the displacement of the particle in going from A to B in time δt and the limit

$$\lim_{\delta t \to 0} \frac{\mathbf{a}(t + \delta t) - \mathbf{a}(t)}{\delta t}$$

is therefore the *velocity* vector of the particle (figure 5.20). This velocity vector will be tangential to the curve along

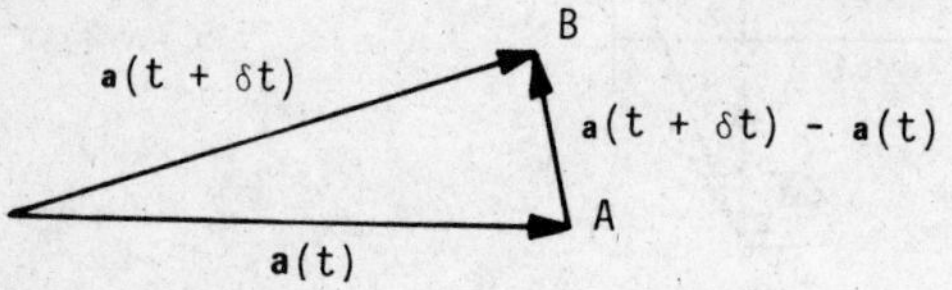

Figure 5.20

which the particle is moving. The second derivative is the *acceleration vector*

$$\ddot{\mathbf{a}}(t) = \frac{d^2}{dt^2}\,\mathbf{a}(t) = \frac{d^2}{dt^2}a_x(t)\hat{\imath} + \frac{d^2}{dt^2}a_y(t)\hat{\jmath} + \frac{d^2}{dt^2}a_z(t)\hat{\mathbf{k}} \tag{5.65}$$

This is related to the force $\mathbf{F}$ on the particle by Newton's law

$$F = m\ddot{\mathbf{a}}(t) \tag{5.66}$$

where m is the mass of the particle.

B. Angular velocity

For a particle rotating in a circle, the angular velocity ω is given by $d\theta/dt$ where θ is the angle swept out (figure 5.21). If the radius of the circle is r, the distance travelled for a rotation θ is $r\theta$. The magnitude of the linear velocity is given by $rd\theta/dt$ or $r\omega$ and its direction is tangential to the circle. The angular velocity ω can be represented by a vector. Consider an infinitesimal rotation of $\delta\theta$ about an axis defined by a unit vector $\hat{\mathbf{e}}$, in which the point moves from $\mathbf{r}$ to $\mathbf{r} + \delta\mathbf{r}$ (figure 5.22). The particle is moving in a circle of radius $\mathbf{r}\sin\phi$, where ϕ is the angle between $\mathbf{r}$ and $\hat{\mathbf{e}}$. The magnitude of $\delta\mathbf{r}$ is therefore $r\sin\phi\delta\theta$ and $\delta\mathbf{r}$ can thus be represented by a vector product

$$\delta\mathbf{r} = \delta\theta\hat{\mathbf{e}} \wedge \mathbf{r} \tag{5.67}$$

since $\delta\mathbf{r}$ is in the plane perpendicular to $\hat{\mathbf{e}}$ and $\mathbf{r}$. The velocity $d\mathbf{r}/dt$ is given by

$$\frac{d\mathbf{r}}{dt} = \lim_{\delta t\to 0} \frac{\delta\mathbf{r}}{\delta t} = \frac{d\theta}{dt}\hat{\mathbf{e}} \wedge \mathbf{r} = \boldsymbol{\omega} \wedge \mathbf{r} \tag{5.68}$$

where $\boldsymbol{\omega} = \hat{\mathbf{e}}\, d\theta/dt$; that is

$$\frac{d\mathbf{r}}{dt} = \mathbf{v} = \boldsymbol{\omega} \wedge \mathbf{r} \tag{5.69}$$

Thus angular velocity can be represented by a vector ω in the direction of the axis of rotation and it can be shown that angular velocities satisfy all the properties of vectors whereas angular displacements (other than infinitesimal ones) are not vectors.

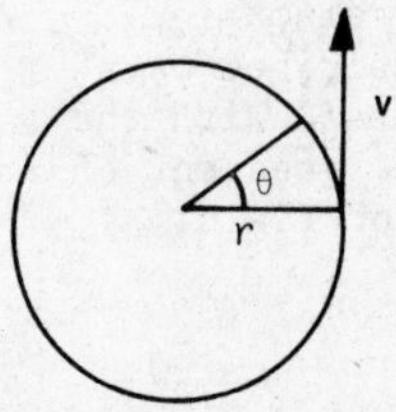

Figure 5.21

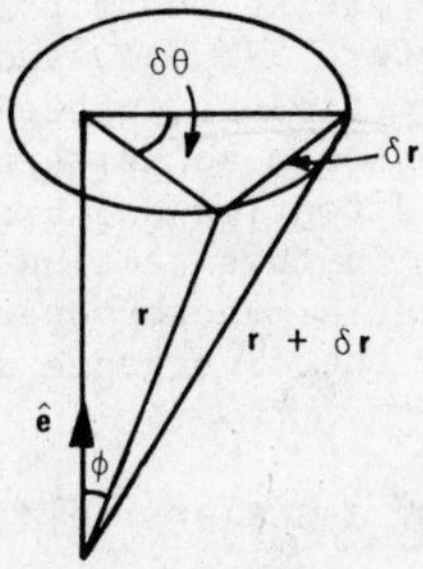

Figure 5.22

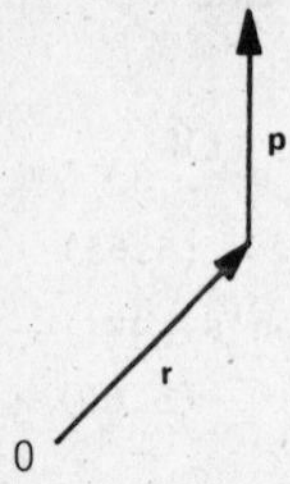

Figure 5.23

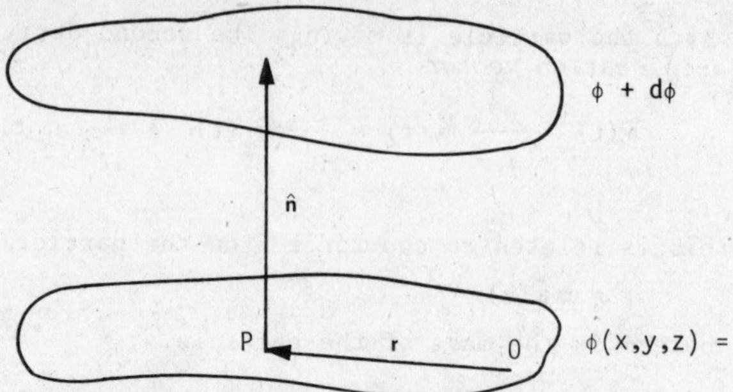

Figure 5.24

C. Angular momentum

The angular momentum **M** of a particle is defined as the *moment* of the momentum **p** about the point O about which rotation is occurring (figure 5.23). By analogy with our definition of moment of a force in equation 5.46, it is given by

$$\mathbf{M} = \mathbf{r} \wedge \mathbf{p}$$

that is

$$\mathbf{M} = \begin{vmatrix} \hat{\mathbf{i}} & \hat{\mathbf{j}} & \hat{\mathbf{k}} \\ r_x & r_y & r_z \\ p_x & p_y & p_z \end{vmatrix} \qquad (5.71)$$

The components are

$$M_x = yp_z - zp_y; \quad M_y = zp_x - xp_z; \quad M_z = xp_y - yp_x \qquad (5.72)$$

where we have replaced r_x, etc. by x, etc. These expressions are the starting point for the quantum-mechanical treatment of angular momentum.

5.5 VECTOR OPERATORS

We have so far divided physical quantities into scalars and vectors. Many physical quantities such as temperature, potential, electric field, temperature gradient are functions of the spatial co-ordinates and are known as *point functions*. Some of these, for example, temperature T(x,y,z) and potential V(x,y,z) have no directional properties associated with them and are *scalar fields*, whereas functions such as temperature gradient and electric field depend on direction and are *vector fields* described by a vector **a**(x,y,z). In this section we shall be concerned with the use of a differential vector operator to obtain the gradient of a scalar field and the divergence and curl of a vector field.

5.5.1 Gradient of a scalar field

If we have a scalar field ϕ(x,y,z), which is a differentiable function of x,y,z in the region of interest, the *gradient* of ϕ, grad ϕ, is a vector function defined by

$$\text{grad}\ \phi = \hat{\mathbf{i}}\frac{\partial\phi}{\partial z} + \hat{\mathbf{j}}\frac{\partial\phi}{\partial y} + \hat{\mathbf{k}}\frac{\partial\phi}{\partial z} \tag{5.73}$$

The components of this vector are the derivatives $\partial\phi/\partial x$, $\partial\phi/\partial y$, $\partial\phi/\partial z$. We must now consider what the physical meaning of this function is. Let us consider a point (x,y,z) defined by a vector $\mathbf{r} = x\hat{\mathbf{i}} + y\hat{\mathbf{j}} + z\hat{\mathbf{k}}$ and a displacement $d\mathbf{r} = dx\,\hat{\mathbf{i}} + dy\,\hat{\mathbf{j}} + dz\,\hat{\mathbf{k}}$ from it. Taking the scalar product of $d\mathbf{r}$ with grad ϕ gives

$$d\mathbf{r}.\text{grad}\ \phi = (\hat{\mathbf{i}}\ dx + \hat{\mathbf{j}}\ dy + \hat{\mathbf{k}}\ dz).\left(\hat{\mathbf{i}}\frac{\partial\phi}{\partial x} + \hat{\mathbf{j}}\frac{\partial\phi}{\partial y} + \hat{\mathbf{k}}\frac{\partial\phi}{\partial z}\right)$$

$$= \frac{\partial\phi}{\partial x}dx + \frac{\partial\phi}{\partial y}dy + \frac{\partial\phi}{\partial z}dz \tag{5.74}$$

which is the total differential $d\phi$ of ϕ, that is, in effect, the change in ϕ as we traverse $d\mathbf{r}$. If $d\mathbf{r}$ has length ds, we can define a unit vector

$$\hat{\mathbf{a}} = \frac{d\mathbf{r}}{ds} \text{ in the direction of } d\mathbf{r}$$

and the derivative of ϕ with respect to s is

$$\frac{d\phi}{ds} = \frac{d\mathbf{r}}{ds}.\text{grad}\ \phi = \hat{\mathbf{a}}.\text{grad}\ \phi \tag{5.75}$$

and therefore $\hat{\mathbf{a}}$.grad ϕ is the rate of change of ϕ along $\mathbf{a}$ and is a *directional derivative*. From the definition of the scalar product we can see that this will have a maximum value when $\hat{\mathbf{a}}$ and grad ϕ are parallel. Therefore grad ϕ is a vector pointing in the *direction of the maximum rate of change of* ϕ.

Let us consider a set of level surfaces defined by $\phi(x,y,z) = c$, for example, contour surfaces or *equipotential surfaces* in potential problems. If we have a point P(x(t),y(t),z(t)), where t is some parameter, on the surface defined by a vector $\mathbf{r}$(x,y,z), then, from page 130, $d\mathbf{r}/dt$ is tangential to the surface at P and the displacement $d\mathbf{r}$ is a tangent vector at P. If we stay on the surface $d\phi$ is zero and hence $d\phi/dt$ is zero. But

$$\frac{d\phi}{dt} = \frac{d\mathbf{r}}{dt}.\text{grad}\ \phi \tag{5.76}$$

Since $d\phi/dt$ is zero, the scalar product is zero; that is

$$\frac{d\mathbf{r}}{dt}.\text{grad}\ \phi = 0 \tag{5.77}$$

and thus grad ϕ is a vector *normal* to the surface at P in the direction of $\hat{\mathbf{n}}$. For example, if we have an *electric potential* V(x,y,z), the electric field $\mathbf{E}$ is given by

$$\mathbf{E} = -\text{grad}\ V$$
$$= -\left[\frac{\partial V}{\partial x}\hat{\mathbf{i}} + \frac{\partial V}{\partial y}\hat{\mathbf{j}} + \frac{\partial V}{\partial z}\hat{\mathbf{k}}\right] \tag{5.78}$$

and is a vector perpendicular to the equipotential surface (figure 5.24).

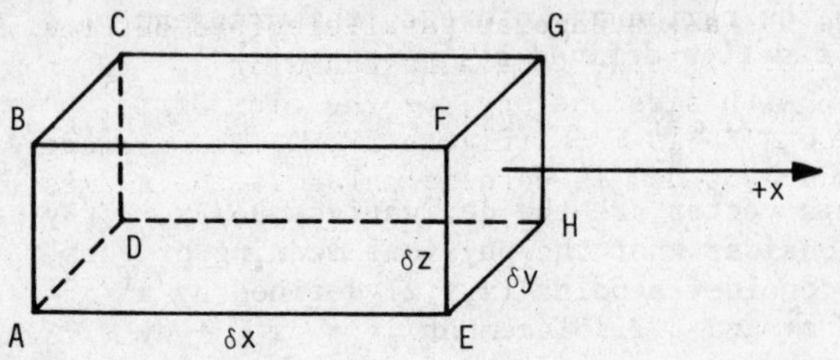

Figure 5.25

We can introduce a *differential vector operator*

$$\nabla = \hat{\mathbf{i}}\frac{\partial}{\partial x} + \hat{\mathbf{j}}\frac{\partial}{\partial y} + \hat{\mathbf{k}}\frac{\partial}{\partial z} \tag{5.79}$$

often called 'del' or 'nabla' and write the gradient as the result of the operation of ∇ on a scalar function

$$\begin{aligned} \text{grad } \phi &= \hat{\mathbf{i}}\frac{\partial \phi}{\partial x} + \hat{\mathbf{j}}\frac{\partial \phi}{\partial y} + \hat{\mathbf{k}}\frac{\partial \phi}{\partial z} \\ &= \nabla\phi \end{aligned} \tag{5.80}$$

5.5.2 Divergence of a vector field

Having introduced the operator ∇, we might well ask whether one can take the scalar and vector products between ∇ and a vector field. If we take the scalar product with a vector field $\mathbf{a}(x,y,z)$ we obtain the *divergence* of $\mathbf{a}$, which is a scalar quantity

$$\begin{aligned} \text{div } \mathbf{a} = \nabla.\mathbf{a} &= \left(\hat{\mathbf{i}}\frac{\partial}{\partial x} + \hat{\mathbf{j}}\frac{\partial}{\partial y} + \hat{\mathbf{k}}\frac{\partial}{\partial z}\right).(a_x\hat{\mathbf{i}} + a_y\hat{\mathbf{j}} + a_z\hat{\mathbf{k}}) \\ &= \frac{\partial}{\partial x}a_x + \frac{\partial}{\partial y}a_y + \frac{\partial}{\partial z}a_z \end{aligned} \tag{5.81}$$

Clearly, in order for div $\mathbf{a}$ to be defined, a_x, a_y and a_z must be differentiable functions of x, y and z.

The divergence can be interpreted physically in terms of *flux* as follows. Let us consider a closed volume V and let $d\mathbf{s}$ be an element of surface area. From equation 5.36, the flux of a vector $\mathbf{a}$ through $d\mathbf{s}$ is $\mathbf{a}.d\mathbf{s}$. The total flux out of the volume is the sum of all such fluxes

$$\text{total flux} = \lim_{d\mathbf{s}\to 0} \sum_{\text{all } d\mathbf{s}} (\mathbf{a}.d\mathbf{s}) = \int_{\text{over surface}} \mathbf{a}.d\mathbf{s} \tag{5.82}$$

This is a *surface integral* and is really a double integral because $d\mathbf{s}$ is an area that will be specified by two co-ordinates. The divergence of $\mathbf{a}$ can be defined formally as

$$\text{div } \mathbf{a} = \lim_{V\to 0}\left[\frac{\text{flux out of V}}{V}\right] \tag{5.83}$$

We can demonstrate this for a rectangular parallelepiped but the result is completely general. If we take a rectangular parallelepiped ABCDEFGH with sides δx, δy, δz the flux of a vector **a** out of the side ABCD is **a**.**ds** (figure 5.25). The element of area **ds** has magnitude $\delta y \delta z$ and is perpendicular to the x-axis and is thus given by

$$\mathbf{ds} = -\mathbf{i}\, \delta y \delta z \tag{5.84}$$

Let this flux be

$$-f(x) = -a_x \delta y \delta z. \tag{5.85}$$

Therefore flux out of EFGH will be $f(x + \delta x)$; that is

$$\text{flux out of EFGH} = f(x) + \frac{\partial f}{\partial x}\delta x$$

so the net flux over ABCD and EFGH is $(\partial f/\partial x).\delta x$; that is

$$\text{net flux over ABCD and EFGH} = \frac{\partial}{\partial x}(a_x \delta y \delta z)\delta x$$

$$= \frac{\partial a_x}{\partial x}\delta x \delta y \delta z. \tag{5.86}$$

Applying the same reasoning to the y and z axes gives the net flux out of the parallelepiped as

$$\left[\frac{\partial a_x}{\partial x} + \frac{\partial a_y}{\partial y} + \frac{\partial a_z}{\partial z}\right]\delta x \delta y \delta z \tag{5.87}$$

and thus the definition of equation 5.82 for the divergence gives

$$\text{div}\,\mathbf{a} = \lim_{V \to 0}\left[\left(\frac{\partial a_x}{\partial x} + \frac{\partial a_y}{\partial y} + \frac{\partial a_z}{\partial z}\right)\frac{\delta x \delta y \delta z}{\delta x \delta y \delta z}\right]$$

$$= \frac{\partial a_x}{\partial x} + \frac{\partial a_y}{\partial y} + \frac{\partial a_z}{\partial z} \tag{5.88}$$

If **V** is the *flux density* of a fluid, that is the total flow per unit cross-sectional area in unit time, $\nabla.\mathbf{V}$ gives the mass of fluid flowing away from a point per unit volume per unit time. If the point is neither a source nor a sink of fluid, this mass change must be equal to the decrease in density $-d\rho/dt$ for a fluid of density ρ; that is

$$\nabla.\mathbf{V} = -\frac{d\rho}{dt} \tag{5.89}$$

This is the *equation of continuity*, which is useful in diffusion problems.

5.5.3 Curl of a vector field

The *curl* of vector field **a** is obtained by taking the vector product of ∇ with **a**

$$\text{curl } \mathbf{a} = \nabla \wedge \mathbf{a} \tag{5.90}$$

$$= \hat{\imath}\left(\frac{\partial a_z}{\partial y} - \frac{\partial a_y}{\partial z}\right) + \hat{\jmath}\left(\frac{\partial a_x}{\partial z} - \frac{\partial a_z}{\partial x}\right) + \hat{k}\left(\frac{\partial a_y}{\partial x} - \frac{\partial a_x}{\partial y}\right)$$

$$= \begin{vmatrix} \hat{\imath} & \hat{\jmath} & \hat{k} \\ \frac{\partial}{\partial x} & \frac{\partial}{\partial y} & \frac{\partial}{\partial z} \\ a_x & a_y & a_z \end{vmatrix} \tag{5.91}$$

This is perhaps of less interest for chemical problems and we only include it for completeness.

There are several important integral theorems involving the divergence and curl. The reader is referred to more advanced books, for example Simons (1970), for a discussion of these.

5.6 PROBLEMS FOR SOLUTION

1. Find $\mathbf{a} + \mathbf{b}$, $\mathbf{a} - \mathbf{b}$, $\mathbf{a}.\mathbf{b}$, $\mathbf{a} \wedge \mathbf{b}$, $(\mathbf{a} + \mathbf{b}).(\mathbf{a} - \mathbf{b})$ for the following pairs of vectors $\mathbf{a}$ and $\mathbf{b}$. What is the angle between $\mathbf{a}$ and $\mathbf{b}$?

(i) $2\hat{\imath} - 3\hat{\jmath} - \hat{k}$, $\hat{\imath} + 4\hat{\jmath} - 2\hat{k}$;
(ii) $2\hat{\imath} - 3\hat{\jmath} - \hat{k}$, $\hat{\imath} + \hat{\jmath} - \hat{k}$;
(iii) $\hat{\imath} - 3\hat{\jmath} + \hat{k}$, $2\hat{\imath} + \hat{\jmath} + \hat{k}$;
(iv) $\hat{\imath} + \hat{\jmath} + \hat{k}$, $2\hat{\imath} + 2\hat{\jmath} + 2\hat{k}$;
(v) $4\hat{\imath} - 2\hat{\jmath} + \hat{k}$, $\hat{\imath} + \hat{\jmath} - 2\hat{k}$;
(vi) $3\hat{\imath} + \hat{\jmath} - \hat{k}$, $\hat{\imath} + 2\hat{\jmath} - 3\hat{k}$.

2. Write down the direction cosines for the following vectors:

(i) $2\hat{\imath} + 3\hat{\jmath} - \hat{k}$; (ii) $\hat{\imath} + 2\hat{\jmath} + \hat{k}$;
(iii) $\hat{\imath} + 3\hat{\jmath} - 4\hat{k}$; (iv) $3\hat{\imath} - \hat{\jmath} + 2\hat{k}$.

3. If two sides of a triangle are defined by the vectors $\mathbf{a} = 2\hat{\imath} + 3\hat{\jmath} + 5\hat{k}$ and $\mathbf{b} = \hat{\imath} - 2\hat{\jmath} + 4\hat{k}$, what is the vector that defines the third side? What is the area of the triangle?

4. A force $\mathbf{F} = 3\hat{\imath} + \hat{\jmath} - 2\hat{k}$ moves an object along the vector $\mathbf{r} = 4\hat{\imath} - 2\hat{\jmath} - 2\hat{k}$. Determine the work done. What is the moment of the force $\mathbf{F}$ about the point defined by the vector $\mathbf{r}$?

5. Evaluate the triple products $\mathbf{a}.(\mathbf{b} \wedge \mathbf{c})$ and $\mathbf{a} \wedge (\mathbf{b} \wedge \mathbf{c})$ for the following sets of vectors a, b, c:

(i) $3\hat{\imath} - \hat{\jmath} + 2\hat{k}$, $2\hat{\imath} + \hat{\jmath} - \hat{k}$, $\hat{\imath} - 2\hat{\jmath} + 3\hat{k}$;
(ii) $\hat{\imath} + 2\hat{\jmath} + 3\hat{k}$, $4\hat{\imath} + 5\hat{\jmath} + 6\hat{k}$, $7\hat{\imath} + 8\hat{\jmath} + 9\hat{k}$;
(iii) $\hat{\imath} + 4\hat{\jmath} - 3\hat{k}$, $2\hat{\imath} - 3\hat{\jmath} + 2\hat{k}$, $-\hat{\imath} + 2\hat{\jmath} - \hat{k}$.

6. Show that for the three vectors $\mathbf{a}$, $\mathbf{b}$, $(\mathbf{c} \wedge \mathbf{d})$

$$(\mathbf{a} \wedge \mathbf{b}) \wedge (\mathbf{c} \wedge \mathbf{d}) = [\mathbf{a}.(\mathbf{c} \wedge \mathbf{d})]\mathbf{b} - [\mathbf{b}.(\mathbf{c} \wedge \mathbf{d})]\mathbf{a}$$

7. Prove that

$$(\mathbf{a} \wedge \mathbf{b}).(\mathbf{c} \wedge \mathbf{d}) = (\mathbf{a}.\mathbf{c})(\mathbf{b}.\mathbf{d}) - (\mathbf{b}.\mathbf{c})(\mathbf{a}.\mathbf{d})$$

(U.W.)

8. Given three vectors **a**, **b**, **c** such that

$$(\mathbf{c} - \mathbf{a}).\mathbf{a} = (\mathbf{c} - \mathbf{b}).\mathbf{b}$$

show that the vectors $(\mathbf{a} - \mathbf{b})$ and $(\mathbf{c} - \mathbf{a} - \mathbf{b})$ are perpendicular. (U.W.)

9. Show that a vector **v** can be expressed as the sum of a vector in the direction of **u** and of a vector perpendicular to **u** by the equation

$$\mathbf{v} = \frac{(\mathbf{u}.\mathbf{v})\mathbf{u}}{(\mathbf{u}.\mathbf{u})} + \frac{\mathbf{u} \wedge (\mathbf{v} \wedge \mathbf{u})}{(\mathbf{u}.\mathbf{u})}$$

10. For a set of vectors **a**, **b**, **c** we can define a set of *reciprocal vectors* **A**, **B** and **C** by the relations

$$\mathbf{A} = \frac{\mathbf{b} \wedge \mathbf{c}}{L}, \quad \mathbf{B} = \frac{\mathbf{c} \wedge \mathbf{a}}{L}, \quad \mathbf{C} = \frac{\mathbf{a} \wedge \mathbf{b}}{L}$$

where $L = \mathbf{a}.(\mathbf{b} \wedge \mathbf{c})$. Show that

$$\mathbf{A}.(\mathbf{B} \wedge \mathbf{C}) = \frac{1}{L}$$

(U.W.)

11. Find the velocity and acceleration of a particle for which the position at time t is given by:

(i) $x = 2t^2 + 3t$, $y = t^3 + 4t + 1$, $z = 2t - 1$;

(ii) $x = 3 \sin t + 1$, $y = \cos 2t - t$, $z = t^2 + 1$.

12. If the velocity **v** of a particle of mass m is given by

$$\mathbf{v} = 3t^2\hat{\mathbf{i}} + (2t + 1)\hat{\mathbf{j}} + t^3\hat{\mathbf{k}}$$

and the position **r** of the particle is given by

$$\mathbf{r} = 3\hat{\mathbf{i}} + 2\hat{\mathbf{j}} - \hat{\mathbf{k}}$$

what is the angular momentum of the particle?

13. Evaluate the gradient of the following scalar fields ϕ:

(i) $\phi = \dfrac{A}{x^2 + y^2 + z^2}$; (ii) $\phi = ax^2 + by^2 + cz^2$;

(iii) $\phi = a(x^2 + y^2 + z^2) + b(xy + xz + yz)$.

14. Evaluate the divergence and curl of the vectors:

(i) $(z^2 + y^2)\hat{\mathbf{i}} + (x^2 + z^2)\hat{\mathbf{j}} + (y^2 + x^2)\hat{\mathbf{k}}$;

(ii) $(2xy - z)\hat{\mathbf{i}} + (x^2 + 2y)\hat{\mathbf{j}} + (xyz + z^2x)\hat{\mathbf{k}}$;

(iii) $(3x - 2y)\hat{\mathbf{i}} + (x^2 + 2yz)\hat{\mathbf{j}} + (3x^2 - z^3)\hat{\mathbf{k}}$.

15. Show that:

(i) div $(a\mathbf{b})$ = a div $\mathbf{b}$ + $\mathbf{b}$.grad a;

(ii) div $(\mathbf{a} \wedge \mathbf{b})$ = $\mathbf{b}$.curl $\mathbf{a}$ − $\mathbf{a}$.curl $\mathbf{b}$;

(iii) $\text{grad}\ (\mathbf{a}.\mathbf{b}) = \mathbf{a} \wedge \text{curl}\ \mathbf{b} + \mathbf{b} \wedge \text{curl}\ \mathbf{a}$
$$+ \left(a_x \frac{\partial}{\partial x} + a_y \frac{\partial}{\partial y} + a_z \frac{\partial}{\partial z}\right)\mathbf{b} + \left(b_x \frac{\partial}{\partial x} + b_y \frac{\partial}{\partial y} + b_z \frac{\partial}{\partial z}\right)\mathbf{a}\,;$$

(iv) $\text{curl grad}\ \phi = 0$;

(v) $\text{div curl}\ \mathbf{a} = 0$.

6

Series, Taylor – Maclaurin Series

By a series we mean a set of numbers a_1, a_2, a_3 ... such that we have a rule for calculating a_2, a_3 etc. from the first number a_1. Series occur in many problems in chemistry such as specific heats of solids, the theory of black-body radiation, solution of the Schrödinger equation, statistical thermodynamics and Fourier series in X-ray crystallography. In this chapter we consider the summation of series and the convergence of infinite series. We shall develop methods for the expansion of functions such as transcendental functions in terms of infinite series.

6.1 SIMPLE SERIES

Two common series are the arithmetical and geometrical progressions.

6.1.1 Arithmetical progression

We generate an arithmetical progression by adding a constant amount, the *common difference* d to the preceding term a; for example

$$a, \quad a + d, \quad a + 2d, \quad a + 3d \tag{6.1}$$

where a is the first term. The sum of n terms, S_n, can be found by adding term by term the series and the series written backwards

$$S_n = a + (a + d) + (a + 2d) + \ldots + [a + (n - 1)d]$$

$$S_n = [a + (n - 1)d] + [a + (n - 2)d] + \ldots + a$$

Thus

$$2S_n = [2a + (n - 1)d] + [2a + (n - 1)d] + \ldots + [2a + (n - 1)d]$$

and

$$S_n = \frac{n}{2}[2a + (n - 1)d] \tag{6.2}$$

The sum of the integers from 1 to n is given by

$$S_n = \frac{n}{2}\,[2 \times 1 + (n - 1) \times 1] = \frac{n(n + 1)}{2}$$

because the first term is 1 and the common difference is 1.

6.1.2 Geometrical progression

We generate successive terms of a geometrical progression by multiplying the preceding term by a constant, the *common ratio*; for example

$$1, 2, 4, 8, 16 \ldots \qquad \text{common ratio} = 2$$

$$1, \frac{1}{2}, \frac{1}{4}, \frac{1}{8}, \frac{1}{16} \ldots \qquad \text{common ratio} = \frac{1}{2}$$

In general we have the series

$$a, ar, ar^2, ar^3 \ldots ar^{n-1} \tag{6.3}$$

where a is the first term and r is the common ratio. We obtain the sum of n terms, S_n, by taking the difference of S_n and rS_n.

$$S_n = a + ar + ar^2 + ar^3 + \ldots + ar^{n-1}$$

$$rS_n = ar + ar^2 + ar^3 + \ldots + ar^{n-1} + ar^n$$

Therefore

$$S_n(1 - r) = a - ar^n$$

So

$$S_n = \frac{a(1 - r^n)}{1 - r} \tag{6.4}$$

If we take 10 terms in the series

1, 2, 4, 8, 16, 32, 64, 128, 256, 512

the sum is

$$S_{10} = \frac{1(1 - 2^{10})}{1 - 2} = 2^{10} - 1 = 1023$$

6.2 CONVERGENCE OF INFINITE SERIES

Arithmetical and geometrical progressions are special cases of series. We can only find an expression for the sum of a series in a limited number of cases. The sums we have been concerned with are *partial sums* because they only include a finite number of terms

$$S_n = a_1 + a_2 + a_3 + \dots a_n = \sum_{r=1}^{n} a_r \qquad (6.5)$$

What can we say about the sum of an infinite number of terms, an *infinite series* Σa_r? Our approach is very similar to that in the case of improper integrals in section 3.4.2 in that we consider the limit of S_n as n goes to infinity. The sum S of an infinite series is given by the limit

$$S = \lim_{n\to\infty} S_n \qquad (6.6)$$

If the limit exists and is finite, the series is *convergent* but if the limit is infinite or oscillatory, the series is *divergent*. We shall consider tests for convergence in section 6.3. However, we can illustrate the situation with the sum of the geometrical progression in equation 6.4

$$S_n = \frac{a(1 - r^n)}{1 - r}$$

Let us now consider what happens as n becomes infinite. There are two cases.

(1) If $r < 1$, r^n will approach zero as n becomes infinite so we can say

$$\lim_{n\to\infty} S_n = \lim_{n\to\infty} \left[\frac{a(1 - r^n)}{1 - r}\right] = \frac{a}{1 - r} \qquad (6.7)$$

Thus in this case the limit exists and is finite, so a geometrical progression is convergent if the common ratio r is less than 1.

(2) If $r > 1$, as n approaches infinity, r^n will also become infinite and in this case there is no finite limit to $\lim S_n$. Thus the series is divergent.

An example of a convergent geometrical progression that occurs in statistical thermodynamics is the infinite series

$$1, e^{-x}, e^{-2x}, e^{-3x}, e^{-4x} \dots$$

If x is positive, e^{-nx} is less than unity, so the series will converge to the sum

$$S_\infty = \frac{1}{1 - e^{-x}} \qquad (6.8)$$

6.3 TESTS FOR CONVERGENCE

Here we only consider a few simple tests for convergence. For a more extensive treatment the reader should consult a more advanced text such as Stephenson (1973) or Green (1958). We consider separately series of positive terms and series of terms with alternating sign.

6.3.1 Series of positive terms

(i) Comparison test

Suppose we know that the series Σb_r is a series of positive terms which is convergent. Then we can say that if Σa_r is a series of positive terms, it will converge if $a_r \leqslant b_r$ for all sufficiently large values of r. However, if Σb_r diverges and if each term in Σa_r satisfies the condition $a_r \geqslant b_r$, then the series will also diverge. We illustrate the use of this test by two examples.

If, in the series

$$\frac{1}{1^2} + \frac{1}{2^2} + \frac{1}{3^2} + \frac{1}{4^2} + \frac{1}{5^2} \ldots \tag{6.9}$$

we group the terms as follows

$$\frac{1}{1^2} + \left[\frac{1}{2^2} + \frac{1}{3^2}\right] + \left[\frac{1}{4^2} + \frac{1}{5^2} + \frac{1}{6^2} + \frac{1}{7^2}\right] + \left[\frac{1}{8^2} + \ldots\right] +$$

we see that each group is equal to or smaller than the corresponding group in

$$\frac{1}{1^2} + \left[\frac{1}{2^2} + \frac{1}{2^2}\right] + \left[\frac{1}{4^2} + \frac{1}{4^2} + \frac{1}{4^2} + \frac{1}{4^2}\right] + \left[\frac{1}{8^2} + \ldots\right] +$$

This new set of numbers is, in fact, the geometrical progression

$$1 + \frac{1}{2} + \frac{1}{4} + \frac{1}{8} \ldots \tag{6.10}$$

which has a common ratio of less than unity and whose sum therefore converges to $1/(1 - \frac{1}{2})$, that is 2. Since series 6.10 is convergent and we can regroup the terms in the series $\Sigma 1/n$ so that each term is less than or equal to a term in the series $\Sigma 1/2^n$, the series $\Sigma 1/n^2$ is convergent.

By contrast, we consider the *harmonic series*

$$1 + \frac{1}{2} + \frac{1}{3} + \frac{1}{4} + \frac{1}{5} \ldots = \sum \frac{1}{r} \tag{6.11}$$

which is divergent. We can group the terms in such a way that the sum of each group is larger than or equal to 1/2; that is

$$1 + \frac{1}{2} + \left(\frac{1}{3} + \frac{1}{4}\right) + \left(\frac{1}{5} + \frac{1}{6} + \frac{1}{7} + \frac{1}{8}\right) + \ldots$$

Thus each term is equal to or larger than each term in the series

$$1 + \frac{1}{2} + \frac{1}{2} + \frac{1}{2} + \frac{1}{2} + \ldots$$

which is obviously divergent.

(ii) d'Alembert's ratio test

This test says that the series Σa_r converges if

$$\lim_{r\to\infty} \frac{a_{r+1}}{a_r} = k, \text{ where } k < 1 \tag{6.12}$$

and diverges if

$$\lim_{r\to\infty} \frac{a_{r+1}}{a_r} = k, \text{ where } k > 1 \tag{6.13}$$

If $k = 1$, the series may converge or diverge. If we have the series

$$\sum_{n=1}^{\infty} \frac{1}{3^n + 2} = \frac{1}{5} + \frac{1}{11} + \frac{1}{29} + \frac{1}{83} + \ldots \tag{6.14}$$

the *test ratio* is

$$\frac{a_{r+1}}{a_r} = \frac{1/(3^{r+1} + 2)}{1/(3^r + 2)} = \frac{3^r + 2}{3^{r+1} + 2}$$

If r is large, $3^{r+1} + 2 \approx 3^{r+1}$ and $3^r + 2 \approx 3^r$ so

$$\frac{a_{r+1}}{a_r} \approx \frac{3^r}{3^{r+1}} \approx \frac{1}{3}$$

Thus the limit $\lim a_{r+1}/a_r = 1/3$ and the series is convergent.

6.3.2 Series of alternating positive and negative terms

If we have a series $a_1, a_2, a_3, a_4 \ldots$ in which the terms are alternately positive and negative and *continually* decrease in magnitude, that is $|a_{r+1}| < |a_r|$, and as n tends to infinity, $\lim_{n\to\infty} a_n = 0$, then the series converges. This can be seen easily by representing the sum S_n graphically by a point on the x-axis. As n increases S_n oscillates with decreasing amplitude about the limit of the sum S_∞ (figure 6.1).

Consider the series

$$1 - \frac{1}{3} + \frac{1}{5} - \frac{1}{7} + \frac{1}{9} - \frac{1}{11} + \ldots$$

and let us represent the partial sums graphically as in figure 6.2.

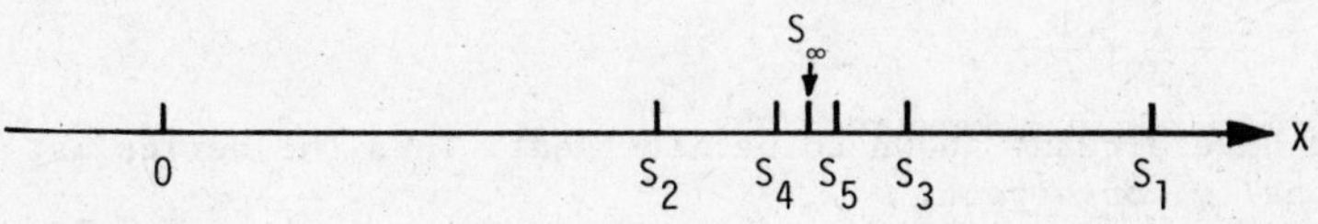

Figure 6.1

Figure 6.2

For series of positive and negative terms we should distinguish between absolute and conditional convergence. Let us consider a series

$$\sum_{r=1}^{\infty} a_r = a_1 + a_2 + a_3 + \ldots \tag{6.15}$$

of alternating positive and negative terms and the associated series

$$\sum_{r=1}^{\infty} |a_r| = |a_1| + |a_2| + |a_3| + \ldots \tag{6.16}$$

in which each term $|a_r|$ is equal to the absolute value of a_r in series 6.15. If series 6.16 is convergent, then series 6.15 is said to be *absolutely convergent*, whereas if $\sum_{r=1}^{\infty} |a_r|$ diverges but $\sum_{r=1} a_r$ converges, then series 6.15 is said to be *conditionally convergent*. The series

$$1 - \frac{1}{2} + \frac{1}{3} - \frac{1}{4} + \frac{1}{5} - \frac{1}{6} + \ldots \tag{6.17}$$

is conditionally convergent and we can see that its sum lies between 1/2 and 1. By grouping the terms as in 6.18

$$\left(1 - \frac{1}{2}\right) + \left(\frac{1}{3} - \frac{1}{4}\right) + \left(\frac{1}{5} - \frac{1}{6}\right) + \ldots \tag{6.18}$$

we get a series of positive terms whose sum is larger than 1/2 and increases as we take more terms, that is $S_{2m+2} \geqslant S_{2m}$. An alternative grouping is

$$1 - \left(\frac{1}{2} - \frac{1}{3}\right) - \left(\frac{1}{4} - \frac{1}{5}\right) - \left(\frac{1}{6} - \frac{1}{7}\right) - \ldots \tag{6.19}$$

in which each term in brackets is positive. We see here that the sum is less than unity and decreases as we take more terms. Thus the two different groupings give us upper and lower limits of 1 and 1/2, respectively, and indicate the existence of a limit. The series of the absolute values is the harmonic series

$$1 + \frac{1}{2} + \frac{1}{3} + \frac{1}{4} + \ldots$$

which we have already shown to be divergent. Thus the series is *conditionally convergent*.

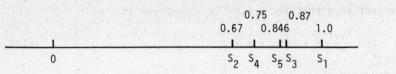

The sum of an absolutely convergent series does not change if the terms in the series are rearranged. However, rearrangement of the terms of a conditionally convergent series may change the sum.

6.4 POWER SERIES

A particularly important type of series is the power series

$$\sum_{r=0}^{\infty} a_r x^r = a_0 + a_1 x + a_2 x^2 + \dots \qquad (6.20)$$

We shall show in the next section how many functions, including transcendental functions, can be expanded in terms of power series. Also, in quantum mechanics we often express wavefunctions in the form of power series. Thus the convergence of such series is of considerable importance. We can apply d'Alembert's ratio test to find the values of x for which the series is convergent. For absolute convergence we require

$$\lim_{r\to\infty} \left| \frac{a_{r+1} x^{r+1}}{a_r x^r} \right|$$

to be less than unity. Rewriting this using the theorem of equation 2.11 gives

$$\lim_{r\to\infty} \left| \frac{a_{r+1} x}{a_r} \right| = |x| \lim_{r\to\infty} \left| \frac{a_{r+1}}{a_r} \right|$$

so we require

$$|x| < R, \text{ where } R = \lim_{r\to\infty} \left| \frac{a_r}{a_{r+1}} \right| \qquad (6.21)$$

R is called the *radius of convergence* and the series will be convergent if x lies in the *interval of convergence* $-R < x < R$. If we take the example

$$\sum_{r=1}^{\infty} \frac{(-1)^r x^r}{r} = \frac{-x}{1} + \frac{x^2}{2} - \frac{x^3}{3} + \frac{x^4}{4} - \dots$$

the radius of convergence is given by

$$R = \lim_{r\to\infty} \left| \frac{a_r}{a_{r+1}} \right| = \lim_{r\to\infty} \left| \frac{(-1)^r / r}{(-1)^{r+1} / (r+1)} \right| = \lim_{r\to\infty} \left| -\frac{(r+1)}{r} \right| = 1$$

so the series is absolutely convergent for $-1 < x < 1$. If x is equal to 1, we get the series

$$-1 + \frac{1}{2} - \frac{1}{3} + \frac{1}{4} \dots$$

which is conditionally convergent, but if $x = -1$ we get the divergent series

$$1 + \frac{1}{2} + \frac{1}{3} + \frac{1}{4} + \dots$$

6.5 TAYLOR AND MACLAURIN SERIES

We mentioned in section 1.1.2 that it is not possible to write down explicit algebraic formulae for many functions such as $\sin x$ and e^x. We discuss in this section how we can express such functions in terms of convergent infinite series. We want to see if we can expand the function $f(x)$ which has the value A_0 at $x = a$ in terms of the power series

$$f(x) = A_0 + A_1(x - a) + A_2(x - a)^2 + \dots + A_n(x - a)^n \tag{6.22}$$

so that the expansion is valid for values of x other than $x = a$. If the expansion is to be valid, the derivatives of $f(x)$ must be equal to the derivatives of the series; that is

$$\begin{aligned} f'(x) &= A_1 + 2A_2(x - a) + 3A_3(x - a)^2 + \dots \\ f''(x) &= 2A_2 + 2 \times 3A_3(x - a) + \dots \\ f'''(x) &= 2 \times 3A_3 + \\ &\quad 2 \times 3 \times 4A_4(x - a) + \dots \end{aligned}$$

and in general the nth derivative will be

$$f^{(n)}(x) = n!A_n + (n + 1)!A_{n+1}(x - a) + \dots \tag{6.23}$$

where $n!$ represents n *factorial*, which is the product $1 \times 2 \times 3 \times \dots \times (n - 1) \times n$ of all the integers from 1 to n.

We can now obtain A_1, A_2, etc. by putting $x = a$.

$$f(a) = A_0;\ f'(a) = A_1;\ f''(a) = 2A_2;$$
$$f'''(a) = 3!A_3;\ \dots\ f^{(n)}(a) = n!A_n \tag{6.24}$$

With these values for A_r, we obtain the series

$$f(x) = f(a) + f'(a)(x - a) + f''(a)\frac{(x - a)^2}{2!} + f'''(a)\frac{(x - a)^3}{3!} + \dots + f^{(n)}(a)\frac{(x - a)^n}{n!} + \dots \tag{6.25}$$

If we restrict ourselves to n terms there will be some error $E_n(x)$, the *remainder*; that is

$$f(x) = \sum_{r=0}^{\infty} \frac{(x - a)^r}{r!} f^{(r)}(a) + E_n(x) \tag{6.26}$$

where $f^{(r)}(a)$ is the value of the rth derivative of f(x) evaluated at x = a. This is *Taylor's theorem* and is valid if f(x) is a continuous single-valued function with continuous derivatives f'(x), f''(x) up to and including $f^{(n)}(x)$ for a given interval $a \leqslant x \leqslant b$ and provided $f^{(n+1)}(x)$ exists for $a \leqslant x \leqslant b$. The remainder is given by

$$E_n(x) = \frac{(x - a)^{n+1}}{(n + 1)!} f^{(n+1)}(\xi) \tag{6.27}$$

where $a < \xi < x$. If $\lim_{n\to\infty} E_n(x) = 0$, then f(x) can be represented by a power series

$$f(x) = f(a) + \frac{(x - a)}{1!} f'(a) + \frac{(x - a)^2}{2!} f''(a) + \ldots$$

$$= \sum_{r=0}^{\infty} \frac{(x - a)^r}{r!} f^{(r)}(a) \tag{6.28}$$

An alternative form is obtained by replacing x by x + a to give

$$f(x + a) = f(a) + \frac{x}{1!} f'(a) + \frac{x^2}{2!} f''(a) + \frac{x^3}{3!} f'''(a) + \ldots \tag{6.29}$$

These are both Taylor expansions of f(x) about x = a. If we have the special case of a = 0, we obtain the *Maclaurin expansion*

$$f(x) = f(0) + \frac{x}{1!} f'(0) + \frac{x^2}{2!} f''(0) + \frac{x^3}{3!} f'''(0) + \ldots \tag{6.30}$$

We should note that $f^{(n)}(a)$ means the value of the nth derivative $f^{(n)}(x)$ of f(x) at x = a.

To derive the first few terms of the Taylor expansion of sin x exp(x), we tabulate the necessary derivatives and their values at x = a

$$\begin{aligned}
f(x) &= \exp(x) \sin x \\
f'(x) &= \exp(x) (\sin x + \cos x) \\
f''(x) &= \exp(x)\ 2 \cos x \\
f'''(x) &= 2 \exp(x) (\cos x - \sin x) \\
f''''(x) &= 4 \exp(x) \sin x \\
f(a) &= \exp(a) \sin a \\
f'(a) &= \exp(a) (\sin a + \cos a) \\
f''(a) &= 2 \exp(a) \cos a \\
f'''(a) &= 2 \exp(a) (\cos a - \sin a) \\
f''''(a) &= 4 \exp(a) \sin a
\end{aligned}$$

Thus

$$\exp(x)\sin x = \exp(a)\sin a + \exp(a)(\sin a + \cos a)x$$
$$+ \frac{x^2}{2!} 2\exp(a)\cos a + \frac{x^3}{3!} 2\exp(a)(\cos a - \sin a) +$$
$$\frac{x^4}{4!} 4\exp(a)\sin a + \ldots$$

We shall now derive Taylor or Maclaurin expansions for a number of standard functions.

6.5.1 Binomial expansion

We tabulate the first few derivatives of the function $f(x) = (1 + x)^{\alpha}$ where α is any general exponent.

$$f(x) = (1 + x)^{\alpha}$$
$$f'(x) = \alpha(1 + x)^{\alpha-1}$$
$$f''(x) = \alpha(\alpha - 1)(1 + x)^{\alpha-2}$$
$$f'''(x) = \alpha(\alpha - 1)(\alpha - 2)(1 + x)^{\alpha-3}$$
$$f^{(p)}(x) = \alpha(\alpha - 1)\ldots(\alpha - p + 1)(1 + x)^{\alpha-p}$$
$$f(0) = 1$$
$$f'(0) = \alpha$$
$$f''(0) = \alpha(\alpha - 1)$$
$$f'''(0) = \alpha(\alpha - 1)(\alpha - 2)$$
$$f^{(p)}(0) = \alpha(\alpha - 1)\ldots(\alpha - p + 1)$$

Thus the Maclaurin expansion is

$$(1 + x)^{\alpha} = 1 + \alpha\frac{x}{1!} + \alpha(\alpha - 1)\frac{x^2}{2!} + \alpha(\alpha - 1)(\alpha - 2)\frac{x^3}{3!}$$
$$+ [\alpha(\alpha - 1)\ldots(\alpha - r + 1)]\frac{x^r}{r!} + \ldots \qquad (6.32)$$

If α is a positive integer n, the series is finite and terminates with $x^n\, n!/n! = x^n$. For this case the expansion can be derived by other means. We have to consider under what conditions the series is convergent when α is not a positive integer. Using the d'Alembert ratio test we require

$$|x| < \lim_{r\to\infty}\left|\frac{a_r}{a_{r+1}}\right| = \lim_{r\to\infty}\left|\frac{[\alpha(\alpha - 1)\ldots(\alpha - r + 2)/(r - 1)!]}{\alpha(\alpha - 1)\ldots(\alpha - r + 1)/r!}\right|$$

$$= \lim_{r\to\infty}\left|\frac{r}{\alpha - r + 1}\right| = \lim_{r\to\infty}\left|\frac{1}{\alpha/r - 1 + 1/r}\right| = 1$$

Thus the binomial series is convergent for $|x| < 1$.

6.5.2 Sine and cosine series

If $f(x) = \sin x$, $f(0) = 0$ and we obtain the following derivatives

$$f'(x) = \cos x = \sin\left(x + \frac{\pi}{2}\right) \qquad f'(0) = 1$$

$$f''(x) = -\sin x = \sin(x + \pi) \qquad f''(0) = 0$$

$$f'''(x) = -\cos x = \sin\left(x + \frac{3\pi}{2}\right) \quad f'''(0) = -1$$

that is

$$f^{(n)}(x) = \sin\left(x + n\frac{\pi}{2}\right)$$

Thus if $n = 1,5,9 \ldots (4m + 1)$; $f^{(n)}(0) = 1$ but if $n = 3,7,11 \ldots (4m + 3)$; $f^{(n)}(0) = -1$ and if n is even $f^{(n)}(0) = 0$. The Maclaurin expansion is therefore

$$\sin x = \frac{x}{1!} - \frac{x^3}{3!} + \frac{x^5}{5!} - \frac{x^7}{7!} + \ldots + \frac{(-1)^{r-1}x^{2r-1}}{(2r-1)!} + \ldots \tag{6.33}$$

The test for convergence gives

$$\lim_{r\to\infty}\left|\frac{a_r}{a_{r+1}}\right| = \lim_{r\to\infty}\left|\frac{[(-1)^{r-1}/(2r-1)!]}{[(-1)^r/(2r+1)!]}\right| = \lim_{r\to\infty}|\,(-1)2r(2r+1)$$

Thus the limit is infinite and the series is convergent for $-\infty < x < \infty$.

Similarly we can derive the expansion for cos x

$$\cos x = 1 - \frac{x^2}{2!} + \frac{x^4}{4!} - \frac{x^6}{6!} + \ldots + (-1)^{r-1}\frac{x^{2r}}{(2r)!} + \ldots \tag{6.34}$$

which is also convergent for $-\infty < x < \infty$.

6.5.3 The exponential series

All derivatives of $f(x) = \exp(x)$ are the same, namely $\exp(x)$ and have the value 1 for $x = 0$. Thus the Maclaurin series for $\exp(x)$ is simply

$$\exp(x) = 1 + \frac{x}{1!} + \frac{x^2}{2!} + \frac{x^3}{3!} + \ldots + \frac{x^r}{r!} + \ldots \tag{6.35}$$

This is convergent for $-\infty < x < \infty$ because the limit

$$\lim_{r\to\infty}\left|\frac{a_r}{a_{r+1}}\right| = \lim_{r\to\infty}\left|\frac{[1/(r-1)!]}{[1/r!]}\right| = \lim_{r\to\infty}|\,r\,|$$

is infinite.

6.5.4 The logarithmic series

We cannot expand ln x as a Maclaurin series because the function is undefined for x = 0. We can, however, expand ln (1 + x). The first few derivatives are

$$f'(x) = \frac{1}{1+x} \qquad f'(0) = 1$$

$$f''(x) = -\frac{1}{(1+x)^2} \qquad f''(0) = -1$$

$$f'''(x) = \frac{2}{(1+x)^3} \qquad f'''(0) = 2$$

$$f^{(r)}(x) = (-1)^{r-1}\frac{(r-1)!}{(1+x)^r} \qquad f^{(r)}(0) = (-1)^{r-1}(r-1)!$$

The expansion is, therefore,

$$\ln(1+x) = x - \frac{x^2}{2} + \frac{x^3}{3} - \frac{x^4}{4} + \ldots + (-1)^{r-1}\frac{x^r}{r} + \ldots \tag{6.36}$$

This series is convergent for the interval $-1 < x < 1$ because

$$\lim_{r\to\infty}\left|\frac{a_r}{a_{r+1}}\right| = \lim_{r\to\infty}\left|-\frac{(r+1)}{r}\right| = \lim_{r\to\infty}\left|-1-\frac{1}{r}\right| = 1$$

Although we cannot expand ln x as a Maclaurin series, we can expand it as Taylor series about x = 1 (or any other value of x except x = 0)

$$\ln x = (x-1) - \frac{1}{2}(x-1)^2 + \frac{1}{3}(x-1)^3 + \ldots \tag{6.37}$$

6.5.5 Legendre polynomials

An interesting application of the Maclaurin expansion arises in potential theory. Suppose we have a unit charge at a point P and we are interested in the potential at the point A, which has polar co-ordinates (r,θ) relative to OP (figure 6.3). If the distance PA is r', the potential at A is $1/4\pi\varepsilon_o r'$, where ε_o is the permittivity of free space. In terms of r, R and θ, the potential V is

$$V = \frac{1}{4\pi\varepsilon_o(R^2 + r^2 - 2Rr\cos\theta)^{\frac{1}{2}}} \tag{6.38}$$

where we have assumed $R < r$. Letting $R/r = x$ and regarding θ as a constant, we can now expand by a Maclaurin series about x = 0 to give

$$V = \frac{1}{4\pi\varepsilon_o r}\left[1 + x\cos\theta + x^2\,\tfrac{1}{2}(3\cos^2\theta - 1) + x^3\,\tfrac{1}{2}(5\cos^3\theta - 3\cos\theta) + \ldots\right] \tag{6.39}$$

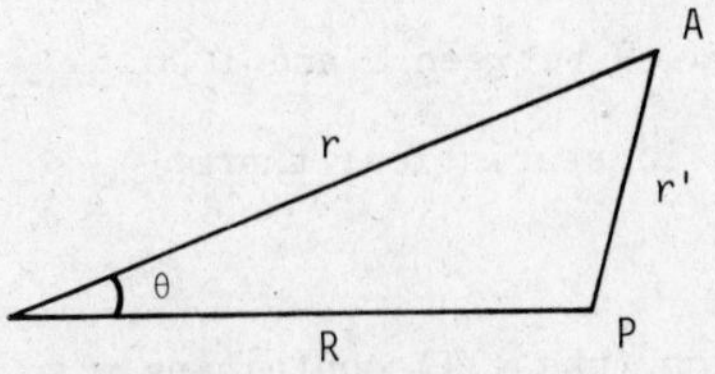

Figure 6.3

The coefficients of x^ℓ are important functions called *Legendre polynomials* and are given the symbol P_ℓ (cos θ). Thus we can write

$$V = \frac{1}{4\pi\varepsilon_o r'} = \frac{1}{4\pi\varepsilon_o} \times \frac{1}{r} \sum_{\ell=0}^{\infty} \left(\frac{R}{r}\right)^\ell P_\ell(\cos\theta) \qquad (6.40)$$

For the case of R > r, we expand in terms of (r/R).

6.6 DIFFERENTIATION OR INTEGRATION OF SERIES

Other useful series can often be obtained by the differentiation or integration of a series. We could, for example, derive the cosine series by differentiating the sine series 6.33.

$$\cos x = \frac{d}{dx}(\sin x) = \frac{d}{dx}\left[x - \frac{x^3}{3!} + \frac{x^5}{5!} + \ldots\right]$$

$$= 1 - \frac{x^2}{2!} + \frac{x^4}{4!} \ldots \qquad (6.41)$$

A more interesting example is the series for $\tan^{-1} x$, which may be obtained by recalling from equation 3.21 that

$$\tan^{-1} x = \int \frac{dx}{1 + x^2} = \int [1 - x^2 + x^4 - x^6 + \ldots] dx$$

for | x | < 1. Performing the integration gives *Gregory's series* for $\tan^{-1} x$

$$\tan^{-1} x = x - \frac{x^3}{3} + \frac{x^5}{5} - \frac{x^7}{7} + \ldots \qquad (6.42)$$

for |x| < 1.

6.7 PROBLEMS FOR SOLUTION

1. Calculate the sum of the even integers from 2 to 1000.

2. Calculate the sum of n terms in the series ax, 2ax, 3ax, 4ax.

3. Calculate the sum of the first 20 terms in the series

$$1, \frac{1}{2}, \frac{1}{4}, \frac{1}{8}, \frac{1}{16}$$

4. Find the sum of all the multiples of 9 between 0 and 1000.

5. The series $\sum_{r=1}^{\infty} \exp(-rh\nu/kT)$ occurs in statistical thermodynamics. Evaluate its sum.

6. Suppose a volume V cm^3 of a solution (phase I) containing w g of a dissolved substance X is repeatedly extracted into phase II with fresh portions of 1 cm^3 of another solvent Y which is immiscible with the first. The distribution coefficient K gives the ratio of the concentration of X in phase I to that in phase II. For a given volume of Y, is it better to divide it into a large number of portions or into a small number of portions?

7. Determine whether the following series are convergent or divergent

$$\text{(i)} \sum_{r=1}^{\infty} \frac{(2r-1)}{r^{3/2}}; \text{ (ii)} \sum_{r=1}^{\infty} \frac{1}{\sqrt{(r^2+r)}};$$

$$\text{(iii)} \sum_{r=1}^{\infty} \frac{3^r}{r \times 2^r}; \text{ (iv)} \sum_{r=1}^{\infty} \frac{1}{2r+1}; \text{ (v)} \sum_{r=0}^{\infty} \frac{r^2}{(r+1)!};$$

$$\text{(vi)} \sum_{r=0}^{\infty} \frac{r^r}{(r+1)!}; \text{ (vii)} \sum_{r=1}^{\infty} \frac{1}{r^3}; \text{ (viii)} \sum_{r=0}^{\infty} \frac{r(r+2)}{(r+1)^3}.$$

8. Test the following series for convergence. Distinguish between absolute and conditional convergence:

$$\text{(i)} \sum_{r=1}^{\infty} (-1)^{r-1} \frac{(2^{r-1}+1)}{2^r}; \text{ (ii)} \sum_{r=1}^{\infty} \frac{(-1)^r}{r^{3/2}};$$

$$\text{(iii)} \sum_{r=0}^{\infty} r \cos\left(\frac{r\pi}{4}\right); \text{ (iv)} \sum_{r=0}^{\infty} \frac{(-1)^{r+1}}{2r-1}.$$

9. For what values of x are the following series convergent?

$$\text{(i)} \sum_{r=0}^{\infty} \frac{x^r}{r^2+1}; \text{ (ii)} \sum_{r=0}^{\infty} (-1)^{r-1} x^{2r-2};$$

$$\text{(iii)} \sum_{r=0}^{\infty} \frac{x^r}{2^{r-1}}; \text{ (iv)} \sum_{r=0}^{\infty} (-1)^{r-1} \frac{x^{2r-1}}{2r-1}.$$

10. Develop Maclaurin expansions for the following functions and specify the values of x for which they are convergent:

$$\text{(i)} \sinh x; \text{ (ii)} \ln\left(\frac{1}{1-x}\right); \text{ (iii)} \sin^2 x;$$

$$\text{(iv)} (1+x)^{1/2}; \text{ (v)} (1+x)^{-3/2}; \text{ (vi)} \cos^{-1} x;$$

$$\text{(vii)} \tan x.$$

11. Derive the first six Legendre polynomials.

7
Complex Numbers

7.1 DEFINITION

So far we have been concerned with *real numbers*. We are familiar with the positive and negative *integers* ±1, ±2, ±3 ..., *rational numbers* p/q, where p and q are integers, *irrational numbers* such as $\sqrt{2}$, π, e, which cannot be expressed exactly as the ratio of two integers and *zero*. Real numbers obey certain rules, which, through familiarity, we have come to regard as self-evident.

(1) Addition is commutative

$$a + b = b + a \tag{7.1}$$

and associative

$$(a + b) + c = a + (b + c) \tag{7.2}$$

(2) In subtraction, the equation

$$a + x = b$$

has the unique solution

$$x = b - a \tag{7.3}$$

(3) The multiplication of real numbers is commutative

$$ab = ba \tag{7.4}$$

and associative

$$(ab)c = a(bc) \tag{7.5}$$

(4) In division, the equation

$$ax = b \quad (a \neq 0)$$

has the unique solution

$$x = \frac{b}{a} \tag{7.6}$$

(5) The distributive law holds

$$(a + b)c = ac + bc \tag{7.7}$$

With only real numbers we are unable to solve the quadratic equation

$$x^2 + 1 = 0$$

However, if we introduce a number $i = \sqrt{-1}$, the square root of minus 1, we can solve any quadratic equation using equation 1.9.

We define a *complex number* as being of the form

$$z = a + ib \tag{7.8}$$

where a and b are real numbers and $i = \sqrt{-1}$. a is called the *real part* of z and b is the *imaginary part* of z, and we can write this as

$$Rz = a, \quad Iz = b \tag{7.9}$$

If $Iz = 0$, then $z = a$ is a real number but if $Rz = 0$, $z = ib$ is *pure imaginary*. A complex number is zero *if and only if* a and b are both zero. Two complex numbers $z_1 = a + ib$, $z_2 = c + id$ are equal *if and only if* $a = c$ and $b = d$.

The complex number $z = a + ib$ is also often written in the form (a,b).

7.2 ALGEBRA OF COMPLEX NUMBERS

We can add, subtract and multiply complex numbers using the same rules as we use for real numbers provided that we remember that $i^2 = -1$. We shall define the process of division later. Any general property of complex numbers is satisfied by real numbers but the converse is *not* true. For complex numbers there is no order relation or positive or negative character.

7.2.1 Addition and subtraction

Addition and subtraction are carried out by performing the operations separately on the real and imaginary parts.

$$(a + ib) + (c + id) = (a + c) + i(b + d) \tag{7.10}$$

For example

$$(6 + 4i) + (3 + 5i) = 9 + 9i$$

$$(a + ib) - (c + id) = (a - c) + i(b - d) \tag{7.11}$$

For example

$$(6 + 4i) - (3 + 5i) = 3 - i$$

7.2.2 Multiplication

This is also a straightforward procedure provided we remember to replace i^2 by -1 wherever it occurs

$$\begin{aligned}(a + ib)(c + id) &= ac + i^2bd + ibc + iad \\ &= (ac - bd) + i(bc + ad)\end{aligned}$$

For example

$$(2 + 3i)(4 + 5i) = (2 \times 4 - 3 \times 5) + i(3 \times 4 + 2 \times 5)$$

This can be extended to expressions of any complexity; for example

$$i(4 + i)(3 + 2i)(2 - 5i) - (2 + i)^2$$
$$= (-1 + 4i)(3 + 2i)(2 - 5i) - (4 + 2i - 1)$$
$$= (-3 - 2i + 12i - 8)(2 - 5i) - (3 + 2i)$$
$$= (-22 + 55i + 20i + 50) - 3 - 2i = 25 + 73i$$

The result of a series of additions, subtractions and multiplications can always be expressed as a single complex number (a + ib).

7.2.3 Division

As yet the quotient (a + ib)/(c + id) is undefined. The easiest way to evaluate it is to multiply top and bottom by (c - id)

$$z = \frac{a + ib}{c + id} = \frac{(a + ib)(c - id)}{(c + id)(c - id)} = \frac{(ac + bd) + i(bc - ad)}{c^2 + d^2} \tag{7.13}$$

which has the effect of reducing the denominator to a real number, for example

$$\frac{2 + 3i}{4 + 5i} = \frac{(2 + 3i)(4 - 5i)}{(4 + 5i)(4 - 5i)} = \frac{(8 + 15) + i(12 - 10)}{16 + 25}$$

Division can be combined with other arithmetical operations in a straightforward manner; for example

$$\frac{(2 + 3i)(4 + 2i)}{(1 + 5i)} = \frac{(2 + 3i)(4 + 2i)(1 - 5i)}{(1 + 5i)(1 - 5i)}$$

7.2.4 Complex conjugate

In the previous section we saw how the product (a + ib)(a - ib) is a real number. The complex numbers (a + ib) and (a - ib) bear an important relation to each other. The number (a - ib) is the *complex conjugate* of (a + ib). The complex conjugate of z is usually given by the symbol z*. Thus the product of a complex number and its complex conjugate is a real number. An example of the importance of this is in the case of the probability distribution in quantum mechanics which is given by the product $\psi^*\psi$ of wavefunction ψ and its complex conjugate ψ^*.

If a complex number z is equal to its complex conjugate z* this means that the number is real. However, if z = -z*, z is pure imaginary. It can be quickly verified that complex conjugates obey the relations

$$(z_1 + z_2)^* = z_1^* + z_2^* \tag{7.14}$$

$$(z_1 z_2)^* = (z_1^*)(z_2^*) \tag{7.15}$$

7.2.5 Modulus of a complex number

We saw above that the product of a complex number with its

complex conjugate is a real positive number, $(a + ib)(a - ib) = a^2 + b^2$. The *modulus* or *absolute value* of the complex number z is defined by

$$|z| = \sqrt{(a^2 + b^2)} = \sqrt{[(Rz)^2 + (Iz)^2]} \quad (7.16)$$

Thus $zz^* = |z|^2$. The modulus is always positive and this definition is consistent with our previous use of the term modulus for real numbers. It is obvious that a complex number and its complex conjugate have the same modulus.

The quotient of two complex numbers z_1 and z_2 can be expressed compactly as

$$\frac{z_1}{z_2} = \frac{z_1 z_2^*}{|z_2|^2} \quad (7.17)$$

7.3 THE ARGAND DIAGRAM

7.3.1 Cartesian co-ordinates

Writing the complex number $z = a + ib$ in the form (a,b) suggests an analogy with the co-ordinates of a point (x,y) in cartesian co-ordinates. So we can plot complex numbers on a diagram in which the x-axis becomes the *real axis* and the y-axis is the *imaginary axis* (figure 7.1). Such a diagram is called an *Argand diagram* and the x-y plane is the *Argand plane*.

Furthermore, the expression $z = a + ib$ is analogous to the resolution of a vector in two dimensions, $\mathbf{a} = a_x\hat{\mathbf{i}} + a_y\hat{\mathbf{j}}$, where instead of the unit vectors $\hat{\mathbf{i}}$ and $\hat{\mathbf{j}}$, we have 1 and i (be careful not to confuse the unit vector $\hat{\mathbf{i}}$ with $i = \sqrt{-1}$). So we can associate a vector OP with the complex number $z = a + ib$. If we like, we can think of the addition and subtraction of complex numbers in terms of the addition and subtraction of vectors in the Argand diagram. The length of the vector represents the modulus.

Using the vector analogy we can readily see (figure 7.2) that the inequality

$$|z_1 + z_2| \leqslant |z_1| + |z_2| \quad (7.18)$$

is true.

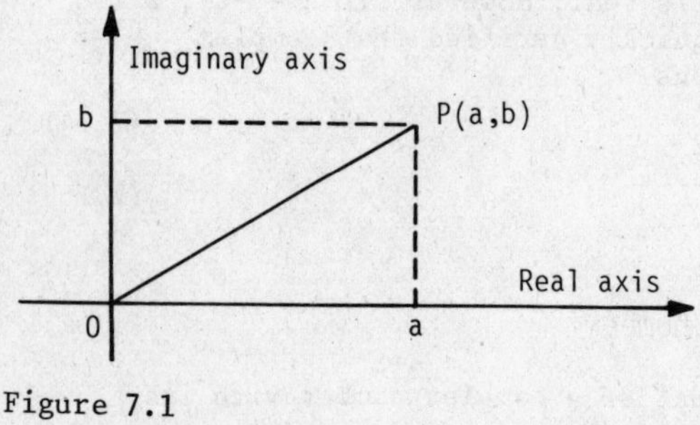

Figure 7.1

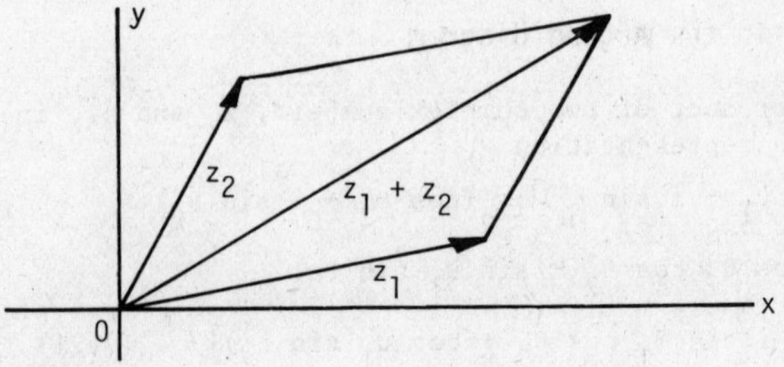

Figure 7.2

7.3.2 The Argand diagram in polar co-ordinates

We have so far discussed the Argand diagram in terms of cartesian co-ordinates. However, the polar co-ordinate form is more useful. We specify the position of the point (x,y) representing the complex number z = x + iy in terms of its distance r from the origin 0 and the angle θ that the line OP makes with the x-axis (figure 7.3). The distance r is obviously equal to the modulus of z

$$r = \sqrt{(x^2 + y^2)} = |z|$$

and

$$\theta = \tan^{-1}\left(\frac{y}{x}\right) \tag{7.19}$$

The convention with regard to the angle θ is that it is restricted to the range $-\pi < \theta \leqslant \pi$. The angle θ is called the *argument* of z

$$\theta = \arg(z)$$

Thus we can rewrite z in the form

$$z = r(\cos\theta + i\sin\theta) \tag{7.20}$$

For example, if z = 1 + 3i

$$r = |z| = \sqrt{10}, \quad \theta = \tan^{-1}(3), \quad \cos\theta = \frac{1}{\sqrt{10}}, \quad \sin\theta = \frac{3}{\sqrt{10}}$$

Therefore

$$z = \sqrt{10}\left(\frac{1}{\sqrt{10}} + i\frac{3}{\sqrt{10}}\right)$$

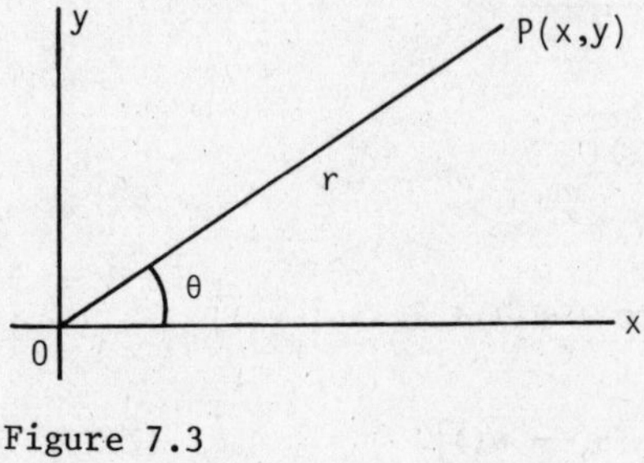

Figure 7.3

7.3.3 Multiplication in the Argand diagram

Let us consider the product of two complex numbers, z_1 and z_2, in the polar co-ordinate representation

$$\begin{aligned} z_1 z_2 &= [r_1(\cos\theta_1 + i\sin\theta_1)][r_2(\cos\theta_2 + i\sin\theta_2)] \\ &= r_1 r_2[(\cos\theta_1\cos\theta_2 - \sin\theta_1\sin\theta_2) \\ &\qquad + i(\sin\theta_1\cos\theta_2 + \cos\theta_1\sin\theta_2)] \qquad (7.21) \\ &= r_1 r_2[\cos(\theta_1 + \theta_2) + i\sin(\theta_1 + \theta_2)] \end{aligned}$$

Thus the modulus of the product is given by the product of the individual moduli $|z_1||z_2| = r_1 r_2$. It would appear that the argument of $z_1 z_2$ is the sum of the arguments of z_1 and z_2. However, we have to be careful to see that $\arg(z_1 z_2)$ lies in the range $-\pi < x \leqslant \pi$; that is

$$\arg(z_1 z_2) = \arg(z_1) + \arg(z_2) + 2\pi k \qquad (7.22)$$

where $k = 0$, 1 or -1, so that $\arg(z_1 z_2)$ lies in the range $-\pi$ to π.

The complex numbers $(1 + i)$ and $(1 + \sqrt{3}i)$, when expressed in polar co-ordinate form are $\sqrt{2}(\cos\pi/4 + i\sin\pi/4)$ and $2(\cos\pi/3 + i\sin\pi/3)$, respectively. Thus the product is given by $z = z_1 z_2$, $(1 + i)(1 + \sqrt{3}i) = 2\sqrt{2}(\cos 7\pi/12 + i\sin 7\pi/12)$. If we wish to multiply z by i we can use the polar co-ordinate form, for

$$|i| = 1,\ \arg(i) = \frac{\pi}{2}$$

so

$$zi = r \times 1\left[\cos\left(\theta + \frac{\pi}{2}\right) + i\sin\left(\theta + \frac{\pi}{2}\right)\right]$$

Thus multiplication by i is equivalent to an anticlockwise rotation of $\pi/2$.

7.3.4 Division

We can also express the quotient of two complex numbers in polar co-ordinate form. If $z_2 \neq 0$, then

$$\begin{aligned} \frac{1}{z_2} &= \frac{z_2^*}{|z_2|^2} = \frac{r_2(\cos\theta_2 - i\sin\theta_2)}{r_2^2} \\ &= \frac{1}{r_2}[\cos(-\theta_2) + i\sin(-\theta_2)] \end{aligned}$$

so

$$\begin{aligned} \frac{z_1}{z_2} &= \frac{r_1}{r_2}(\cos\theta_1 + i\sin\theta_1)[\cos(-\theta_2) + i\sin(-\theta_2)] \\ &= \frac{r_1}{r_2}[\cos(\theta_1 - \theta_2) + i\sin(\theta_1 - \theta_2)] \qquad (7.23) \end{aligned}$$

Thus

$$\left|\frac{z_1}{z_2}\right| = \frac{r_1}{r_2}$$

and

$$\arg\left(\frac{z_1}{z_2}\right) = \arg z_1 - \arg z_2 + 2\pi k$$

where k = 0, 1, -1, so that $\arg(z_1/z_2)$ lies in the range $-\pi$ to π. For example

$$\frac{1 + i}{1 + \sqrt{3}i} = \frac{\sqrt{2}}{2}\left[\frac{\cos(\pi/4) + i \sin(\pi/4)}{\cos(\pi/3) + i \sin(\pi/3)}\right]$$

$$= \frac{1}{\sqrt{2}}\left(\cos\left(\frac{-\pi}{12}\right) + i \sin\left(\frac{-\pi}{12}\right)\right)$$

7.4 DE MOIVRE'S THEOREM

This is an important and useful theorem in complex-number theory and can be derived from the product of two complex numbers in polar co-ordinate form

$$z_1z_2 = r_1r_2[\cos(\theta_1 + \theta_2) + i \sin(\theta_1 + \theta_2)]$$

If $z_1 = z_2 = z$, that is, $r_1 = r_2 = r$, $\theta_1 = \theta_2 = \theta$, we obtain the expression

$$z^2 = r^2(\cos 2\theta + i \sin 2\theta)$$

Multiplying by z once more gives

$$z^3 = r^3(\cos 3\theta + i \sin 3\theta)$$

so we can see that the general result is

$$z^n = r^n[\cos(n\theta) + i \sin (n\theta)] \qquad (7.24)$$

If we take the case where r = 1, we obtain *de Moivre's theorem*

$$(\cos \theta + i \sin \theta)^n = \cos(n\theta) + i \sin(n\theta) \qquad (7.25)$$

We have derived this for a positive value of n. However it is valid for negative values also because if n = -q,

$$\begin{aligned}(\cos \theta + i \sin \theta)^n &= [(\cos \theta + i \sin \theta)^q]^{-1} \\ &= [\cos(q\theta) + i \sin(q\theta)]^{-1} \\ &= \cos(-q\theta) + i \sin(-q\theta) \\ &= \cos(n\theta) + i \sin(n\theta) \qquad (7.26)\end{aligned}$$

By using a combination of the results for positive and negative values we can show that the theorem is also applicable to fractional values of n.

7.4.1 Application to trigonometric formulae

The multiple-angle formula 1.27 can be easily derived from de Moivre's theorem. Let us consider sin 3θ and cos 3θ. From equation 7.25 we have

$$(\cos 3\theta + i \sin 3\theta) = (\cos \theta + i \sin \theta)^3$$

$$= \cos^3 \theta - 3 \cos \theta \sin^2 \theta$$

$$+ 3i \sin \theta \cos^2 \theta - i \sin^3 \theta$$

$$= (4 \cos^3 \theta - 3 \cos \theta)$$

$$+ i(3 \sin \theta - 4 \sin^3 \theta)$$

If we equate the real parts on each side of the equation we see that

$$\cos 3\theta = 4 \cos^3 \theta - 3 \cos \theta \qquad (7.27)$$

and from the imaginary parts we get

$$\sin 3\theta = 3 \sin \theta - 4 \sin^3 \theta \qquad (7.28)$$

We can also use de Moivre's theorem to obtain expressions for $\cos^n \theta$ and $\sin^n \theta$. If $z = \cos \theta + i \sin \theta$

$$z^{-1} = \frac{z^*}{|z|^2} = \cos \theta - i \sin \theta$$

From de Moivre's theorem

$$z^n = \cos n\theta + i \sin n\theta; \quad z^{-n} = \cos n\theta - i \sin n\theta$$

Using these expressions to obtain expressions for cos θ, sin θ, cos nθ and sin nθ gives

$$\begin{aligned} z + z^{-1} &= 2 \cos \theta & \qquad z - z^{-1} &= 2i \sin \theta \\ z^n + z^{-n} &= 2 \cos n\theta & \qquad z^n - z^{-n} &= 2i \sin n\theta \end{aligned} \qquad (7.29)$$

To obtain $\cos^n \theta$, we expand $(z + z^{-1})^n$ by the binomial theorem (equation 6.32); for example

$$(z + z^{-1})^3 = (z^3 + z^{-3}) + 3(z + z^{-1})$$

and substitute for $(z^n + z^{-n})$ from equation 7.29. Thus in our example

$$(2 \cos \theta)^3 = (z + z^{-1})^3 = 2 \cos 3\theta + 3 \times 2 \cos \theta$$

so

$$4 \cos^3 \theta = \cos 3\theta + 3 \cos \theta \qquad (7.30)$$

7.4.2 Roots of complex numbers

Another important application of de Moivre's theorem is to the calculation of roots of numbers. Suppose we require the nth roots of the number $z = r(\cos\theta + i\sin\theta)$. We can add any integral multiple of 2π to θ without changing the number; that is

$$z = r[\cos(\theta + 2\pi k) + i\sin(\theta + 2\pi k)]$$

We can now use de Moivre's theorem to write the nth roots as

$$\begin{aligned} z^{1/n} &= r^{1/n}[\cos(\theta + 2\pi k) + i\sin(\theta + 2\pi k)]^{1/n} \\ &= r^{1/n}\left[\cos\left(\frac{\theta + 2\pi k}{n}\right) + i\sin\left(\frac{\theta + 2\pi k}{n}\right)\right] \end{aligned} \tag{7.31}$$

and we allow k to take values 0, 1 ... (n - 1) so that we obtain n distinct roots.

To find the fifth roots of $(\sqrt{3} + i)$, we first express z in terms of polar co-ordinates

$$z = 2\left[\cos\left(\frac{\pi}{6}\right) + i\sin\left(\frac{\pi}{6}\right)\right]$$

Therefore

$$\begin{aligned} z^{1/5} &= 2^{1/5}\left[\cos\left(\frac{\pi}{6}\right) + i\sin\left(\frac{\pi}{6}\right)\right]^{1/5} \\ &= 2^{1/5}\left[\cos\frac{1}{5}\left(\frac{\pi}{6} + 2\pi k\right) + i\sin\frac{1}{5}\left(\frac{\pi}{6} + 2\pi k\right)\right] \end{aligned}$$

Here k will take the values 0, 1, 2, 3, 4 and we obtain the five distinct roots

$$\begin{aligned} &2^{1/5}\left(\cos\frac{\pi}{30} + i\sin\frac{\pi}{30}\right);\ 2^{1/5}\left(\cos\frac{13\pi}{30} + i\sin\frac{13\pi}{30}\right); \\ &2^{1/5}\left(\cos\frac{25\pi}{30} + i\sin\frac{25\pi}{30}\right);\ 2^{1/5}\left(\cos\frac{37\pi}{30} + i\sin\frac{37\pi}{30}\right); \\ &2^{1/5}\left(\cos\frac{49\pi}{30} + i\sin\frac{49\pi}{30}\right). \end{aligned} \tag{7.32}$$

Letting k take values of 5 and over would only repeat some of these roots.

7.5 THE EXPONENTIAL FUNCTION

Just as we can have functions of real variables, we can also have functions of complex variables. An important example is the exponential function for a complex argument. We have seen in section 6.5.3 that the exponential function of a real variable x can be written as a power series

$$\exp(x) = 1 + \frac{x}{1!} + \frac{x^2}{2!} + \frac{x^3}{3!} + \frac{x^4}{4!} + \ldots \tag{7.33}$$

If we have a variable z that is a complex number, we can write

$$\exp(z) = 1 + \frac{z}{1!} + \frac{z^2}{2!} + \frac{z^3}{3!} + \frac{z^4}{4!} + \ldots \tag{7.34}$$

and exp(z) obeys all the rules obeyed by exp(x).

If z is a pure imaginary number, iθ (where θ is real), we obtain

$$\exp(i\theta) = 1 + \frac{i\theta}{1!} + \frac{i^2\theta^2}{2!} + \frac{i^3\theta^3}{3!} + \frac{i^4\theta^4}{4!} + \ldots$$

Eliminating powers of i higher than the first gives

$$\exp(i\theta) = 1 + \frac{i\theta}{1!} - \frac{\theta^2}{2!} - \frac{i\theta^3}{3!} + \frac{\theta^4}{4!} + \cdots \qquad (7.35)$$

and collecting together the real and imaginary parts we obtain

$$\exp(i\theta) = \left[1 - \frac{\theta^2}{2!} + \frac{\theta^4}{4!} \ldots\right] + i\left[\frac{\theta}{1!} - \frac{\theta^3}{3!} + \frac{\theta^5}{5!} + \ldots\right] \qquad (7.36)$$

Comparing the real and imaginary parts with the expansions for sin θ and cos θ in equations 6.33 and 6.34, we see that we can write

$$\exp(i\theta) = \cos\theta + i\sin\theta \qquad (7.37)$$

This is known as *Euler's formula*. Thus we can write cos θ and sin θ in terms of exp(iθ) and exp(-iθ)

$$\cos\theta = \frac{1}{2}\left[\exp(i\theta) + \exp(-i\theta)\right]$$
$$\qquad (7.38)$$
$$\sin\theta = \frac{1}{2i}\left[\exp(i\theta) - \exp(-i\theta)\right]$$

which can be compared with equation 1.39 defining the hyperbolic cosine and sine.

Euler's formula gives us another route to de Moivre's theorem because

$$(\cos\theta + i\sin\theta)^m = \left[\exp(i\theta)\right]^m = \cos(m\theta) + i\sin(m\theta) \qquad (7.39)$$

The exponential function exp(iθ) is a periodic function with period 2π because

$$\exp\left[i(\theta + 2\pi m)\right] = \cos(\theta + 2\pi m) + i\sin(\theta + 2\pi m)$$
$$= \cos\theta + i\sin\theta \qquad (7.40)$$

An application of the exponential of an imaginary variable arises in atomic-orbital theory. For example, the p-orbitals in the hydrogen atom are of the form

$$p_{+1} = \frac{1}{\sqrt{2}} f(r)\sin\theta\exp(i\phi)$$

$$p_{-1} = \frac{1}{\sqrt{2}} f(r)\sin\theta\exp(-i\phi) \qquad (7.41)$$

$$p_0 = f(r)\cos\theta$$

where f(r) is a function of the variable r. These are the functions that emerge naturally from the solution of the Schrödinger equation and are a most suitable form for spectroscopic considerations. However, for a discussion of bonding in molecules, it is preferable to have the oribitals in real form. This is simply done by taking linear combinations of p_{+1} and p_{-1}

$$p_x = \frac{1}{\sqrt{2}}(p_{+1} + p_{-1}) = f(r)\sin\theta\cos\phi$$

$$p_y = \frac{1}{i\sqrt{2}}(p_{+1} - p_{-1}) = f(r)\sin\theta\sin\phi \qquad (7.42)$$

to obtain the familiar dumbell p_x and p_y orbitals. The d-orbitals can be treated similarly. The imaginary forms are

$$d_2 = F(r)\sin^2\theta\,\exp(2i\phi)$$

$$d_{-2} = F(r)\sin^2\theta\,\exp(-2i\phi)$$

$$d_{+1} = 2F(r)\sin\theta\cos\theta\,\exp(i\phi) \qquad (7.43)$$

$$d_{-1} = 2F(r)\sin\theta\cos\theta\,\exp(-i\phi)$$

$$d_0 = \sqrt{\left(\frac{2}{3}\right)}F(r)\,\frac{1}{2}(3\cos^2\theta - 1)$$

and the real forms are obtained by taking the linear combinations

$$d_{x^2-y^2} = \frac{1}{\sqrt{2}}(d_{+2} + d_{-2}) = \sqrt{2}F(r)\sin^2\theta\cos 2\phi$$

$$d_{xy} = \frac{1}{i\sqrt{2}}(d_{+2} - d_{-2}) = \sqrt{2}F(r)\sin^2\theta\sin 2\phi$$

$$d_{xz} = \frac{1}{\sqrt{2}}(d_{+1} + d_{-1}) = 2\sqrt{2}F(r)\sin\theta\cos\theta\cos\phi \qquad (7.44)$$

$$d_{yz} = \frac{1}{i\sqrt{2}}(d_{+1} - d_{-1}) = 2\sqrt{2}F(r)\sin\theta\cos\theta\sin\phi$$

$$d_{z^2} = d_0$$

Another important application in quantum chemistry is that one can show by symmetry considerations that the π-electron molecular orbitals ψ_ℓ for benzene can be written in terms of the atomic orbitals χ_k on the carbon atom in the form

$$\psi_\ell = N_\ell \sum_{k=0}^{5} \exp\left(\frac{2\pi ik\ell}{6}\right)\chi_k \qquad (7.45)$$

where N_ℓ is a numerical constant. It can easily be shown that these are simply linear combinations of the familiar real forms. This is an example of a *Bloch sum*, an idea widely used in the theory of the solid state.

7.6 PROBLEMS FOR SOLUTION

1. Express each of the following as a single complex number and

write down its complex conjugate

(i) $7 + 5i + 2(3 - 4i)$; (ii) $(7 + 5i)(3 - 4i)$;

(iii) $(3 - 4i)(5 - 6i)$; (iv) $(\sqrt{2} + 3i)(\sqrt{2} - 4i)$;

(v) $(\sqrt{3} + i\sqrt{2})(\sqrt{3} - i\sqrt{2})$; (vi) $\dfrac{7 + 4i}{6 - 5i}$; (vii) $\dfrac{4 - i}{1 + i}$;

(viii) $\dfrac{\sqrt{3} - i\sqrt{2}}{\sqrt{3} + i\sqrt{2}}$; (ix) $(3 + 4i)^2(4 + 3i) - (2 + 3i)^2$.

2. Find the modulus and argument of each of the following complex numbers:

(i) $4 + 3i$; (ii) $5 + 12i$; (iii) $1 + i\sqrt{3}$; (iv) i; (v) $1 + i/2$; (vi) $3 + i$.

3. Express in the form $x + yi$ the complex numbers z having:

(i) $|z| = 2$, $\arg z = 1/4$; (ii) $|z| = 3$, $\arg z = 2/3\pi$;

(iii) $|z| = 5$, $\arg z = \tan^{-1}(3/4)$, (iv) $|z| = 2$, $\arg z = -1/4\pi$.

4. Form the product and quotient of the complex numbers z_1 and z_2 where:

(i) $z_1 = 3\left(\cos\frac{\pi}{6} + i\sin\frac{\pi}{6}\right)$; $z_2 = \frac{1}{2}\left(\cos\frac{\pi}{3} + i\sin\frac{\pi}{3}\right)$;

(ii) $z_1 = 2\left(\cos\frac{\pi}{4} + i\sin\frac{\pi}{4}\right)$; $z_2 = \frac{1}{3}\left(\cos\frac{\pi}{6} + i\sin\frac{\pi}{6}\right)$.

5. Using de Moivre's theorem derive expressions for $\sin 4\theta$, $\cos 4\theta$, $\sin 5\theta$, $\cos 5\theta$.

6. Show that

(i) $\cos^4\theta = \frac{1}{8}(\cos 4\theta + 4\cos 2\theta + 3)$;

(ii) $\sin^4\theta = \frac{1}{8}(\cos 4\theta - 4\cos 2\theta + 3)$;

(iii) $\cos^5\theta = \frac{1}{16}(\cos 5\theta + 5\cos 3\theta + 10\cos\theta)$;

(iv) $\sin^5\theta = \frac{1}{16}(\sin 5\theta - 5\sin 3\theta + 10\sin\theta)$.

7. Using de Moivre's theorem prove that

$$\frac{(1 + i\sqrt{3})^4(\sqrt{3} + i)^6}{(1 - i\sqrt{3})^3(\sqrt{3} - i)^4} = 8$$

(U.W.)

8. Prove that

$$\frac{1 + \cos x + i\sin x}{1 - \cos x + i\sin x} = -i\exp(ix)\cot\left(\frac{x}{2}\right)$$

(U.W.)

9. If $z_1 = \cos\theta + i\sin\theta$ and $z_2 = \cos\phi + i\sin\phi$, show that:

(i) $\cos(\theta + \phi) = \frac{1}{2}(z_1 z_2 + z_1^{-1} z_2^{-1})$; (ii) $\dfrac{1 + z_1}{1 - z_1} = i\cot\left(\dfrac{\theta}{2}\right)$.

(U.W.)

10. Show that

(i) $\ln\left[\dfrac{1}{\sqrt{2}}(1 + i)\right] = \dfrac{i\pi}{4}$;

(ii) $\ln(a + ib) = \ln|a + ib| + i\tan^{-1}\left(\dfrac{b}{a}\right)$;

(iii) $\tan(x + iy) = \dfrac{\sin x\cos x + i\sinh y\cosh y}{\cos^2 x\cosh^2 y + \sin^2 x\sinh^2 y}$.

(U.W.)

11. Express the following in the form $x + iy$:

(i) $\exp(\pi i/4)$; (ii) $\exp(3\pi i/4)$; (iii) $\exp(5\pi i/4)$;

(iv) $\exp(7\pi i/4)$; (v) $\exp(\pi i/2)$; (vi) $\exp(3\pi i/2)$.

12. Find the cube roots of 2.

13. Find the fourth roots of $3 + 2i$.

14. Write out the functions ψ_ℓ of equation 7.45 for $\ell = 0, \pm 1, \pm 2, 3$.

8
Orthogonal Functions and Fourier Series

8.1 THE RELATION BETWEEN VECTORS AND FUNCTIONS

In chapter 5 we discussed vectors in three dimensions and expressed such vectors in terms of their components in the x,y and z directions; for example

$$\mathbf{a} = a_x\hat{\mathbf{i}} + a_y\hat{\mathbf{j}} + a_z\hat{\mathbf{k}}$$

and (8.1)

$$\mathbf{b} = b_x\hat{\mathbf{i}} + b_y\hat{\mathbf{j}} + b_z\hat{\mathbf{k}}$$

Two vectors are equal only if all their components are separately equal, that is only if $a_x = b_x$, $a_y = b_y$, $a_z = b_z$. We performed vector addition by adding the components. For example if $\mathbf{c} = \mathbf{a} + \mathbf{b}$, then $c_x = a_x + b_x$, $c_y = a_y + b_y$, $c_z = a_z + b_z$.

These ideas, provided we do not try to interpret them in geometrical terms in three dimensions, can be extended to any number of dimensions. We can define a vector $\mathbf{a}$ in n dimensions in terms of components $\hat{\mathbf{1}}, \hat{\mathbf{2}}, \ldots \hat{\mathbf{n}}$.

$$\mathbf{a} = a_1\hat{\mathbf{1}} + a_2\hat{\mathbf{2}} + a_3\hat{\mathbf{3}} + \ldots + a_n\hat{\mathbf{n}} \tag{8.2}$$

Just as we can represent a three-dimensional vector by its components $\mathbf{a} = (a_1,a_2,a_3)$, we can write our n-dimensional vector $\mathbf{a} = (a_1,a_2,a_3 \ldots a_n)$. Conversely we can regard a string of n numbers $(a_1,a_2 \ldots a_n)$ as being represented by a vector

$$\mathbf{a} = (a_1,a_2 \ldots a_n) \tag{8.3}$$

in n dimensions.

If we have a continuous function f(x), we can specify this function by specifying its values $f(x_i)$ for a series of points x_i. Clearly the best description would require an infinite number of points. We can think of these values $f(x_i)$ as being represented by a vector

$$\mathbf{f} = (f(x_1),f(x_2),f(x_3) \ldots f(x_n) \ldots) \tag{8.4}$$

If we have another function g(x), the condition for equality with f(x) is that $g(x_i) = f(x_i)$ for all x_i. The sum of g(x) and f(x) is defined by

$$h(x) = f(x) + g(x) \tag{8.5}$$

where $h(x_i) = f(x_i) + g(x_i)$.

We defined the scalar product of two three-dimensional vectors in equation 5.26 by the expression

$$\begin{aligned}\mathbf{a}.\mathbf{b} &= a_x b_x + a_y b_y + a_z b_z \\ &= \sum_{i=x,y,z} a_i b_i\end{aligned} \tag{8.6}$$

We can generalise this to n dimensions by writing

$$\mathbf{a}.\mathbf{b} = \sum_{i=1}^{n} a_i b_i \tag{8.7}$$

If we represent the functions f(x) and g(x) by vectors, the analogy of the scalar product is

$$\mathbf{f}(x).\mathbf{g}(x) = \sum_i f(x_i)g(x_i) \tag{8.8}$$

However, as we go to the limit of an infinite number of points, we have the replace the summation by an integral and we tentatively define the scalar product of $\mathbf{f}(x)$ and $\mathbf{g}(x)$ by

$$\mathbf{f}(x).\mathbf{g}(x) = \int f(x)g(x)dx \tag{8.9}$$

However, we recall that the length of a vector $\mathbf{a}$ is given by $\surd(\mathbf{a}.\mathbf{a})$ so the corresponding entity for the function $\mathbf{f}(x)$ is $\surd(\mathbf{f}(x).\mathbf{f}(x)) = \surd[\int \mathbf{f}(x)\mathbf{f}(x)\,dx]$. We run into a difficulty at this point if $\mathbf{f}(x)$ is a complex function, for example exp(ikx) because $\surd[\int \exp(ikx)\exp(ikx)\,dx]$ will also be a complex number and the analogy with length clearly fails. In order to get a real number, we have to have a real integrand. This can be achieved by redefining the scalar product of $\mathbf{f}(x)$ and $\mathbf{g}(x)$ as $\int[\mathbf{f}(x)]^*\mathbf{g}(x)\,dx$. We shall represent this by the symbol $(\mathbf{f}(x),\mathbf{g}(x))$.

$$(\mathbf{f}(x), \mathbf{g}(x)) = \int[\mathbf{f}(x)]^*\mathbf{g}(x)\,dx \tag{8.10}$$

Thus the quantity analogous to the length of a vector is

$$[\int[\mathbf{f}(x)]^*\mathbf{f}(x)\,dx]^{1/2}$$

We said in section 5.31 that if the scalar product of two vectors is zero, the vectors are perpendicular or *orthogonal*. We extend this concept to functions and say that if, for the functions $\mathbf{f}(x)$ and $\mathbf{g}(x)$, the scalar product is zero, that is

$$\int[\mathbf{f}(x)]^*\,\mathbf{g}(x)\,dx = 0 \tag{8.11}$$

then the functions f(x) and g(x) are orthogonal. From our discussion of definite integrals in section 3.4.1, we see at once that if we are concerned with a symmetrical interval $-a \leqslant x \leqslant a$, then any even function will be orthogonal to an odd function.

8.2 EXPANSION IN TERMS OF ORTHOGONAL FUNCTIONS

In three dimensions, any arbitrary vector $\mathbf{a}$ can be expressed in terms of the three unit vectors $\hat{\mathbf{i}}$, $\hat{\mathbf{j}}$, and $\hat{\mathbf{k}}$ which are directed along the x, y and z axes. The unit vectors are *orthogonal* because $\hat{\mathbf{i}}.\hat{\mathbf{j}} = 0$, etc., and are *normalised* because they are unit vectors satisfying the condition

$$\hat{\mathbf{i}}.\hat{\mathbf{i}} = \hat{\mathbf{j}}.\hat{\mathbf{j}} = \hat{\mathbf{k}}.\hat{\mathbf{k}} = 1$$

We resolve $\mathbf{a}$ thus

$$\mathbf{a} = a_x\hat{\mathbf{i}} + a_y\hat{\mathbf{j}} + a_z\hat{\mathbf{k}} \tag{8.12}$$

where we obtain a_x, a_y, a_z by taking the scalar product of $\hat{\mathbf{i}}$, $\hat{\mathbf{j}}$ and $\hat{\mathbf{k}}$, respectively with $\mathbf{a}$

$$\hat{\mathbf{i}}.\mathbf{a} = a_x\hat{\mathbf{i}}.\hat{\mathbf{i}} + a_y\hat{\mathbf{i}}.\hat{\mathbf{j}} + a_z\hat{\mathbf{i}}.\hat{\mathbf{k}} = a_x \tag{8.13}$$

Thus

$$a_x = \hat{\mathbf{i}}.\mathbf{a},\ a_y = \hat{\mathbf{j}}.\mathbf{a},\ a_z = \hat{\mathbf{k}}.\mathbf{a} \tag{8.14}$$

We can express an arbitrary vector $\mathbf{a}$ in terms of any three vectors $\mathbf{p}$, $\mathbf{q}$, $\mathbf{r}$ provided they are *independent* and form a *complete set*. By independent we mean that it is not possible to expresss any one of the vectors, say $\mathbf{p}$, in terms of the other two. More generally, $\mathbf{p}$, $\mathbf{q}$ and $\mathbf{r}$ are independent if there is *no* relation

$$a_1\mathbf{p} + a_2\mathbf{q} + a_3\mathbf{r} = 0 \tag{8.15}$$

other than the trivial case of $a_1 = a_2 = a_3 = 0$. If there is such a relation, then clearly we can express any one vector in terms of the other two.

We explain the term *complete set of vectors* by illustration. Obviously we can only write

$$\mathbf{a} = a_x\hat{\mathbf{i}} + a_y\hat{\mathbf{j}}$$

if $\mathbf{a}$ lies in the x-y plane. We cannot express any arbitrary three-dimensional vector $\mathbf{a}$ in terms of $\hat{\mathbf{i}}$ and $\hat{\mathbf{j}}$. For such a vector, $\hat{\mathbf{i}}$ and $\hat{\mathbf{j}}$ form an incomplete set of unit vectors whereas $\hat{\mathbf{i}}$, $\hat{\mathbf{j}}$ and $\hat{\mathbf{k}}$ form a complete set.

Just as we can resolve an arbitrary vector in terms of a complete set of independent vectors, we can expand any arbitrary function f(x) in terms of a complete set of independent functions $\phi_i(x)$. For the set of functions to be independent there must be no relation

$$c_1\phi_1(x) + c_2\phi_2(x) + c_3\phi_3(x) + \ldots + c_n\phi_n(x) = 0 \tag{8.16}$$

other than the completely trivial case where

$$c_1 = c_2 = c_3 = \ldots = c_n = 0$$

We may require an infinite number of functions in order to have a complete set.

Thus we can expand f(x) in terms of the functions $\phi_i(x)$

$$f(x) = \sum_{i=1}^{n} c_i \phi_i(x) \quad (8.17)$$

and we assume the set of functions $\{\phi_i(x)\}$ to be *orthogonal* and *normalised*, that is

$$\int \phi_i^*(x)\phi_j(x)\, dx = \begin{cases} 1, & \text{if } i = j \\ 0, & \text{if } i \neq j \end{cases} \quad (8.18)$$

We say that the functions are *orthonormal*. This relation can be expressed compactly using the *Kroenecker delta* δ_{ij}, which is equal to 1 if i = j and zero otherwise; that is

$$\int \phi_i^*(x)\phi_j(x)\, dx = \delta_{ij} \quad (8.19)$$

The determination of the expansion coefficients is analogous to the vector case. Taking the scalar product of $\phi_j^*(x)$ with f(x) gives

$$\int \phi_j^*(x) f(x)\, dx = \int \phi_j^*(x) \sum_{i=1}^{n} c_i \phi_i(x) dx$$

$$= \sum_{i=1}^{n} c_i \int \phi_j^*(x)\phi_i(x) dx \quad (8.20)$$

However, the integral will only be nonzero if i = j so we obtain

$$\int \phi_j^*(x) f(x) dx = \sum_{i=1}^{n} c_i \delta_{ij} = c_j \quad (8.21)$$

so

$$c_j = \int \phi_j^*(x) f(x) dx \quad (8.22)$$

This technique is very frequently used in quantum mechanics.

8.3 FOURIER SERIES

Fourier series are an important example of the expansion of a function in terms of a complete set of orthonormal functions. Provided that certain conditions are obeyed, we can expand a periodic function in terms of either sines and cosines

$$f(x) = a_0 + \sum_{k=1}^{\infty} (a_k \cos kx + b_k \sin kx) \quad (8.23)$$

or in terms of the functions $1/\surd(2\pi)\exp(ikx)$

$$f(x) = \sum_{k=-\infty}^{\infty} c_k \frac{1}{\surd(2\pi)} \exp(ikx) \quad (8.24)$$

Both of these expansions are periodic with period 2π, so we usually consider the interval $-\pi < x \leqslant \pi$. The function must satisfy *Dirichlet's conditions*, which are:

(1) the function must be single valued;
(2) in any range of width 2π it can have at most a finite number of discontinuities
(3) it must have a finite number of maxima and minima.

Fourier-series expansions differ from Taylor-series expansions in that the Fourier expansion is applicable to functions that may not be continuous or differentiable in the interval of interest. The method is useful for expanding functions such as a saw-tooth wave (figure 8.1a) or a square wave (figure 8.1b), and is used extensively in crystallography.

We can readily verify that for the interval $-\pi < x \leqslant \pi$, the functions $\phi_k(x) = 1/\sqrt{(2\pi)}\exp(ikx)$ form an orthonormal set.

(i) Orthogonality

$$\int_{-\pi}^{\pi} \phi_k^*(x)\phi_\ell(x)dx = \frac{1}{2\pi}\int_{-\pi}^{\pi} \exp(-ikx)\exp(i\ell x)dx$$

$$= \frac{1}{2\pi i(\ell - k)} \exp\left[i(\ell - k)x\right]\Big|_{-\pi}^{\pi} \quad (k \neq \ell)$$

$$= \frac{1}{2\pi i(\ell - k)}\left[\exp(i(\ell - k)\pi) - \exp(-i(\ell - k)\pi)\right]$$

$$= 0 \tag{8.25}$$

(ii) Normalisation

$$\int_{-\pi}^{\pi} \phi_k^*(x)\phi_k(x)dx = \frac{1}{2\pi}\int_{-\pi}^{\pi} \exp(-ikx)\exp(ikx)dx$$

$$= \frac{1}{2\pi}\int_{-\pi}^{\pi} dx = 1 \tag{8.26}$$

The coefficients c_k in the expansion of f(x)

$$f(x) = \sum_{k=-\infty}^{\infty} \frac{c_k}{\sqrt{(2\pi)}} \exp(ikx) \tag{8.27}$$

are given by

$$c_k = \frac{1}{\sqrt{(2\pi)}}\int_{-\pi}^{\pi} \exp(-ikx)f(x)dx \tag{8.28}$$

Fourier expansions are used to analyse complicated periodic functions in terms of the *Fourier components* exp(ikx). Thus Fourier series can be used to extract the *weight* c_k of a particular component exp(ikx) from the complicated function f(x).

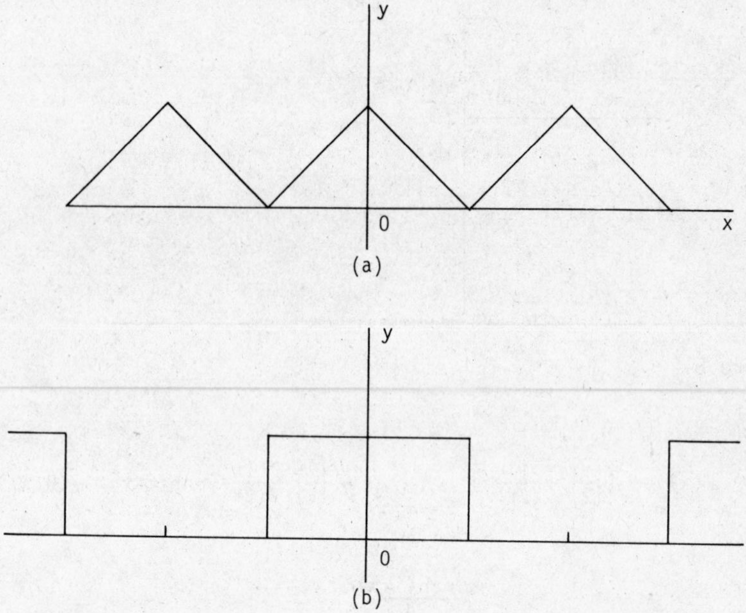

Figure 8.1

Let us take the *step function* as an example (figure 8.2)

$$f(x) = 1, \text{ if } -\pi < x \leqslant 0$$

and $f(x) = 0$, if $0 < x \leqslant \pi$

If

$$f(x) = \frac{1}{\sqrt{(2\pi)}} \sum_{k=-\infty}^{\infty} c_k \exp(ikx)$$

$$c_k = \frac{1}{\sqrt{(2\pi)}} \int_{-\pi}^{\pi} \exp(-ikx) f(x) dx$$

$$= \frac{1}{\sqrt{(2\pi)}} \left[\int_{-\pi}^{0} \exp(-ikx) 1 \, dx + \int_{0}^{\pi} 0 \, dx \right]$$

$$= -\frac{1}{ik\sqrt{2\pi}} [1 - \exp(ik\pi)] \quad k \neq 0 \tag{8.29}$$

There are two cases

(i) If k is odd, $\exp(ik\pi) = -1$ and $c_k = (i/k)\sqrt{(2/\pi)}$.

(ii) If k is even, $\exp(ik\pi) = 1$ and $c_k = 0$.

Taking the case of $k = 0$ gives

$$c_\theta = \frac{1}{\sqrt{2\pi}} \int_{-\pi}^{0} dx = \sqrt{\left(\frac{\pi}{2}\right)} \tag{8.30}$$

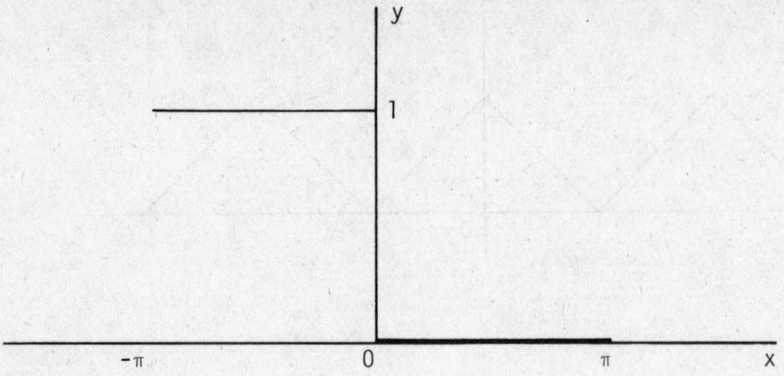

Figure 8.2

Thus

$$f(x) = \sqrt{\left(\frac{\pi}{2}\right)}\,\frac{1}{\sqrt{(2\pi)}} + \sum_{\substack{k=-\infty\\ k\text{ odd},\neq 0}}^{\infty} \frac{i}{k}\sqrt{\left(\frac{2}{\pi}\right)}\,\frac{1}{\sqrt{(2\pi)}}\exp(ikx) \qquad (8.31)$$

$$= \frac{1}{2} + \frac{i}{\pi}\sum_{\substack{k=-\infty\\ k\text{ odd},\neq 0}}^{\infty} \frac{\exp(ikx)}{k}$$

$$= \frac{1}{2} + \frac{i}{\pi}\sum_{\substack{k=-\infty\\ k\text{ odd},\neq 0}}^{\infty} \left[\frac{\cos kx}{k} + \frac{i\sin kx}{k}\right] \qquad (8.32)$$

Because cos(-kx) = cos(kx), the cosine terms will all cancel out because of the factor 1/k. However

$$\frac{\sin kx}{k} = \frac{\sin -kx}{-k}$$

so we get

$$f(x) = \frac{1}{2} - \frac{2}{\pi}\sum_{\substack{k=1\\ k\text{ odd}}}^{\infty} \frac{\sin kx}{k} \qquad (8.33)$$

Thus we arrive at a real expansion, which is consistent with our starting with a real function. Figure 8.3 compares the actual function f(x) with expansions of various lengths. We also note that f(x) is an odd function and find that the expansion is in terms of sine functions.

We have illustrated expansion in the *complex form*. The expansion in real form

$$f(x) = a_0 + \sum_{k=1}^{\infty} (a_k \cos kx + b_k \sin kx) \qquad (8.34)$$

is entirely equivalent for real functions because the coefficients c_k in the complex expansion will in general be complex numbers of the form $c_k = p_k - iq_k$. Thus

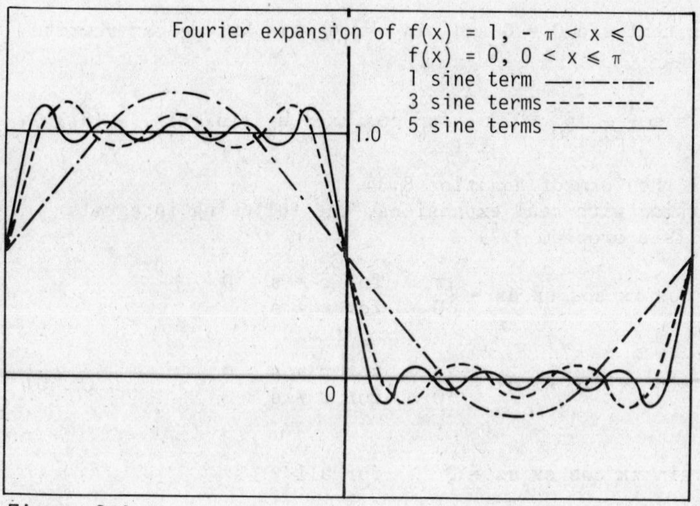

Figure 8.3

$$f(x) = \frac{1}{\sqrt{(2\pi)}} \sum_{k=-\infty}^{\infty} (p_k - iq_k)\exp(ikx)$$

$$= \frac{1}{\sqrt{(2\pi)}} \sum_{k=-\infty}^{\infty} (p_k - iq_k)(\cos kx + i \sin kx) \qquad (8.35)$$

$$= \frac{1}{\sqrt{(2\pi)}} \sum_{k=-\infty}^{\infty} \left[(p_k \cos kx + q_k \sin kx) + i(p_k \sin kx - q_k \cos kx)\right]$$

Since we are expanding a real function, the imaginary part of 8.35 will be zero, so we can write

$$f(x) = \frac{1}{\sqrt{(2\pi)}} \sum_{k=-\infty}^{\infty} (p_k \cos kx + q_k \sin kx) \qquad (8.36)$$

In the expansion in equation 8.27

$$c_k = \frac{1}{\sqrt{(2\pi)}} \int_{-\pi}^{\pi} \exp(-ikx)f(x)dx$$

$$= \frac{1}{\sqrt{(2\pi)}} \int_{-\pi}^{\pi} \cos kx\, f(x)dx - \frac{i}{\sqrt{(2\pi)}} \int \sin kx\, f(x)dx \qquad (8.37)$$

that is

$$p_k = \frac{1}{\sqrt{(2\pi)}} \int_{-\pi}^{\pi} \cos kx\, f(x)dx = \int_{-\pi}^{\pi} \cos(-kx)f(x)dx = p_{-k}$$

$$q_k = \frac{1}{\sqrt{(2\pi)}} \int_{-\pi}^{\pi} \sin kx\, f(x)dx = -\int_{-\pi}^{\pi} \sin(-kx)f(x)dx = -q_{-k} \qquad (8.38)$$

Remembering that sin 0 = 0 and sin -kx = -sin kx, we can rewrite the series as

$$f(x) = \frac{1}{\sqrt{(2\pi)}}\left[p_0 + 2\sum_{k=1}^{\infty}(p_k \cos kx + q_k \sin kx)\right] \qquad (8.39)$$

which is of the form of equation 8.34.

When working with real expansions, the following integrals are useful (see problem 3.7)

$$\int_{-\pi}^{\pi} \cos rx \cos sx \, dx = \begin{cases}\pi & \text{for } r = s > 0\\ 0 & \text{for } r \neq s\end{cases}$$

$$\int_{-\pi}^{\pi} \sin rx \sin sx \, dx = \begin{cases}\pi & \text{for } r = s > 0\\ 0 & \text{for } r \neq s\end{cases} \qquad (8.40)$$

$$\int_{-\pi}^{\pi} \sin rx \cos sx \, dx = 0 \qquad \text{for all } r, s$$

8.4 THE FOURIER TRANSFORM

An important new technique is Fourier transform spectroscopy. We briefly describe the Fourier transform in this section. The Fourier expansion of f(x) is

$$f(x) = \sum_{k=-\infty}^{\infty} c_k \frac{\exp(ikx)}{2\pi} \qquad (8.41)$$

where

$$c_k = \int_{-\pi}^{\pi} \frac{\exp(-ikx)}{\sqrt{(2\pi)}} f(x)dx$$

Let us make the range of integration $-\ell$ to ℓ by introducing a new variable $y = \ell x/\pi$. The expansion becomes

$$f(y) = \sum_{k=-\infty}^{\infty} \frac{c_k}{\sqrt{(2\pi)}} \exp\left(\frac{i\pi ky}{\ell}\right) \qquad (8.42)$$

where

$$c_k = \frac{\pi}{\ell}\frac{1}{\sqrt{(2\pi)}}\int_{-\ell}^{\ell} \exp\left(\frac{-ik\pi y}{\ell}\right) f(y)dy \qquad (8.43)$$

remembering that dx becomes (π/ℓ)dy. Substituting for c_k in equation 8.42 and introducing a new variable t under the integral sign gives

$$f(y) = \frac{1}{2\ell}\sum_{k=-\infty}^{\infty}\int_{-\ell}^{\ell} f(t)\exp\left(\frac{ik\pi(y - t)}{\ell}\right)dt \qquad (8.44)$$

If δ is a small quantity equal to π/ℓ and we let ℓ go to infinity, the summation can then be replaced by an integration with respect to a variable u to give the Fourier *integral theorem*

$$f(y) = \frac{1}{2\pi}\int_{-\infty}^{\infty} du \int_{-\infty}^{\infty} f(t)\exp[-iu(t - y)]dt \qquad (8.45)$$

This can be written in two separate steps

$$f(y) = \frac{1}{\sqrt{(2\pi)}}\int_{-\infty}^{\infty} F(u)\exp(iuy)du \qquad (8.46)$$

where

$$F(u) = \frac{1}{\sqrt{(2\pi)}}\int_{-\infty}^{\infty} f(t)\exp(-iut)dt \qquad (8.47)$$

The function F(u) is the *Fourier transform* of f(t) and is analogous to the coefficient of exp(ikx) in the expansion

$$f(x) = \sum_{k=-\infty}^{\infty} c_k \exp(ikx) \qquad (8.49)$$

The difference is that the range of integration for F(u) is from $-\infty$ to ∞.

In nuclear magnetic resonance, the Fourier transform is used to obtain the frequency spectrum from the exponential decay curve obtained in pulse experiments.

8.5 PROBLEMS FOR SOLUTION

1. Evaluate the scalar products for $-1 \leqslant x \leqslant 1$, and show that the Legendre polynomials $P_0(x) = 1$, $P_1(x) = x$, $P_2(x) = \frac{1}{2}(3x^2 - 1)$, $P_3(x) = \frac{1}{2}(5x^3 - 3x)$ are mutually orthogonal.

2. Show that the functions $\exp[2n\pi ix/(b - a)]$ are orthogonal for $a \leqslant x \leqslant b$.

3. Find a Fourier series expansion for the function

$$\begin{aligned} f(x) &= x + \pi; \quad -\pi \leqslant x \leqslant -\frac{\pi}{2} \\ &= x + \frac{\pi}{2}; \quad -\frac{\pi}{2} < x \leqslant 0 \\ &= x; \quad 0 < x \leqslant \frac{\pi}{2} \\ &= x - \frac{\pi}{2}; \quad \frac{\pi}{2} < x \leqslant \pi \end{aligned}$$

in the range $-\pi \leqslant x \leqslant \pi$. (U.W.)

4. Expand the function f(x) defined by

$$f(x) = -x^2; \quad -\pi \leqslant x \leqslant 0$$

$$= x^2; \quad 0 < x \leqslant \pi$$

as a Fourier series in the range $-\pi \leqslant x \leqslant \pi$.

5. Show that the Fourier expansion of f(x) in the interval $-\ell \leqslant x \leqslant \ell$ is given by

$$f(x) = \sum_{k=-\infty}^{\infty} C_k \frac{1}{\surd(2\ell)} \exp(ik\pi x/\ell)$$

where

$$C_k = \frac{1}{\surd(2\ell)} \int_{-\ell}^{\ell} f(x)\exp(-ik\pi x/\ell)dx$$

6. Derive the Fourier-series expansion for the saw-tooth function

$$f(x) = x + 1; \quad -1 \leqslant x \leqslant 0$$

$$= -x + 1; \quad 0 < x \leqslant 1$$

in the interval $-1 \leqslant x \leqslant 1$.

7. Derive the Fourier-series expansion for the square-wave potential

$$y = 0; \quad -a \leqslant x \leqslant -a/2$$

$$= 1; \quad -a/2 < x \leqslant a/2$$

$$= 0; \quad a/2 < x \leqslant a.$$

8. Find the Fourier-series expansion of the function f(x) defined by

$$f(x) = \cos x; \quad -\pi/2 < x < \pi/2$$

$$= 0; \quad \pi/2 \leqslant |x| \leqslant \pi$$

in the range $-\pi \leqslant x \leqslant \pi$.

(U.W.)

9
Determinants

9.1 SIMULTANEOUS EQUATIONS AND DETERMINANTS

9.1.1 Second-order determinants

The solution of simultaneous equations in two variables is an elementary exercise in algebra. If we have the equations

$$a_{11}x + a_{12}y = b_1 \tag{9.1}$$

$$a_{21}x + a_{22}y = b_2 \tag{9.2}$$

we can obtain a value for y by eliminating x from the equations. This is done by multiplying equation 9.1 by a_{21}, 9.2 by a_{11} and subtracting the second result from the first. Thus

$$a_{21}a_{11}x + a_{21}a_{12}y = a_{21}b_1$$

$$a_{11}a_{21}x + a_{11}a_{22}y = a_{11}b_2$$

and

$$(a_{21}a_{12} - a_{11}a_{22})y = a_{21}b_1 - a_{11}b_2$$

so

$$y = \frac{a_{21}b_1 - a_{11}b_2}{a_{21}a_{12} - a_{11}a_{22}} \tag{9.3}$$

x can then be obtained by substituting for y in one of the original equations. However, it is more instructive to obtain x by eliminating y from equations 9.1 and 9.2. Doing this, we get

$$(a_{22}a_{11} - a_{12}a_{21})x = a_{22}b_1 - a_{12}b_2$$

that is

$$x = -\frac{(a_{12}b_2 - a_{22}b_1)}{(a_{11}a_{22} - a_{12}a_{21})} \tag{9.4}$$

provided that $a_{11}a_{22} - a_{12}a_{21} \neq 0$. Thus we can express x and y in similar forms

$$x = \frac{(b_1a_{22} - b_2a_{12})}{(a_{11}a_{22} - a_{12}a_{21})}; \quad y = \frac{(a_{11}b_2 - a_{21}b_1)}{(a_{11}a_{22} - a_{12}a_{21})} \tag{9.5}$$

This result can be expressed more compactly if we define a *determinant*. A second-order determinant is defined by the relation

$$\begin{vmatrix} a_{11} & a_{12} \\ a_{21} & a_{22} \end{vmatrix} = a_{11}a_{22} - a_{21}a_{12} \qquad (9.6)$$

Thus we can rewrite equation 9.5 as

$$x = \frac{\begin{vmatrix} b_1 & a_{12} \\ b_2 & a_{22} \end{vmatrix}}{\begin{vmatrix} a_{11} & a_{12} \\ a_{21} & a_{22} \end{vmatrix}} \qquad y = \frac{\begin{vmatrix} a_{11} & b_1 \\ a_{21} & b_2 \end{vmatrix}}{\begin{vmatrix} a_{11} & a_{12} \\ a_{21} & a_{22} \end{vmatrix}} \qquad (9.7)$$

You will note that the determinants in the numerator are obtained by replacing the coefficients of x or y appearing in the determinant in the denominator by b_1, b_2.

Thus if we have the equations

$$2x + 3y = 7$$

$$3x - y = 4$$

the solutions are

$$x = \frac{\begin{vmatrix} 7 & 3 \\ 4 & -1 \end{vmatrix}}{\begin{vmatrix} 2 & 3 \\ 3 & -1 \end{vmatrix}} = \frac{-7 \quad -12}{-2 \quad -9} = \frac{19}{11}; \quad y = \frac{\begin{vmatrix} 2 & 7 \\ 3 & 4 \end{vmatrix}}{-11} = \frac{8 \quad -21}{-11} = \frac{13}{11} \qquad (9.8)$$

Although this expresses the solutions in a compact manner, it is not very interesting unless it can be applied to more complicated systems.

9.1.2 Third-order determinants

If we have the equations

$$a_{11}x + a_{12}y + a_{13}z = b_1 \qquad (9.9)$$

$$a_{21}x + a_{22}y + a_{23}z = b_2 \qquad (9.10)$$

$$a_{31}x + a_{32}y + a_{33}z = b_3 \qquad (9.11)$$

we can still solve by elementary techniques. Eliminating y from equations 9.9 and 9.10 and from equations 9.9 and 9.11 gives

$$x(a_{12}a_{21} - a_{22}a_{11}) + z(a_{12}a_{23} - a_{22}a_{13}) = a_{12}b_2 - a_{22}b_1$$

$$x(a_{12}a_{31} - a_{32}a_{11}) + z(a_{12}a_{33} - a_{32}a_{13}) = a_{12}b_3 - a_{32}b_1$$

Elimination of z gives

$$x[(a_{12}a_{21} - a_{22}a_{11})(a_{12}a_{33} - a_{32}a_{13}) - (a_{12}a_{31} - a_{32}a_{11}) \times (a_{12}a_{23} - a_{22}a_{13})]$$

$$= (a_{12}b_2 - a_{22}b_1)(a_{12}a_{33} - a_{32}a_{13}) - (a_{12}b_3 - a_{32}b_1)(a_{12}a_{23} - a_{22}a_{13})$$

so

$$x = \frac{b_1a_{23}a_{32} - b_1a_{22}a_{33} + b_2a_{12}a_{33} - b_2a_{32}a_{13} + b_3a_{22}a_{13} - b_3a_{12}a_{23}}{a_{12}a_{21}a_{33} - a_{22}a_{11}a_{33} + a_{13}a_{31}a_{22} + a_{32}a_{23}a_{11} - a_{21}a_{32}a_{13} - a_{12}a_{31}a_{23}} \tag{9.12}$$

The manipulation, however, is rather tedious and some way of systematising the calculation would be advantageous. This can be done by introducing determinants of higher order. The third-order determinant is given by

$$\begin{vmatrix} a_{11} & a_{12} & a_{13} \\ a_{21} & a_{22} & a_{23} \\ a_{31} & a_{32} & a_{33} \end{vmatrix} = a_{11}a_{22}a_{33} - a_{11}a_{23}a_{32} - a_{12}a_{21}a_{33} + a_{12}a_{31}a_{23} + a_{13}a_{21}a_{32} - a_{13}a_{31}a_{22} \tag{9.13}$$

Using this definition, we can rewrite the solution of equations 9.9 to 9.11 as

$$x = \frac{\begin{vmatrix} b_1 & a_{12} & a_{13} \\ b_2 & a_{22} & a_{23} \\ b_3 & a_{32} & a_{33} \end{vmatrix}}{\begin{vmatrix} a_{11} & a_{12} & a_{13} \\ a_{21} & a_{22} & a_{23} \\ a_{31} & a_{32} & a_{33} \end{vmatrix}} \quad y = \frac{\begin{vmatrix} a_{11} & b_1 & a_{13} \\ a_{21} & b_2 & a_{23} \\ a_{31} & b_3 & a_{33} \end{vmatrix}}{\begin{vmatrix} a_{11} & a_{12} & a_{13} \\ a_{21} & a_{22} & a_{23} \\ a_{31} & a_{32} & a_{33} \end{vmatrix}} \quad z = \frac{\begin{vmatrix} a_{11} & a_{12} & b_1 \\ a_{21} & a_{22} & b_2 \\ a_{31} & a_{32} & b_3 \end{vmatrix}}{\begin{vmatrix} a_{11} & a_{12} & a_{13} \\ a_{21} & a_{22} & a_{23} \\ a_{31} & a_{32} & a_{33} \end{vmatrix}}$$

The solution of the equations

$$3x - y + z = 3$$
$$x - 2y = 2$$
$$-x + y - 3z = -7$$

is given by

$$x = \frac{\begin{vmatrix} 3 & -1 & 1 \\ 2 & -2 & 0 \\ -7 & 1 & -3 \end{vmatrix}}{\Delta}; \quad y = \frac{\begin{vmatrix} 3 & 3 & 1 \\ 1 & 2 & 0 \\ -1 & -7 & -3 \end{vmatrix}}{\Delta}; \quad z = \frac{\begin{vmatrix} 3 & -1 & 3 \\ 1 & -2 & 2 \\ -1 & 1 & -7 \end{vmatrix}}{\Delta}$$

where

$$\Delta = \begin{vmatrix} 3 & -1 & 1 \\ 1 & -2 & 0 \\ -1 & 1 & -3 \end{vmatrix}$$

Evaluating the determinants gives

$$x = \frac{0}{14} = 0;\ y = -\frac{14}{14} = -1;\ z = \frac{28}{14} = 2 \qquad (9.15)$$

If we examine the expansion of the determinant in equation 9.13 we see that

$$\begin{vmatrix} a_{11} & a_{12} & a_{13} \\ a_{21} & a_{22} & a_{23} \\ a_{31} & a_{32} & a_{33} \end{vmatrix}$$

$$= a_{11}(a_{22}a_{33} - a_{23}a_{32}) - a_{12}(a_{21}a_{33} - a_{31}a_{23}) + a_{13}(a_{21}a_{32} - a_{31}a_{22})$$

$$= a_{11}\begin{vmatrix} a_{22} & a_{23} \\ a_{32} & a_{33} \end{vmatrix} - a_{12}\begin{vmatrix} a_{21} & a_{23} \\ a_{31} & a_{33} \end{vmatrix} + a_{13}\begin{vmatrix} a_{21} & a_{22} \\ a_{31} & a_{32} \end{vmatrix} \qquad (9.16)$$

In this expression, the second-order determinants are obtained by striking out from the third-order determinant the row and column containing a_{ij}, where a_{ij} is the element multiplying that second-order determinant. These second-order determinants are called *minors* of the determinant. Let us denote the minor of the element a_{ij} by A_{ij}. We can now write the expansion of the determinant as

$$\begin{vmatrix} a_{11} & a_{12} & a_{13} \\ a_{21} & a_{22} & a_{23} \\ a_{31} & a_{32} & a_{33} \end{vmatrix} = (-1)^{1+1}a_{11}A_{11} + (-1)^{1+2}a_{12}A_{12} + (-1)^{1+3}a_{13}A_{13} \qquad (9.17)$$

9.1.3 Determinants of general order

Determinants of higher order can be defined in the same way. For example we can expand a fourth-order determinant in terms of minors of order three

$$\begin{vmatrix} a_{11} & a_{12} & a_{13} & a_{14} \\ a_{21} & a_{22} & a_{23} & a_{24} \\ a_{31} & a_{32} & a_{33} & a_{34} \\ a_{41} & a_{42} & a_{43} & a_{44} \end{vmatrix} = a_{11}\begin{vmatrix} a_{22} & a_{23} & a_{24} \\ a_{32} & a_{33} & a_{34} \\ a_{42} & a_{43} & a_{44} \end{vmatrix} - a_{12}\begin{vmatrix} a_{21} & a_{23} & a_{24} \\ a_{31} & a_{33} & a_{34} \\ a_{41} & a_{43} & a_{44} \end{vmatrix}$$

$$+ a_{13}\begin{vmatrix} a_{21} & a_{22} & a_{24} \\ a_{31} & a_{32} & a_{34} \\ a_{41} & a_{42} & a_{44} \end{vmatrix} - a_{14}\begin{vmatrix} a_{21} & a_{22} & a_{23} \\ a_{31} & a_{32} & a_{33} \\ a_{41} & a_{42} & a_{43} \end{vmatrix}$$

$$= (-1)^{1+1}A_{11} + (-1)^{1+2}A_{12} + (-1)^{1+3}A_{13} + (-1)^{1+4}A_{14} \tag{9.18}$$

The solution of the equations

$$\begin{aligned} a_{11}w + a_{12}x + a_{13}y + a_{14}z &= b_1 \\ a_{21}w + a_{22}x + a_{23}y + a_{24}z &= b_2 \\ a_{31}w + a_{32}x + a_{33}y + a_{34}z &= b_3 \\ a_{41}w + a_{42}x + a_{43}y + a_{44}z &= b_4 \end{aligned} \tag{9.19}$$

can be expressed neatly in terms of determinants whereas solution by elementary algebraic techniques would be very tedious. Thus

$$\frac{w}{\begin{vmatrix} b_1 & a_{12} & a_{13} & a_{14} \\ b_2 & a_{22} & a_{23} & a_{24} \\ b_3 & a_{32} & a_{33} & a_{34} \\ b_4 & a_{42} & a_{43} & a_{44} \end{vmatrix}} = \frac{x}{\begin{vmatrix} a_{11} & b_1 & a_{13} & a_{14} \\ a_{21} & b_2 & a_{23} & a_{24} \\ a_{31} & b_3 & a_{33} & a_{34} \\ a_{41} & b_4 & a_{43} & a_{44} \end{vmatrix}} \tag{9.20}$$

$$= \frac{y}{\begin{vmatrix} a_{11} & a_{12} & b_1 & a_{14} \\ a_{21} & a_{22} & b_2 & a_{24} \\ a_{31} & a_{32} & b_3 & a_{34} \\ a_{41} & a_{42} & b_4 & a_{44} \end{vmatrix}} = \frac{z}{\begin{vmatrix} a_{11} & a_{12} & a_{13} & b_1 \\ a_{21} & a_{22} & a_{23} & b_2 \\ a_{31} & a_{32} & a_{33} & b_3 \\ a_{41} & a_{42} & a_{43} & b_4 \end{vmatrix}}$$

$$= \frac{1}{\begin{vmatrix} a_{11} & a_{12} & a_{13} & a_{14} \\ a_{21} & a_{22} & a_{23} & a_{24} \\ a_{31} & a_{32} & a_{33} & a_{34} \\ a_{41} & a_{42} & a_{43} & a_{44} \end{vmatrix}}$$

9.2 PROPERTIES OF DETERMINANTS

In the above section we have shown how the solution of inhomogeneous simultaneous equations can be formalised by the introduction of the determinant. However, it is probably clear that the evaluation of determinants of high order can be tedious. Determinants have many important properties that often lead to considerable simplification in their evaluation. These properties are completely general but we shall illustrate them with third-order determinants.

(1) If we *transpose* the determinant, that is change the columns into rows and the rows into columns, the value of the determinant is unchanged. If

$$\Delta = \begin{vmatrix} a_{11} & a_{12} & a_{13} \\ a_{21} & a_{22} & a_{23} \\ a_{31} & a_{32} & a_{33} \end{vmatrix}$$

interchanging rows and columns gives the determinant

$$\tilde{\Delta} = \begin{vmatrix} a_{11} & a_{21} & a_{31} \\ a_{12} & a_{22} & a_{32} \\ a_{13} & a_{23} & a_{33} \end{vmatrix}$$

$$= a_{11}(a_{22}a_{33} - a_{23}a_{32}) - a_{21}(a_{12}a_{33} - a_{13}a_{32})$$

$$+ a_{31}(a_{12}a_{23} - a_{13}a_{22}) \tag{9.21}$$

This is identical to the expansion in equation 9.13, so $\tilde{\Delta} = \Delta$. Thus we can expand the determinant Δ in terms of the elements of the first column and their minors

$$\Delta = (-1)^{1+1}a_{11}A_{11} + (-1)^{2+1}a_{21}A_{21} + (-1)^{3+1}a_{31}A_{31} \tag{9.22}$$

(2) A determinant changes sign if two rows or two columns are interchanged

$$\begin{vmatrix} a_{12} & a_{11} & a_{13} \\ a_{22} & a_{21} & a_{23} \\ a_{32} & a_{31} & a_{33} \end{vmatrix}$$

$$= a_{12}(a_{21}a_{33} - a_{31}a_{23}) - a_{11}(a_{22}a_{33} - a_{32}a_{23})$$

$$+ a_{13}(a_{22}a_{31} - a_{32}a_{21})$$

$$= -[a_{11}(a_{22}a_{33} - a_{32}a_{23}) - a_{12}(a_{21}a_{33} - a_{31}a_{23})$$

$$+ a_{13}(a_{21}a_{32} - a_{31}a_{22})]$$

$$= -\begin{vmatrix} a_{11} & a_{12} & a_{13} \\ a_{21} & a_{22} & a_{23} \\ a_{31} & a_{32} & a_{33} \end{vmatrix} \tag{9.23}$$

$$\begin{vmatrix} a_{21} & a_{22} & a_{23} \\ a_{11} & a_{12} & a_{13} \\ a_{31} & a_{32} & a_{33} \end{vmatrix}$$

$$= a_{21}(a_{12}a_{33} - a_{32}a_{13}) - a_{22}(a_{11}a_{33} - a_{31}a_{13})$$

$$+ a_{23}(a_{11}a_{32} - a_{31}a_{12})$$

$$= -[a_{11}(a_{22}a_{33} - a_{23}a_{32}) - a_{12}(a_{21}a_{33} - a_{31}a_{23})$$

$$+ a_{13}(a_{21}a_{32} - a_{22}\,a_{31})]$$

$$= - \begin{vmatrix} a_{11} & a_{12} & a_{13} \\ a_{21} & a_{22} & a_{23} \\ a_{31} & a_{32} & a_{33} \end{vmatrix} \tag{9.24}$$

Since the expansion is shorter if the coefficient of a minor is zero, we can use this property to bring zeros to the first row.

(3) If we multiply each element of a row or column by a number k, the value of the determinant is multiplied by k. If

$$\Delta = \begin{vmatrix} a_{11} & a_{12} & a_{13} \\ a_{21} & a_{22} & a_{23} \\ a_{31} & a_{32} & a_{33} \end{vmatrix}$$

then

$$\begin{vmatrix} ka_{11} & ka_{12} & ka_{13} \\ a_{21} & a_{22} & a_{23} \\ a_{31} & a_{32} & a_{33} \end{vmatrix}$$

$$= ka_{11}(a_{22}a_{33} - a_{32}a_{23}) - ka_{12}(a_{21}a_{33} - a_{31}a_{23})$$

$$+ ka_{13}(a_{21}a_{32} - a_{31}a_{22}) = k\Delta \tag{9.25}$$

(4) If a determinant has two identical rows or two identical columns, then the determinant is zero

$$\begin{vmatrix} a_{11} & a_{12} & a_{13} \\ a_{11} & a_{12} & a_{13} \\ a_{31} & a_{32} & a_{33} \end{vmatrix}$$

$$= a_{11}(a_{12}a_{33} - a_{32}a_{13}) - a_{12}(a_{11}a_{33} - a_{31}a_{13})$$

$$+ a_{13}(a_{11}a_{32} - a_{31}a_{12}) = 0 \tag{9.26}$$

Using property (3) we can extend this to say that any determinant in which one row is a multiple of another or in which one column is a multiple of another is zero.

(5) We can add any multiple of one row to another row or add a multiple of one column to another column without affecting the value of the determinant.

$$\begin{vmatrix} ka_{21}+a_{11} & ka_{22}+a_{12} & ka_{23}+a_{13} \\ a_{21} & a_{22} & a_{23} \\ a_{31} & a_{32} & a_{33} \end{vmatrix}$$

$$= (ka_{21}+a_{11})\begin{vmatrix} a_{22} & a_{23} \\ a_{32} & a_{33} \end{vmatrix} - (ka_{22}+a_{12})\begin{vmatrix} a_{21} & a_{23} \\ a_{31} & a_{33} \end{vmatrix}$$

$$+ k(a_{23}+a_{13})\begin{vmatrix} a_{21} & a_{22} \\ a_{31} & a_{32} \end{vmatrix}$$

$$= a_{11}\begin{vmatrix} a_{22} & a_{23} \\ a_{32} & a_{33} \end{vmatrix} - a_{12}\begin{vmatrix} a_{21} & a_{23} \\ a_{31} & a_{33} \end{vmatrix} + a_{13}\begin{vmatrix} a_{21} & a_{22} \\ a_{31} & a_{32} \end{vmatrix}$$

$$+ k\left[a_{21}\begin{vmatrix} a_{22} & a_{23} \\ a_{32} & a_{33} \end{vmatrix} - a_{22}\begin{vmatrix} a_{21} & a_{23} \\ a_{31} & a_{33} \end{vmatrix} + a_{23}\begin{vmatrix} a_{21} & a_{22} \\ a_{31} & a_{32} \end{vmatrix}\right]$$

$$= \begin{vmatrix} a_{11} & a_{12} & a_{13} \\ a_{21} & a_{22} & a_{23} \\ a_{31} & a_{32} & a_{33} \end{vmatrix} + k\begin{vmatrix} a_{21} & a_{22} & a_{23} \\ a_{21} & a_{22} & a_{23} \\ a_{31} & a_{32} & a_{33} \end{vmatrix}$$

$$= \begin{vmatrix} a_{11} & a_{12} & a_{13} \\ a_{21} & a_{22} & a_{23} \\ a_{31} & a_{32} & a_{33} \end{vmatrix} \qquad (9.27)$$

This property is very useful because it can be used to create zeros in the determinant. Suppose we wish to evaluate the determinant

$$\begin{vmatrix} 1 & 2 & 3 \\ 4 & 5 & 6 \\ 7 & 8 & 9 \end{vmatrix}$$

If we subtract twice the first column from the second column we get

$$\begin{vmatrix} 1 & 0 & 3 \\ 4 & -3 & 6 \\ 7 & -6 & 9 \end{vmatrix}$$

and then subtracting three times the first column from the third gives

$$\begin{vmatrix} 1 & 0 & 0 \\ 4 & -3 & -6 \\ 7 & -6 & -12 \end{vmatrix}$$

This reduces to the second-order determinant

$$\begin{vmatrix} -3 & -6 \\ -6 & -12 \end{vmatrix}$$

which is in fact zero because the second row is twice the first row. This technique can be applied to larger determinants and we shall discuss a systematic method for doing this in chapter 13.

Thus if any row (or column) is a linear combination of the other rows (or columns) of the determinant, the determinant is zero. The converse is also true: in any determinant that is zero, one row (or column) is a linear combination of the others.

(6) If the elements in any row or column can be written as sums of two terms, then we can split the determinant into two separate determinants.

$$\begin{vmatrix} a_{11}+b_1 & a_{12}+b_2 & a_{13}+b_3 \\ a_{21} & a_{22} & a_{23} \\ a_{31} & a_{32} & a_{33} \end{vmatrix}$$

$$= (a_{11}+b_1)\begin{vmatrix} a_{22} & a_{23} \\ a_{32} & a_{33} \end{vmatrix} - (a_{12}+b_2)\begin{vmatrix} a_{21} & a_{23} \\ a_{31} & a_{33} \end{vmatrix}$$

$$+ (a_{13}+b_3)\begin{vmatrix} a_{21} & a_{22} \\ a_{31} & a_{32} \end{vmatrix}$$

$$= a_{11}\begin{vmatrix} a_{22} & a_{23} \\ a_{32} & a_{33} \end{vmatrix} - a_{12}\begin{vmatrix} a_{21} & a_{23} \\ a_{31} & a_{33} \end{vmatrix} + a_{13}\begin{vmatrix} a_{21} & a_{22} \\ a_{31} & a_{32} \end{vmatrix}$$

$$+ b_1\begin{vmatrix} a_{22} & a_{23} \\ a_{32} & a_{33} \end{vmatrix} - b_2\begin{vmatrix} a_{21} & a_{23} \\ a_{31} & a_{33} \end{vmatrix} + b_3\begin{vmatrix} a_{21} & a_{22} \\ a_{31} & a_{32} \end{vmatrix}$$

$$= \begin{vmatrix} a_{11} & a_{12} & a_{13} \\ a_{21} & a_{22} & a_{23} \\ a_{31} & a_{32} & a_{33} \end{vmatrix} + \begin{vmatrix} b_1 & b_2 & b_3 \\ a_{21} & a_{22} & a_{23} \\ a_{31} & a_{32} & a_{33} \end{vmatrix} \qquad (9.28)$$

(7) An application. It is convenient to express atomic and molecular wavefunctions in terms of *Slater determinants*. Consider, for example, the ground state of the beryllium atom in which the 1s and 2s orbitals are each doubly occupied. The wavefunction can be written as

$$\begin{vmatrix} 1s(1)\alpha(1) & 1s(1)\beta(1) & 2s(1)\alpha(1) & 2s(1)\beta(1) \\ 1s(2)\alpha(2) & 1s(2)\beta(2) & 2s(2)\alpha(2) & 2s(2)\beta(2) \\ 1s(3)\alpha(3) & 1s(3)\beta(3) & 2s(3)\alpha(3) & 2s(3)\beta(3) \\ 1s(4)\alpha(4) & 1s(4)\beta(4) & 2s(4)\alpha(4) & 2s(4)\beta(4) \end{vmatrix} \quad (9.29)$$

where $1s(1)\alpha(1)$ represents a 1s orbital occupied by electron 1 with spin α. On expansion, this determinant would yield twenty-four terms that would include all the permutations of the electron labels 1, 2, 3, 4 among the orbitals 1s and 2s with α and β spin occupancy, thus allowing for the indistinguishability of the electrons. We see at once that if we try to construct a wavefunction in which we put two electrons into the same orbital in violation of the Pauli principle, we shall get zero because the resulting determinant will have two identical columns. For example

$$\begin{vmatrix} 1s(1)\alpha(1) & 1s(1)\alpha(1) & 2s(1)\alpha(1) & 2s(1)\beta(1) \\ 1s(2)\alpha(2) & 1s(2)\alpha(2) & 2s(2)\alpha(2) & 2s(2)\beta(2) \\ 1s(3)\alpha(3) & 1s(3)\alpha(3) & 2s(3)\alpha(3) & 2s(3)\beta(3) \\ 1s(4)\alpha(4) & 1s(4)\alpha(4) & 2s(4)\alpha(4) & 2s(4)\beta(4) \end{vmatrix}$$

We can also readily see that if we interchange two electron labels, for example, 1 and 2 in our wavefunction, the wavefunction changes sign, that is, is *antisymmetric* because we have interchanged two rows.

9.3 MINORS AND COFACTORS

In section 9.2 we defined the minor A_{ik} of an element a_{ik} of a determinant Δ_n of order n as being the determinant of order (n - 1) obtained by striking out row i and column k from Δ_n. If we have

$$\Delta_4 = \begin{vmatrix} a_{11} & a_{12} & a_{13} & a_{14} \\ a_{21} & a_{22} & a_{23} & a_{24} \\ a_{31} & a_{32} & a_{33} & a_{34} \\ a_{41} & a_{42} & a_{43} & a_{44} \end{vmatrix}$$

then the minor A_{22} would be

$$A_{22} = \begin{vmatrix} a_{11} & a_{13} & a_{14} \\ a_{31} & a_{33} & a_{34} \\ a_{41} & a_{43} & a_{44} \end{vmatrix} \quad (9.30)$$

We expressed the expansion of the determinant Δ_n in terms of minors thus

$$\Delta_n = \sum_{i=1}^{n} (-1)^{1+i} a_{1i} A_{1i} \tag{9.31}$$

We could expand by other rows or other columns and write, in general

$$\Delta_n = \sum_{i=1}^{n} (-1)^{j+i} a_{ji} A_{ji} = \sum_{i=1}^{n} (-1)^{i+j} a_{ij} A_{ij} \tag{9.32}$$

If we attach the sign $(-1)^{i+j}$ to the minor A_{ij}, we obtain the *cofactor* $\mathcal{A}_{ij}$, which is sometimes more useful than the minor. Expanding the determinant in terms of cofactors gives

$$\Delta_n = \sum_{i=1}^{n} a_{ij} \mathcal{A}_{ij} = \sum_{i=1}^{n} a_{ji} \mathcal{A}_{ji} \tag{9.33}$$

9.4 SOLUTION OF LINEAR EQUATIONS

9.4.1 Inhomogeneous equations

In section 9.1.2 we considered the solution of the equations

$$\begin{aligned} a_{11}x + a_{12}y + a_{13}z &= b_1 \\ a_{21}x + a_{22}y + a_{23}z &= b_2 \\ a_{31}x + a_{32}y + a_{33}z &= b_3 \end{aligned} \tag{9.34}$$

These equations are known as *inhomogeneous* equations because they have non-zero constant terms b_1, b_2, b_3. In terms of determinants the solution of these equation is

$$x = \frac{\begin{vmatrix} b_1 & a_{12} & a_{13} \\ b_2 & a_{22} & a_{23} \\ b_3 & a_{32} & a_{33} \end{vmatrix}}{\Delta}; \quad y = \frac{\begin{vmatrix} a_{11} & b_1 & a_{13} \\ a_{21} & b_2 & a_{23} \\ a_{31} & b_3 & a_{33} \end{vmatrix}}{\Delta};$$

$$z = \frac{\begin{vmatrix} a_{11} & a_{12} & b_1 \\ a_{21} & a_{22} & b_2 \\ a_{31} & a_{32} & b_3 \end{vmatrix}}{\Delta}$$

where

$$\Delta = \begin{vmatrix} a_{11} & a_{12} & a_{13} \\ a_{21} & a_{22} & a_{23} \\ a_{31} & a_{32} & a_{33} \end{vmatrix} \tag{9.35}$$

This is known as *Cramer's rule*. It is clearly applicable to systems of any size. However, for systems of equations with more than three unknowns it is better to use the matrix method, which will be developed in section 10.3, or the method of gaussian elimination (see section 13.4). Clearly we shall only get finite values of x, y and z if $\Delta \neq 0$. If the determinant Δ is zero two cases may arise. Suppose we have the equations

$$\begin{aligned} x + y + z &= 3 \\ x - 2y + 3z &= 6 \\ x + 4y - z &= 2 \end{aligned} \qquad (9.36)$$

for which

$$\begin{vmatrix} 1 & 1 & 1 \\ 1 & -2 & 3 \\ 1 & 4 & -1 \end{vmatrix} = 0$$

If we add the second and third equations we obtain

$$2x + 2y + 2z = 8 \qquad (9.37)$$

But the first equation is

$$x + y + z = 3 \qquad (9.38)$$

which is inconsistent with equation 9.37. Thus we say that the equations are *inconsistent* and no solution is possible.

Suppose, on the other hand, we have the equations

$$\begin{aligned} x + y + z &= 4 \\ x - 2y + 3z &= 6 \\ x + 4y - z &= 2 \end{aligned} \qquad (9.39)$$

This time the equations are consistent, but we see that the sum of the second and third equations is equal to twice the first equation. Thus the first equation is redundant because it doesn't give us any more information than the second and third. We have three unknowns and two equations and therefore cannot obtain a unique solution. The two equations are

$$\begin{aligned} x - 2y + 3z &= 6 \\ x + 4y - z &= 2 \end{aligned} \qquad (9.40)$$

which are satisfied by an infinity of solutions. We can let one of the variables, x, y or z take on an arbitrary value and express the other two in terms of this. For example, letting z take the arbitrary value λ we get

$$x = \frac{8}{3} - \frac{5\lambda}{3}; \; y = \frac{-2}{3} + \frac{2\lambda}{3}$$

9.4.2 Homogeneous equations

If, in equation 9.34, b_1, b_2, b_3 are zero, we have the set of *homogeneous linear equations*

$$a_{11}x + a_{12}y + a_{13}z = 0$$
$$a_{21}x + a_{22}y + a_{23}z = 0 \qquad (9.41)$$
$$a_{31}x + a_{32}y + a_{33}z = 0$$

Applying the techniques we have developed so far to this set of equations gives the *trivial solution* x = y = z = 0, for the case of $\Delta \neq 0$. This is clearly not very interesting. However, in certain cases it is possible to obtain solutions for two of the variables in terms of the third. We may, for example, be able to obtain x and y in terms of z. In order to do this it has to be possible to express one of the equations as a linear combination of the other two. The condition for us to be able to do this is that the determinant of the coefficients a_{ij} should be zero.

$$\begin{vmatrix} a_{11} & a_{12} & a_{13} \\ a_{21} & a_{22} & a_{23} \\ a_{31} & a_{32} & a_{33} \end{vmatrix} = 0 \qquad (9.42)$$

Let us consider the equations

$$x + y + z = 0$$
$$x - 2y + 3z = 0 \qquad (9.43)$$
$$x + 4y - z = 0$$

These are not independent because the sum of the second and third is

$$2x + 2y + 2z = 0 \qquad (9.44)$$

which is equal to twice the first equation. Thus we can take as our independent equations

$$x - 2y + 3z = 0$$
$$x + 4y - z = 0 \qquad (9.45)$$

and, for example, solve for x and y in terms of z to give $x = -(5z/3)$, $y = 2z/3$.

Important applications of this arise in molecular-orbital theory and in the theory of molecular vibrations. In Hückel molecular orbital theory we obtain the set of equations

$$C_1(H_{11} - ES_{11}) + C_2(H_{12} - ES_{12}) + \ldots + C_n(H_{1n} - ES_{1n}) = 0$$
$$C_1(H_{21} - ES_{21}) + C_2(H_{22} - ES_{22}) + \ldots + C_n(H_{2n} - ES_{2n}) = 0$$
$$C_1(H_{n1} - ES_{n1}) + C_2(H_{n2} - ES_{n2}) + \ldots + C_n(H_{nn} - ES_{nn}) = 0$$
$$(9.46)$$

where H_{ij} and S_{ij} are assigned values. We require the values of E for which these equations, the *secular equations* have a nontrivial solution. The required values of E are those for which which the *secular determinant*

$$\begin{vmatrix} (H_{11} - ES_{11})\ (H_{12} - ES_{12}) \ldots\ (H_{1n} - ES_{1n}) \\ \\ (H_{n1} - ES_{n1})\ \ldots\ldots\ldots\ldots\ldots\ (H_{nn} - ES_{nn}) \end{vmatrix} \qquad (9.47)$$

is equal to zero. The determinant can be expanded to give a polynomial f(E) in E of degree n, which can then be solved (by approximate methods if necessary - see section 13.1) to give n values of E.

The elements H_{ij} and S_{ij} are integrals over atomic orbitals χ_i and χ_j; that is

$$H_{ij} = \int \chi_i H \chi_j \, d\tau \qquad S_{ij} = \int \chi_i \chi_j \, d\tau$$

where H is the Hamiltonian operator. For hydrocarbon π-electron systems H_{ij} and S_{ij} are never evaluated explicitly but are assigned values according to the following assumptions:

1. $S_{ij} = 1$, if $i = j$
   $= 0$, if $i \neq j$;
2. $H_{ii} = \alpha$, the Coulomb integral, for all i;
3. $H_{ij} = \beta$, the resonance integral, if i and j are adjacent
   $= 0$, otherwise.

Thus for benzene, with the carbon atoms labelled as in figure 9.1 the secular determinant is

$$\begin{vmatrix} \alpha - E & \beta & 0 & 0 & 0 & \beta \\ \beta & \alpha - E & \beta & 0 & 0 & 0 \\ 0 & \beta & \alpha - E & \beta & 0 & 0 \\ 0 & 0 & \beta & \alpha - E & \beta & 0 \\ 0 & 0 & 0 & \beta & \alpha - E & \beta \\ \beta & 0 & 0 & 0 & \beta & \alpha - E \end{vmatrix} = 0 \qquad (9.49)$$

This is transformed to a determinant amenable to solution by dividing throughout by β and writing $(\alpha - E)/\beta$ as x to give

$$\begin{vmatrix} x & 1 & 0 & 0 & 0 & 1 \\ 1 & x & 1 & 0 & 0 & 0 \\ 0 & 1 & x & 1 & 0 & 0 \\ 0 & 0 & 1 & x & 1 & 0 \\ 0 & 0 & 0 & 1 & x & 1 \\ 1 & 0 & 0 & 0 & 1 & x \end{vmatrix} = 0 \qquad (9.50)$$

This can be reduced to the determinant

$$(x + 2)(x - 2)(x - 1) \begin{vmatrix} (x + 1) & 2 & 0 \\ 0 & (x - 1) & 0 \\ 0 & (1 - x) & (x + 1) \end{vmatrix} = 0 \qquad (9.51)$$

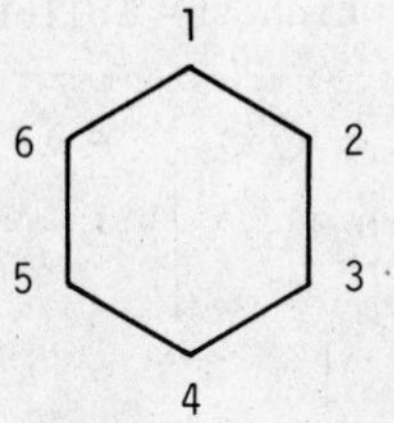

Figure 9.1

by a series of manipulations of rows and columns. The full expansion of the determinant is thus

$$(x + 2)(x - 2)(x + 1)^2(x - 1)^2 = 0 \qquad (9.52)$$

so x = 2, 1, 1, −1, −1, −2. Therefore the secular determinant (equation 9.49) is zero for $E = \alpha + 2\beta$, $\alpha + \beta$, $\alpha - \beta$ and $\alpha - 2\beta$.

9.5 PROBLEMS FOR SOLUTION

1. Evaluate the determinants:

(i) $\begin{vmatrix} 1 & 4 & 7 \\ 2 & 3 & 1 \\ 0 & 1 & 5 \end{vmatrix}$; (ii) $\begin{vmatrix} 2 & 1 & 0 \\ 5 & -7 & 1 \\ 0 & 1 & 3 \end{vmatrix}$; (iii) $\begin{vmatrix} 1 & -2 & 5 & 1 \\ 0 & 3 & -7 & 2 \\ 5 & 4 & -3 & 1 \\ 3 & 2 & 4 & -1 \end{vmatrix}$;

(iv) $\begin{vmatrix} 5 & 1 & -2 & 4 \\ 6 & -1 & 3 & 1 \\ 0 & 2 & 5 & 1 \\ 5 & 7 & -2 & 4 \end{vmatrix}$

2. Show, without expanding, that the following determinants vanish:

(i) $\begin{vmatrix} y - z & z - x & x - y \\ z - x & x - y & y - z \\ x - y & y - z & z - x \end{vmatrix}$; (ii) $\begin{vmatrix} 0 & c & -b \\ -c & 0 & a \\ b & -a & 0 \end{vmatrix}$; (iii) $\begin{vmatrix} b + c & 1 & a \\ c + a & 1 & b \\ b + a & 1 & c \end{vmatrix}$

(U.W.)

3. Show that

$$\begin{vmatrix} 1 & a & a^2 & a^3 + bcd \\ 1 & b & b^2 & b^3 + cda \\ 1 & c & c^2 & c^3 + abd \\ 1 & d & d^2 & d^3 + abc \end{vmatrix} = 0$$

(U.W.)

4. Find the values of λ for which the following determinants vanish:

(i) $\begin{vmatrix} 10-\lambda & -6 & 2 \\ -6 & 9-\lambda & -4 \\ 2 & -4 & 5-\lambda \end{vmatrix}$; (ii) $\begin{vmatrix} 7-\lambda & 5 & -4 \\ 1 & -\lambda & 3 \\ 2 & 0 & 1-\lambda \end{vmatrix}$;

(iii) $\begin{vmatrix} 3-\lambda & 4 & 2 \\ 4 & -7-\lambda & 1 \\ 2 & 1 & 2-\lambda \end{vmatrix}$

5. Without expanding show that

$$\begin{vmatrix} a^2 & b^2 & c^2 \\ a & b & c \\ 1 & 1 & 1 \end{vmatrix} = (a-b)(a-c)(b-c)$$

6. Solve the following sets of simultaneous equations:

(i) $4x + 2y + z = 11$, $x - y - z = -4$, $x + y + z = 6$

(ii) $x + y + z = 2$, $2x - y + z = 0$, $x + 2y - z = 4$

(iii) $2x + 4y - 7z = 44$, $3x - 2y + z = -4$, $x + 3y - 2z = 19$

(iv) $4x + 3y + 5z = 11$, $9x + 4y + 15z = 13$, $12x + 10y - 3z = 4$

(U.W.)

7. Solve the simultaneous equations

$$ax + y + 2z = 1$$
$$x + ay + 2z = 1$$
$$2x + 2y + az = 1$$

when (i) $a = 1$, (ii) $a = -1$, (iii) $a = (\sqrt{33} - 1)/2$.

8. Find the values of k (if any) for which the equations

$$x + y + z = 1$$
$$x + 2y + kz = 2$$
$$x + 4y + k^2z = 3$$

have (i) no solution, (ii) more than one solution. (U.W.)

9. Why is not possible to solve the equations

$$5x - 8y + 17z = 4$$
$$2x - y + 3z = k$$
$$3x + 4y - 5z = k^2$$

for all values of k? For what value of k does a solution exist? Find the solution for this case.

10. Solve the equations

$$x + ky = 2$$

$$y - kz = 3$$

$$kx - z = -5$$

when (i) $k \neq -1$, (ii) $k = -1$.

11. Do the following sets of equations have unique solutions?

(i)
$$y + z = 3$$
$$w - 2x - z = 2$$
$$-w - 2x - y + z = -1$$
$$3w + 6x + 2y - 3z = 3$$

(ii)
$$w + x + 2y - 3z = 1$$
$$-w + 2x + y = -3$$
$$-2w + 3x + y + z = 2$$
$$3w - 2x + y - 4z = 4$$

12. For what values of c do the equations

$$x + y + z = 0$$

$$x + 2y + cz = 0$$

$$x + 4y + c^2 z = 0$$

have nontrivial solutions? Find the solutions for these values of c.

(U.W.)

13. Solve the following sets of equations

(i)
$$5x - 8y + 17z = 0$$
$$2x - y + 3z = 0$$
$$3x + 4y - 5z = 0$$

(ii)
$$2x + 4y - 3z = 0$$
$$3x + y + 2z = 0$$
$$-x + 3y - 5z = 0$$

(iii)
$$x + 2y - z = 0$$
$$-2x + 5y + 3z = 0$$
$$4x + y + 4z = 0$$

10

Matrices

In chapter 9 we defined a square *array* of numbers called a *determinant* and discussed the evaluation of the determinant which has a definite value. In this chapter we introduce a new algebraic concept, the *matrix*. This is also a rectangular array of numbers; for example

$$\begin{pmatrix} 1 & 3 & 4 & 7 \\ 2 & 4 & 6 & 9 \\ 8 & 1 & 5 & 3 \end{pmatrix}$$

In contrast with a determinant, a matrix does *not* have a value. It is an algebraic entity and as in the case of vectors and complex numbers, we shall have to develop a new algebra.

The introduction of the concept of a matrix and the matrix algebra that we develop will enable us to consider the solution of simultaneous equations in a more systematic way and to express the result more compactly. Matrices are also used to describe transformations from one co-ordinate system to another. Familiarity with matrix methods is essential for the application of symmetry and group-theoretical methods to molecular problems.

If a matrix has m rows and n columns it is a matrix of order (m × n). We label the *elements* by subscripts i j; for example a_{ij} is the element in row i and column j of the matrix **A**

$$\mathbf{A} = \begin{pmatrix} a_{11} & a_{12} & a_{13} & a_{14} \\ a_{21} & a_{22} & a_{23} & a_{24} \\ a_{31} & a_{32} & a_{33} & a_{34} \end{pmatrix} \qquad (10.1)$$

10.1 MATRIX ALGEBRA

We have to consider three basic operations: the addition of two matrices, multiplication of a matrix by a constant and the multiplication of two matrices.

10.1.1 Matrix addition

We can only add two matrices **A** and **B** together if they are of the same order, that is both **A** and **B** have to be (m × n) matrices.

The sum of **A** and **B** is a new matrix **C**

$$\mathbf{C} = \mathbf{A} + \mathbf{B} \tag{10.2}$$

whose elements c_{ij} are given by

$$c_{ij} = a_{ij} + b_{ij} \tag{10.3}$$

Thus, for example

$$\begin{pmatrix} 1 & 2 & 4 \\ 3 & 4 & 7 \\ 2 & 1 & 0 \end{pmatrix} + \begin{pmatrix} 2 & 0 & 1 \\ 3 & 2 & 4 \\ 8 & 1 & 3 \end{pmatrix} = \begin{pmatrix} 3 & 2 & 5 \\ 6 & 6 & 11 \\ 10 & 2 & 3 \end{pmatrix} \tag{10.4}$$

The addition of matrices obeys the commutative and associative laws of addition

$$\left.\begin{aligned} \mathbf{A} + \mathbf{B} &= \mathbf{B} + \mathbf{A} \\ \mathbf{A} + (\mathbf{B} + \mathbf{C}) &= (\mathbf{A} + \mathbf{B}) + \mathbf{C} \end{aligned}\right\} \tag{10.5}$$

The difference **D** of two matrices **A** and **B**

$$\mathbf{D} = \mathbf{A} - \mathbf{B} \tag{10.6}$$

is a matrix with elements

$$d_{ij} = a_{ij} - b_{ij} \tag{10.7}$$

and thus subtraction is simply a special case of addition.

10.1.2 Equality of matrices

For two matrices **A** and **B** to be equal, they have to be of the same order $(m \times n)$ and satisfy the condition

$$a_{ij} = b_{ij}, \text{ for all } i, j \tag{10.8}$$

10.1.3 Multiplication by a constant

The effect of multiplying a matrix **A** by a constant k is to multiply each element of **A** by k. Thus

$$k\mathbf{A} = k\begin{pmatrix} a_{11} & a_{12} & a_{13} \\ a_{21} & a_{22} & a_{23} \\ a_{31} & a_{32} & a_{33} \end{pmatrix} = \begin{pmatrix} ka_{11} & ka_{12} & ka_{13} \\ ka_{21} & ka_{22} & ka_{23} \\ ka_{31} & ka_{32} & ka_{33} \end{pmatrix} \tag{10.9}$$

The reader should be most careful to note the difference between this and the multiplication of a determinant by a constant as discussed in section 9.2.3.

10.1.4 Matrix multiplication

In order to evaluate the matrix product **AB**, the matrices **A** and **B** have to be *conformable*; that is, the number of columns in **A** has to be equal to the number of rows in **B**. Thus if **A** is of the order ($\ell \times m$), **B** has to be of order ($m \times n$). ℓ and n can have any values. The product **AB** is a matrix **C**

$$\mathbf{C} = \mathbf{AB} \tag{10.10}$$

whose elements c_{ij} are given by

$$c_{ij} = \sum_{k=1}^{m} a_{ik} b_{kj} \tag{10.11}$$

that is, the element c_{ij} of **C** is obtained by taking row i of **A** with column j of **B**. Thus the product of the matrices

$$\mathbf{A} = \begin{pmatrix} 1 & 2 & 4 \\ 3 & 5 & 1 \\ 2 & 1 & 3 \end{pmatrix} \text{ and } \mathbf{B} = \begin{pmatrix} 2 & 3 & 2 \\ 4 & 6 & 1 \\ 3 & 2 & 5 \end{pmatrix}$$

is given by

$$\begin{pmatrix} 1 & 2 & 4 \\ 3 & 5 & 1 \\ 2 & 1 & 3 \end{pmatrix} \begin{pmatrix} 2 & 3 & 2 \\ 4 & 6 & 1 \\ 3 & 2 & 5 \end{pmatrix}$$

$$= \begin{pmatrix} 1\times 2 + 2\times 4 + 4\times 3 & 1\times 3 + 2\times 6 + 4\times 2 & 1\times 2 + 2\times 1 + 4\times 5 \\ 3\times 2 + 5\times 4 + 1\times 3 & 3\times 3 + 5\times 6 + 1\times 2 & 3\times 2 + 5\times 1 + 1\times 5 \\ 2\times 2 + 1\times 4 + 3\times 3 & 2\times 3 + 1\times 6 + 3\times 2 & 2\times 2 + 1\times 1 + 3\times 5 \end{pmatrix}$$

$$= \begin{pmatrix} 22 & 23 & 24 \\ 29 & 41 & 16 \\ 17 & 18 & 20 \end{pmatrix} \tag{10.12}$$

It is important to note that, in general, matrix multiplication is not commutative; that is the products **AB** and **BA** are usually quite different. In our example

$$\mathbf{BA} = \begin{pmatrix} 2 & 3 & 2 \\ 4 & 6 & 1 \\ 3 & 2 & 5 \end{pmatrix} \begin{pmatrix} 1 & 2 & 4 \\ 3 & 5 & 1 \\ 2 & 1 & 3 \end{pmatrix}$$

$$= \begin{pmatrix} 2\times 1 + 3\times 3 + 2\times 2 & 2\times 2 + 3\times 5 + 2\times 1 & 2\times 4 + 3\times 1 + 2\times 3 \\ 4\times 1 + 6\times 3 + 1\times 2 & 4\times 2 + 6\times 5 + 1\times 1 & 4\times 4 + 6\times 1 + 1\times 3 \\ 3\times 1 + 2\times 3 + 5\times 2 & 3\times 2 + 2\times 5 + 5\times 1 & 3\times 4 + 2\times 1 + 5\times 3 \end{pmatrix}$$

$$= \begin{pmatrix} 15 & 21 & 17 \\ 24 & 39 & 25 \\ 19 & 21 & 29 \end{pmatrix} \tag{10.13}$$

Matrix multiplication does, however, obey the associative and distributive laws

$$\mathbf{A}(\mathbf{BC}) = (\mathbf{AB})\mathbf{C} \qquad (10.14)$$

$$\mathbf{A}(\mathbf{B} + \mathbf{C}) = \mathbf{AB} + \mathbf{AC} \qquad (10.15)$$

In the triple product $\mathbf{M} = \mathbf{ABC}$, if $\mathbf{A}$ is of order $(\ell \times m)$ and $\mathbf{C}$ is of order $(n \times p)$ then $\mathbf{B}$ must be of order $(m \times n)$. The elements d_{ir} of $\mathbf{D}$, the product of $\mathbf{A}$ and $\mathbf{B}$, are given by

$$d_{ir} = \sum_{s=1}^{m} a_{is} b_{sr}$$

and the elements m_{ij} of $\mathbf{M}$ are

$$m_{ij} = \sum_{r=1}^{n} d_{ir} c_{rj} = \sum_{r=1}^{n} \left(\sum_{s=1}^{m} a_{is} b_{sr} \right) c_{rj}$$

$$= \sum_{r=1}^{n} \sum_{s=1}^{m} a_{is}\, b_{sr} c_{rj} \qquad (10.16)$$

We can interchange the order of the summation signs since a_{is}, b_{sr} and c_{rj} are simply numbers and write

$$m_{ij} = \sum_{s=1}^{m} a_{is} \left(\sum_{r=1}^{n} b_{sr} c_{rj} \right) \qquad (10.17)$$

thus proving that

$$(\mathbf{AB})\mathbf{C} = \mathbf{A}(\mathbf{BC}) \qquad (10.18)$$

10.2 SOME IMPORTANT SPECIAL MATRICES

In using matrices we shall meet several important types of matrix. In this section we discuss these special cases.

10.2.1 Row and column vectors

Very frequently we encounter matrices with either a single row or a single column. These are known as *row and column vectors*, respectively, because of their relation to the n-dimensional vectors defined in section 8.1. We shall use the symbol $\lfloor \mathbf{A} \rfloor$ to denote a row vector

$$\lfloor \mathbf{A} \rfloor = (a_1 \;\; a_2 \;\; a_3 \;\; a_4 \;\; \ldots) \qquad (10.19)$$

and denote a column vector thus

$$\{\mathbf{A}\} = \begin{Bmatrix} a_1 \\ a_2 \\ a_3 \\ \vdots \end{Bmatrix} \qquad (10.20)$$

The product $[\mathbf{A}]\{\mathbf{A}\}$ is a (1×1) matrix - that is, it is a number - and is in fact the scalar product of the n-dimensional vector **a** with itself.

$$[\mathbf{A}]\{\mathbf{A}\} = (a_1 a_2 a_3 \ldots a_n) \begin{pmatrix} a_1 \\ a_2 \\ a_3 \\ \vdots \\ a_n \end{pmatrix} = \sum_{i=1}^{n} a_i a_i \qquad (10.21)$$

However, if we perform the multiplication the other way round, we get a matrix of order $(n \times n)$

$$\{\mathbf{A}\}[\mathbf{A}] = \begin{pmatrix} a_1 \\ a_2 \\ \\ a_n \end{pmatrix} (a_1 a_2 a_3 \ldots a_n)$$

$$= \begin{pmatrix} a_1 a_1 & a_1 a_2 & a_1 a_3 \ldots & a_1 a_n \\ a_2 a_1 & \ldots & \ldots & a_2 a_n \\ \vdots & & & \vdots \\ a_n a_1 & \ldots & \ldots & a_n a_n \end{pmatrix} \qquad (10.22)$$

We can now use row or column vectors to write the simultaneous equations 9.9-9.11 in matrix form. Thus

$$\begin{pmatrix} a_{11} & a_{12} & a_{13} \\ a_{21} & a_{22} & a_{23} \\ a_{31} & a_{32} & a_{33} \end{pmatrix} \begin{pmatrix} x \\ y \\ z \end{pmatrix} = \begin{pmatrix} b_1 \\ b_2 \\ b_3 \end{pmatrix}$$

or $\mathbf{A}\{\mathbf{X}\} = \{\mathbf{B}\}$ (10.23)

where

$$\mathbf{A} = \begin{pmatrix} a_{11} & a_{12} & a_{13} \\ a_{21} & a_{22} & a_{23} \\ a_{31} & a_{32} & a_{33} \end{pmatrix}; \ \{\mathbf{X}\} = \begin{pmatrix} x \\ y \\ z \end{pmatrix}; \ \{\mathbf{B}\} = \begin{pmatrix} b_1 \\ b_2 \\ b_3 \end{pmatrix}$$

Alternatively we can write

$$(x\ y\ z) \begin{pmatrix} a_{11} & a_{21} & a_{31} \\ a_{12} & a_{22} & a_{32} \\ a_{13} & a_{23} & a_{33} \end{pmatrix} = (b_1\ b_2\ b_3)$$

which can be written

$$[X]\tilde{A} = [B] \tag{10.24}$$

where $\tilde{A}$ is the matrix obtained by interchanging the rows and columns of **A** (see section 10.2.7).

10.2.2 Null matrix

The *null matrix* **0** consists entirely of zeros

$$\mathbf{0} = \begin{pmatrix} 0 & 0 & 0 & 0 & \cdots \\ 0 & 0 & & & \\ \vdots & & & & \end{pmatrix} \tag{10.25}$$

From what we have said in section 9.1, it is clear that

$$\mathbf{A} + \mathbf{0} = \mathbf{A} \tag{10.26}$$

$$\mathbf{A0} = \mathbf{0A} = \mathbf{0} \tag{10.27}$$

10.2.3 Square matrix

Apart from column and row vectors, most of the matrices we shall encounter will have the same number of rows and columns. Such matrices are known as *square matrices*. The matrix **A** in equation 10.23 is an example of a square matrix. If we have two square matrices **A** and **B** of order $(n \times n)$, we can form two products by *premultiplying* **A** by **B** to give **BA** or by *postmultiplying* **A** by **B** to give **AB**. These products will, in general, be different.

10.2.4 Diagonal matrix

A particularly important type of square matrix is the *diagonal matrix* for which the elements a_{ij} are only nonzero for $i = j$. Such a matrix is of the form

$$\mathbf{A} = \begin{pmatrix} a_{11} & 0 & 0 \\ 0 & a_{22} & 0 \\ 0 & 0 & a_{33} \end{pmatrix} \tag{10.28}$$

The multiplication of a diagonal matrix **B** by a diagonal matrix **A** is commutative

$$\mathbf{AB} = \begin{pmatrix} a_{11} & 0 & 0 \\ 0 & a_{22} & 0 \\ 0 & 0 & a_{33} \end{pmatrix} \begin{pmatrix} b_{11} & 0 & 0 \\ 0 & b_{22} & 0 \\ 0 & 0 & b_{33} \end{pmatrix}$$

$$= \begin{pmatrix} a_{11}b_{11} & 0 & 0 \\ 0 & a_{22}b_{22} & 0 \\ 0 & 0 & a_{33}b_{33} \end{pmatrix}$$

$$= \begin{pmatrix} b_{11} & 0 & 0 \\ 0 & b_{22} & 0 \\ 0 & 0 & b_{33} \end{pmatrix} \begin{pmatrix} a_{11} & 0 & 0 \\ 0 & a_{22} & 0 \\ 0 & 0 & a_{33} \end{pmatrix} = \mathbf{BA} \tag{10.29}$$

10.2.5 The unit matrix

The *unit matrix* **1** is a diagonal matrix in which the elements a_{ii} are equal to unity.

$$\mathbf{1} = \begin{pmatrix} 1 & 0 & 0 \\ 0 & 1 & 0 \\ 0 & 0 & 1 \end{pmatrix} \tag{10.30}$$

A matrix **A** is unchanged by multiplication by a unit matrix of the same order

$$\mathbf{1A} = \mathbf{A1} = \mathbf{A} \tag{10.31}$$

10.2.6 Determinant of a matrix

If the matrix **A** is square, we can evaluate its determinant by the methods of chapter 9. Thus if we have the matrix

$$\mathbf{A} = \begin{pmatrix} 1 & 3 & 6 \\ 2 & 1 & 0 \\ 0 & 3 & 5 \end{pmatrix}$$

then

$$\det \mathbf{A} = \begin{vmatrix} 1 & 3 & 6 \\ 2 & 1 & 0 \\ 0 & 3 & 5 \end{vmatrix} = 1 \times 5 - 3 \times 10 + 6 \times 6 = 11 \tag{10.32}$$

If the determinant of the matrix **A** is zero, then **A** is said to be *singular*. If the determinant is nonzero, the matrix is *nonsingular*.

10.2.7 Transpose of a matrix

If we interchange the rows and columns of a matrix **A**, that is, if we interchange the elements a_{ij} and a_{ji} – we obtain the *transpose* of **A**, $\tilde{\mathbf{A}}$. For example, if

$$\mathbf{A} = \begin{pmatrix} 2 & 4 & 1 \\ 3 & 1 & 2 \\ 5 & 7 & 9 \end{pmatrix} \quad \text{then} \quad \tilde{\mathbf{A}} = \begin{pmatrix} 2 & 3 & 5 \\ 4 & 1 & 7 \\ 1 & 2 & 9 \end{pmatrix} \tag{10.33}$$

The transpose of a matrix of order $(m \times n)$, which is not square, is a matrix of order $(n \times m)$. If

$$\mathbf{B} = \begin{pmatrix} 2 & 6 \\ 3 & 4 \\ 5 & 1 \end{pmatrix} \quad \text{then} \quad \tilde{\mathbf{B}} = \begin{pmatrix} 2 & 3 & 5 \\ 6 & 4 & 1 \end{pmatrix} \tag{10.34}$$

If **C** is the product of two matrices **AB**, what can we say about the transpose $\tilde{\mathbf{C}}$ of **C**? Can we relate it to the transposes of **A** and **B**? We show below that the transpose of **C** is given by

$$\tilde{\mathbf{C}} = \tilde{\mathbf{B}}\tilde{\mathbf{A}} \tag{10.35}$$

The rule for matrix multiplication gives the elements of **C** as

$$c_{ij} = \sum_k a_{ik} b_{kj} \tag{10.36}$$

Therefore the elements of the transposed matrix $\tilde{\mathbf{C}}$ are given by

$$(\tilde{c})_{ij} = c_{ji} = \sum_k a_{jk} b_{ki} \tag{10.37}$$

But $a_{jk} = (\tilde{a})_{kj}$; $b_{ki} = (\tilde{b})_{ik}$ where $(\tilde{c})_{ij}$, etc., represent elements of the transposed matrices. Therefore

$$(\tilde{c})_{ij} = \sum_k (\tilde{b})_{ik} (\tilde{a})_{kj}$$

that is

$$\tilde{\mathbf{C}} = \tilde{\mathbf{B}}\tilde{\mathbf{A}} \tag{10.38}$$

Thus using the matrices **A** and **B** from equations 10.33 and 10.34 we obtain

$$\mathbf{C} = \mathbf{AB} = \begin{pmatrix} 2 & 4 & 1 \\ 3 & 1 & 2 \\ 5 & 7 & 9 \end{pmatrix} \begin{pmatrix} 2 & 6 \\ 3 & 4 \\ 5 & 1 \end{pmatrix}$$

$$= \begin{pmatrix} 2 \times 2 + 4 \times 3 + 1 \times 5 & 2 \times 6 + 4 \times 4 + 1 \times 1 \\ 3 \times 2 + 1 \times 3 + 2 \times 5 & 3 \times 6 + 1 \times 4 + 2 \times 1 \\ 5 \times 2 + 7 \times 3 + 9 \times 5 & 5 \times 6 + 7 \times 4 + 9 \times 1 \end{pmatrix}$$

$$= \begin{pmatrix} 21 & 29 \\ 19 & 24 \\ 76 & 67 \end{pmatrix}$$

and

$$\tilde{\mathbf{B}}\tilde{\mathbf{A}} = \begin{pmatrix} 2 & 3 & 5 \\ 6 & 4 & 1 \end{pmatrix} \begin{pmatrix} 2 & 3 & 5 \\ 4 & 1 & 7 \\ 1 & 2 & 9 \end{pmatrix} = \begin{pmatrix} 21 & 19 & 76 \\ 29 & 24 & 67 \end{pmatrix} = \tilde{\mathbf{C}} \tag{10.39}$$

This can be extended to the product of any number of matrices. If $\mathbf{P} = \mathbf{ABCD} \ldots$, then $\tilde{\mathbf{P}} = \ldots \tilde{\mathbf{D}}\tilde{\mathbf{C}}\tilde{\mathbf{B}}\tilde{\mathbf{A}}$.

10.2.8 Symmetric matrix

A matrix for which $a_{ij} = a_{ji}$ for all i and j is a *symmetric matrix*. A symmetric matrix is obviously equal to its transpose. An example is the matrix

$$\mathbf{A} = \begin{pmatrix} 1 & 2 & 3 \\ 2 & 4 & 5 \\ 3 & 5 & 6 \end{pmatrix} \tag{10.40}$$

10.2.9 Complex matrices

So far, all the elements of the matrices in our examples have been real numbers, but in general matrix elements may be real or complex; for example

$$\mathbf{A} = \begin{pmatrix} 1 + i & 2 - i & 5 + 2i \\ 3 + 4i & 7 - 2i & 1 + 3i \\ 1 - i & 2 + 4i & 3 + i \end{pmatrix} \tag{10.41}$$

The *complex conjugate* $\mathbf{A}^*$ of $\mathbf{A}$ is obtained by taking the complex conjugate of each element of $\mathbf{A}$

$$\mathbf{A}^* = \begin{pmatrix} 1 - i & 2 + i & 5 - 2i \\ 3 - 4i & 7 + 2i & 1 - 3i \\ 1 + i & 2 - 4i & 3 - i \end{pmatrix} \tag{10.42}$$

An important matrix in quantum mechanics is the *Hermitean adjoint* $\mathbf{A}^+$, which is the transpose of $\mathbf{A}^*$ or the complex conjugate of $\tilde{\mathbf{A}}$

$$\mathbf{A}^+ = \widetilde{(\mathbf{A}^*)} = (\tilde{\mathbf{A}})^* \tag{10.43}$$

Thus the Hermitean adjoint of the matrix in equation 10.41 is

$$\mathbf{A}^+ = \begin{pmatrix} 1 - i & 3 - 4i & 1 + i \\ 2 + i & 7 + 2i & 2 - 4i \\ 5 - 2i & 1 - 3i & 3 - i \end{pmatrix} \tag{10.44}$$

The nomenclature is rather confused here because 'adjoint matrix' has another meaning. However, in physics the term 'adjoint' usually refers to the matrix $\mathbf{A}^+$ defined above.

If $\mathbf{A}^+ = \mathbf{A}$, then the matrix is said to be *Hermitean*. An example is

$$\mathbf{B} = \begin{pmatrix} 3 & 1 - 2i & 3 + 4i \\ 1 + 2i & 7 & 4 - i \\ 3 - 4i & 4 + i & 1 \end{pmatrix} \tag{10.45}$$

10.2.10 The inverse matrix

In equation 10.23 we expressed a set of simultaneous equations in matrix notation

$$\mathbf{A}\{\mathbf{X}\} = \{\mathbf{B}\} \tag{10.46}$$

or

$$\begin{pmatrix} a_{11} & a_{12} & a_{13} \\ a_{21} & a_{22} & a_{23} \\ a_{31} & a_{32} & a_{33} \end{pmatrix} \begin{pmatrix} x \\ y \\ z \end{pmatrix} = \begin{pmatrix} b_1 \\ b_2 \\ b_3 \end{pmatrix}$$

If we can find a matrix $\mathbf{A}^{-1}$ such that

$$\mathbf{A}^{-1}\mathbf{A} = \mathbf{1} \tag{10.47}$$

we can readily write down the solution of these equations; thus

$$\{\mathbf{X}\} = \mathbf{A}^{-1}\{\mathbf{B}\} \tag{10.48}$$

The matrix $\mathbf{A}^{-1}$ is called the *inverse matrix* of $\mathbf{A}$ and is defined by the relation

$$\mathbf{A}^{-1} = \frac{\text{adj } \mathbf{A}}{\det \mathbf{A}} \tag{10.49}$$

where adj $\mathbf{A}$ is the *adjoint matrix* (not to be confused with the Hermitean adjoint defined in the previous section). The adjoint matrix is obtained by taking the transpose of the matrix consisting of the cofactors of the elements of $\mathbf{A}$. Thus if $\mathbf{A}$ is the matrix

$$\mathbf{A} = \begin{pmatrix} a_{11} & a_{12} & a_{13} \\ a_{21} & a_{22} & a_{23} \\ a_{31} & a_{32} & a_{33} \end{pmatrix}$$

and the cofactors of the elements a_{ij} are A_{ij}, then adj $\mathbf{A}$ is given by

$$\text{adj } \mathbf{A} = \begin{pmatrix} A_{11} & A_{21} & A_{31} \\ A_{12} & A_{22} & A_{32} \\ A_{13} & A_{23} & A_{33} \end{pmatrix} \tag{10.50}$$

Clearly we can only define an inverse matrix when the determinant of the matrix is nonzero; that is the matrix has to be nonsingular. We illustrate with the calculation of the inverse of the matrix $\mathbf{A}$

$$\mathbf{A} = \begin{pmatrix} 1 & 4 & 3 \\ 2 & 1 & 0 \\ 1 & 3 & 2 \end{pmatrix}$$

The matrix of cofactors is

$$\begin{pmatrix} (1\times 2-3\times 0) & -(2\times 2-1\times 0) & (2\times 3-1\times 1) \\ -(4\times 2-3\times 3) & (1\times 2-1\times 3) & -(1\times 3-1\times 4) \\ (4\times 0-1\times 3) & -(1\times 0-2\times 3) & (1\times 1-2\times 4) \end{pmatrix}$$

$$= \begin{pmatrix} 2 & -4 & 5 \\ 1 & -1 & 1 \\ -3 & 6 & -7 \end{pmatrix}$$

Thus the adjoint of $\mathbf{A}$, adj $\mathbf{A}$, is

$$\text{adj}\ \mathbf{A} = \begin{pmatrix} 2 & 1 & -3 \\ -4 & -1 & 6 \\ 5 & 1 & -7 \end{pmatrix}$$

$$\det \mathbf{A} = 1(1\times 2-3\times 0) - 4(2\times 2-1\times 0) + 3(2\times 3-1\times 1) = 1$$

Therefore the inverse matrix is

$$\mathbf{A}^{-1} = \begin{pmatrix} 2 & 1 & -3 \\ -4 & -1 & 6 \\ 5 & 1 & -7 \end{pmatrix} \tag{10.51}$$

$$\mathbf{A}^{-1}\mathbf{A} = \begin{pmatrix} 2 & 1 & -3 \\ -4 & -1 & 6 \\ 5 & 1 & -7 \end{pmatrix}\begin{pmatrix} 1 & 4 & 3 \\ 2 & 1 & 0 \\ 1 & 3 & 2 \end{pmatrix}$$

$$= \begin{pmatrix} 1 & 0 & 0 \\ 0 & 1 & 0 \\ 0 & 0 & 1 \end{pmatrix} \tag{10.52}$$

Multiplication of $\mathbf{A}$ by its inverse is commutative; that is

$$\mathbf{A}^{-1}\mathbf{A} = \mathbf{A}\mathbf{A}^{-1} = \mathbf{1} \tag{10.53}$$

If $\mathbf{C}$ is the product $\mathbf{AB}$ of the matrices $\mathbf{A}$ and $\mathbf{B}$, we can express the inverse of $\mathbf{C}$ in terms of the inverses of $\mathbf{A}$ and $\mathbf{B}$ as follows

$$\mathbf{C}\mathbf{C}^{-1} = (\mathbf{AB})(\mathbf{AB})^{-1} = \mathbf{1} \tag{10.54}$$

Let us multiply on the left first by $\mathbf{A}^{-1}$ and then by $\mathbf{B}^{-1}$ to give

$$\mathbf{B}^{-1}\mathbf{A}^{-1}(\mathbf{AB})(\mathbf{AB})^{-1} = \mathbf{B}^{-1}\mathbf{A}^{-1}\mathbf{1} = \mathbf{B}^{-1}\mathbf{A}^{-1}$$

Since matrix multiplication is associative we can rewrite this as

$$\mathbf{B}^{-1}\mathbf{A}^{-1} = \mathbf{B}^{-1}(\mathbf{A}^{-1}\mathbf{A})\mathbf{B}(\mathbf{AB})^{-1}$$

$$= \mathbf{B}^{-1}\mathbf{1}\mathbf{B}(\mathbf{AB})^{-1} = \mathbf{B}^{-1}\mathbf{B}(\mathbf{AB})^{-1} = \mathbf{1}(\mathbf{AB})^{-1} = (\mathbf{AB})^{-1}$$

Hence

$$\mathbf{C}^{-1} = (\mathbf{AB})^{-1} = \mathbf{B}^{-1}\mathbf{A}^{-1} \qquad (10.55)$$

10.2.11 Orthogonal and unitary matrices

These matrices occur frequently in quantum mechanics and group theory. An *orthogonal matrix* is a matrix whose inverse is equal to its transpose

$$\mathbf{A}^{-1} = \tilde{\mathbf{A}} \qquad (10.56)$$

An example of this is the matrix

$$\begin{pmatrix} \cos\theta & -\sin\theta & 0 \\ \sin\theta & \cos\theta & 0 \\ 0 & 0 & 1 \end{pmatrix} \qquad (10.57)$$

where the inverse matrix is

$$\begin{pmatrix} \cos\theta & \sin\theta & 0 \\ -\sin\theta & \cos\theta & 0 \\ 0 & 0 & 1 \end{pmatrix} \qquad (10.58)$$

The inverse of a *unitary matrix* is equal to its Hermitean conjugate.

$$\mathbf{A}^{-1} = \mathbf{A}^{+} \qquad (10.59)$$

An example of a unitary matrix is

$$\psi = \begin{pmatrix} \cos\theta & i\sin\theta \\ i\sin\theta & \cos\theta \end{pmatrix} \qquad (10.60)$$

10.3 SOLUTION OF SIMULTANEOUS EQUATIONS

We said in the previous section that provided we can define an inverse matrix, we can compactly express the solution to the inhomogeneous simultaneous equations

$$\mathbf{A}\{\mathbf{X}\} = \{\mathbf{B}\}$$

in terms of the inverse matrix

$$\{\mathbf{X}\} = \mathbf{A}^{-1}\{\mathbf{B}\} \qquad (10.61)$$

Thus in the case of the equations

$$x + 4y + 3z = 3$$

$$2x + y = 2$$

$$x + 3y + 2z = 4$$

the inverse of the matrix

$$\mathbf{A} = \begin{pmatrix} 1 & 4 & 3 \\ 2 & 1 & 0 \\ 1 & 3 & 2 \end{pmatrix}$$

is

$$\mathbf{A}^{-1} = \begin{pmatrix} 2 & 1 & -3 \\ -4 & -1 & 6 \\ 5 & 1 & -7 \end{pmatrix}$$

and the solution is given by

$$\begin{pmatrix} x \\ y \\ z \end{pmatrix} = \begin{pmatrix} 2 & 1 & -3 \\ -4 & -1 & 6 \\ 5 & 1 & -7 \end{pmatrix}\begin{pmatrix} 3 \\ 2 \\ 4 \end{pmatrix} = \begin{pmatrix} -4 \\ 10 \\ -11 \end{pmatrix}$$

that is

$$x = -4, \quad y = 10, \quad z = -11 \tag{10.62}$$

As well as being more elegant than the determinantal method, the matrix solution involves less calculation. It is only necessary to calculate the inverse matrix whereas the determinantal method requires the computation of (n + 1) determinants where n is the number of unknowns. Well-established routines are available for the inversion of large matrices on computers.

If the matrix $\mathbf{A}$ is singular, the inverse $\mathbf{A}^{-1}$ does not exist and the method is not applicable. In such cases we have to apply the considerations of section 9.4.1.

A set of homogeneous equations can be written in matrix notation as

$$\mathbf{A}\{\mathbf{X}\} = \{\mathbf{0}\} \tag{10.63}$$

As we saw in section 9.4.2, we can only obtain solutions for such a set of equations when det $\mathbf{A}$ is zero. In this case the matrix $\mathbf{A}^{-1}$ does not exist and the matrix method is not applicable.

10.4 EIGENVALUES AND EIGENVECTORS

We can rewrite the secular equations 9.46 in matrix notation thus

$$(\mathbf{H} - E\mathbf{S})\{\mathbf{C}\} = \mathbf{0} \tag{10.64}$$

In many applications the elements S_{ij} of $\mathbf{S}$ are zero unless $i = j$; that is often $\mathbf{S}$ is the unit matrix $\mathbf{1}$, so we write

$$(\mathbf{H} - E\mathbf{1})\{\mathbf{C}\} = \mathbf{0}$$

or

$$\mathbf{H}\{\mathbf{C}\} = E\{\mathbf{C}\} \tag{10.65}$$

This is an equation of the same general form as the eigenvalue equation 2.32. If we multiply $\{\mathbf{C}\}$ by the matrix $\mathbf{H}$, we obtain the column vector $\{\mathbf{C}\}$ multiplied by a constant. We say that E is an *eigenvalue* of the matrix $\mathbf{H}$ and $\{\mathbf{C}\}$ is an *eigenvector*. In general we have

$$\mathbf{A}\{\mathbf{X}\} = \lambda\{\mathbf{X}\} \tag{10.66}$$

where λ is the eigenvalue and $\{\mathbf{X}\}$ the eigenvector. This problem occurs commonly in quantum mechanics and in the theory of molecular vibrations. If we require λ and $\{\mathbf{X}\}$ to be such that

$$(\mathbf{A} - \lambda\mathbf{1})\{\mathbf{X}\} = 0 \tag{10.67}$$

and we are interested in nontrivial eigenvectors, from the considerations of section 9.4.2 we require $\det(\mathbf{A} - \lambda\mathbf{1})$ to be zero. As mentioned in that section, the values of λ for which this is true can be obtained from the expansion of $\det(\mathbf{A} - \lambda\mathbf{1})$ as a polynomial in λ. The calculation of eigenvalues and eigenvectors for matrices of order greater than (3 × 3) is most readily done on a computer and there are several efficient routines for doing this.

An example that occurs in the application of Hückel molecular-orbital theory to the allyl radical is the matrix

$$\begin{pmatrix} 0 & 1 & 0 \\ 1 & 0 & 1 \\ 0 & 1 & 0 \end{pmatrix} \tag{10.68}$$

We require the values of λ for which the determinant

$$\begin{vmatrix} -\lambda & 1 & 0 \\ 1 & -\lambda & 1 \\ 0 & 1 & -\lambda \end{vmatrix} \tag{10.69}$$

is zero. Expanding the determinant gives

$$-\lambda(\lambda^2 - 1) - 1(-\lambda) = 0$$

that is

$$\lambda(\lambda^2 - 2) = 0$$

so the eigenvalues are $\lambda = 0, \pm\sqrt{2}$.

We now require the column vectors for which

$$\begin{pmatrix} -\lambda_i & 1 & 0 \\ 1 & -\lambda_i & 1 \\ 0 & 1 & -\lambda_i \end{pmatrix} \begin{pmatrix} x_{i1} \\ x_{i2} \\ x_{i3} \end{pmatrix} = \begin{pmatrix} 0 \\ 0 \\ 0 \end{pmatrix} \tag{10.70}$$

for each of the three possible values of λ_i. Since these are homogeneous equations, we cannot obtain a unique solution. We can only express two of the x_{ij} in terms of the third. If $\lambda_1 = 0$, we have the equations

$$\left.\begin{aligned} x_{12} &= 0 \\ x_{11} + x_{13} &= 0 \\ x_{12} &= 0 \end{aligned}\right\} \tag{10.71}$$

from which we see that $x_{11} = -x_{13}$, $x_{12} = 0$. For $\lambda_2 = \sqrt{2}$ the equations are

$$\left.\begin{aligned} -\sqrt{2}x_{21} + x_{22} &= 0 \\ x_{21} - \sqrt{2}x_{22} + x_{23} &= 0 \\ x_{22} - \sqrt{2}x_{23} &= 0 \end{aligned}\right\} \qquad (10.72)$$

Thus in terms of x_{23} we have $x_{21} = x_{23}$, $x_{22} = \sqrt{2}x_{23}$. Similarly for $\lambda_3 = -\sqrt{2}$ we get $x_{21} = x_{23}$, $x_{22} = -\sqrt{2}x_{23}$.

The absolute values of the coefficients are usually fixed by requiring the eigenvectors to be normalised. In the Hückel method the condition for this is that

$$\sum_{j=1}^{n} x_{ij}^{\ 2} = 1$$

so we obtain the following normalised eigenvectors

$$\lambda = 0 \quad : x_{11} = -x_{13} = \frac{1}{\sqrt{2}},\ x_{12} = 0$$

$$\lambda = \sqrt{2} \quad : x_{21} = x_{23} = \frac{1}{2},\ x_{22} = \frac{\sqrt{2}}{2}$$

$$\lambda = -\sqrt{2} : x_{31} = x_{33} = \frac{1}{2},\ x_{32} = -\frac{\sqrt{2}}{2}$$

The eigenvalues λ_i are related to the energy E of the molecular orbital ψ_i by the relation $-\lambda = (\alpha - E)/\beta$, so $E = \alpha + \lambda\beta$. The numbers x_{ij} are coefficients of the atomic orbital χ_j in molecular orbital i. Taking β as a negative quantity, we can draw a molecular-orbital diagram (figure 10.1).

E

$\alpha - \sqrt{2}\beta$ —— $\psi_3 = \frac{1}{2}(\chi_1 - \sqrt{2}\chi_2 + \chi_3)$

α —— $\psi_2 = \frac{1}{\sqrt{2}}(\chi_1 - \chi_3)$

$\alpha + \sqrt{2}\beta$ —— $\psi_1 = \frac{1}{2}(\chi_1 + \sqrt{2}\chi_2 + \chi_3)$

Figure 10.1

10.5 LINEAR TRANSFORMATIONS

One of the most important uses of matrices in molecular problems arises in the application of group theory to symmetry properties. Symmetry operations can be described in terms of matrices. This is a particular application of a *linear transformation*. Let us illustrate this by considering the rotation of a vector **p** about the z-axis (figure 10.2).

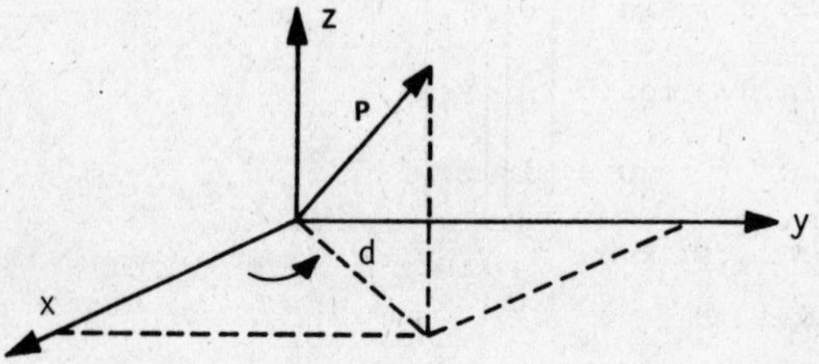

Figure 10.2

We define the positive sense as that which takes x into y as we rotate about the z-axis. In terms of the unit vectors $\hat{\imath}$, $\hat{\jmath}$ and $\hat{k}$, **p** is given by

$$\mathbf{p} = x_1\hat{\imath} + y_1\hat{\jmath} + z_1\hat{k} \tag{10.73}$$

Let us now rotate by an angle θ about the z-axis to give a new vector $\mathbf{p}'$. The z-component remains unchanged so we can restrict ourselves to the xy plane and take d to be the length of the projection of **p** on to this plane. Let this projection initially make an angle φ with the x-axis (figure 10.3). Then

$$\begin{aligned} x_2 &= d\cos(\theta + \phi) = d\cos\theta\cos\phi - d\sin\theta\sin\phi \\ &= d\cos\theta\left(\frac{x_1}{d}\right) - d\sin\theta\left(\frac{y_1}{d}\right) \\ &= x_1\cos\theta - y_1\sin\theta \end{aligned} \tag{10.74}$$

Similarly

$$\begin{aligned} y_2 &= d\sin(\theta + \phi) = d\sin\theta\cos\phi + d\cos\theta\sin\phi \\ &= d\sin\theta\left(\frac{x_1}{d}\right) + d\cos\theta\left(\frac{y_1}{d}\right) = x_1\sin\theta + y_1\cos\theta \end{aligned} \tag{10.75}$$

Thus we can relate the components (x_2, y_2, z_2) of $\mathbf{p}'$ to those of **p** by the matrix relation

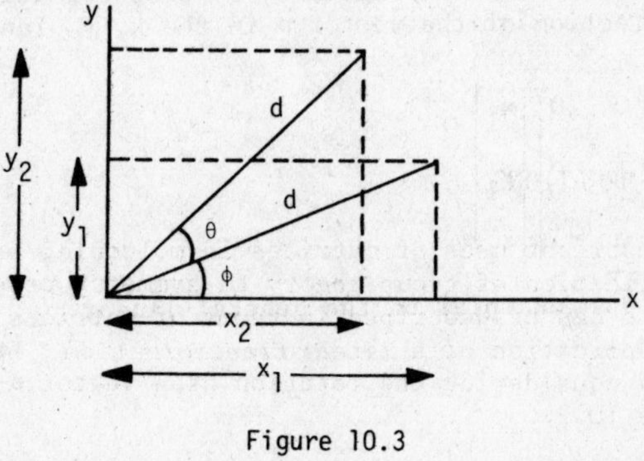

Figure 10.3

$$\begin{pmatrix} x_2 \\ y_2 \\ z_2 \end{pmatrix} = \begin{pmatrix} \cos\theta & -\sin\theta & 0 \\ \sin\theta & \cos\theta & 0 \\ 0 & 0 & 1 \end{pmatrix} \begin{pmatrix} x_1 \\ y_1 \\ z_1 \end{pmatrix} \tag{10.76}$$

that is

$$\{\mathbf{X}_2\} = \mathbf{R}\{\mathbf{X}_1\}$$

We used this transformation matrix in section 10.2.1 as an example of an orthogonal matrix. The physical interpretation of this is that the length of the vector $\mathbf{p}$ is unchanged by the operation. The inverse transformation is given by the inverse matrix $\mathbf{R}^{-1}$

$$\begin{pmatrix} x_1 \\ y_1 \\ z_1 \end{pmatrix} = \begin{pmatrix} \cos\theta & \sin\theta & 0 \\ -\sin\theta & \cos\theta & 0 \\ 0 & 0 & 1 \end{pmatrix} \begin{pmatrix} x_2 \\ y_2 \\ z_2 \end{pmatrix} \tag{10.77}$$

that is

$$\{\mathbf{X}_1\} = \mathbf{R}^{-1}\{\mathbf{X}_2\}$$

Successive rotations are described by a matrix product. If a further rotation θ_1 is carried out the result is

$$\begin{pmatrix} x_3 \\ y_3 \\ z_3 \end{pmatrix} = \begin{pmatrix} \cos\theta_1 & -\sin\theta_1 & 0 \\ \sin\theta_1 & \cos\theta_1 & 0 \\ 0 & 0 & 1 \end{pmatrix} \begin{pmatrix} x_2 \\ y_2 \\ z_2 \end{pmatrix}$$

$$= \begin{pmatrix} \cos\theta_1 & -\sin\theta_1 & 0 \\ \sin\theta_1 & \cos\theta_1 & 0 \\ 0 & 0 & 1 \end{pmatrix} \begin{pmatrix} \cos\theta & -\sin\theta & 0 \\ \sin\theta & \cos\theta & 0 \\ 0 & 0 & 1 \end{pmatrix} \begin{pmatrix} x_1 \\ y_1 \\ z_1 \end{pmatrix} \tag{10.78}$$

Reflections can be described similarly by transformation matrices. The reflection of the vector $\mathbf{p}$ in the x, y plane is given by

$$\begin{pmatrix} x_2 \\ y_2 \\ z_2 \end{pmatrix} = \begin{pmatrix} 1 & 0 & 0 \\ 0 & 1 & 0 \\ 0 & 0 & -1 \end{pmatrix} \begin{pmatrix} x_1 \\ y_1 \\ z_1 \end{pmatrix} \tag{10.79}$$

These are just two examples of the general linear transformation

$$\begin{pmatrix} y_1 \\ y_2 \\ y_3 \\ \cdot \\ \cdot \\ \cdot \\ y_n \end{pmatrix} \begin{pmatrix} a_{11} & a_{12} & \cdots & a_{im} \\ a_{21} & a_{22} & \cdots & \\ \cdot & & & \\ \cdot & & & \\ \cdot & & & \\ \cdot & & & \\ a_{n1} & \cdots & \cdots & a_{nm} \end{pmatrix} \begin{pmatrix} x_1 \\ x_2 \\ \cdot \\ \cdot \\ \cdot \\ \cdot \\ \cdot \\ x_m \end{pmatrix} \tag{10.80}$$

in which n variables $y_1 \ldots y_n$ are expressed in terms of m variables $x_1 \ldots x_m$.

10.6 PROBLEMS FOR SOLUTION

1. For the pairs of matrices **A**, **B** given below, write down the matrices **A** + **B**, **A** − **B**, **AB**, **BA**, $\tilde{\mathbf{A}}$, $\tilde{\mathbf{B}}$, $\tilde{\mathbf{A}}\tilde{\mathbf{B}}$, $\mathbf{A}^{-1}$, $\mathbf{B}^{-1}$, $\mathbf{A}^{-1}\mathbf{B}^{-1}$:

(i) $\begin{pmatrix} 1 & -1 & 2 \\ 3 & 7 & 5 \\ 0 & 4 & 3 \end{pmatrix}$; $\begin{pmatrix} 2 & 3 & -1 \\ -1 & 2 & 4 \\ 5 & 1 & 0 \end{pmatrix}$;

(ii) $\begin{pmatrix} 5 & 2 & -3 \\ 6 & 0 & 1 \\ 1 & 3 & 2 \end{pmatrix}$; $\begin{pmatrix} 3 & 1 & 0 \\ 1 & 5 & 2 \\ 0 & 2 & -1 \end{pmatrix}$;

(iii) $\begin{pmatrix} 1 & 7 & 2 \\ 7 & 3 & 1 \\ 1 & 1 & 5 \end{pmatrix}$; $\begin{pmatrix} 3 & 1 & 0 \\ 1 & 5 & 2 \\ 0 & 2 & -1 \end{pmatrix}$;

(iv) $\begin{pmatrix} 1/2 & \sqrt{3}/2 & 0 \\ -\sqrt{3}/2 & 1/2 & 0 \\ 0 & 0 & 1 \end{pmatrix}$; $\begin{pmatrix} \sqrt{3}/2 & 1/2 & 0 \\ -1/2 & \sqrt{3}/2 & 0 \\ 0 & 0 & 1 \end{pmatrix}$

2. Evaluate the products **AB** and **BA** for the pairs of matrices given below:

(i) $\begin{pmatrix} 1 \\ 3 \\ 2 \end{pmatrix}$, $(2 \;\; 0 \;\; 1)$; (ii) $\begin{pmatrix} 4 \\ 7 \\ 2 \end{pmatrix}$, $(3 \;\; 2 \;\; 5)$;

(iii) $\begin{pmatrix} 1 \\ -2 \\ 3 \end{pmatrix}$; $(1 \;\; -1 \;\; -1)$; (iv) $\begin{pmatrix} 2 \\ 1 \\ 0 \end{pmatrix}$, $(-1 \;\; 2 \;\; 1)$.

3. Write down the Hermitean adjoints of the following matrices. State whether the matrices are Hermitean.

(i) $\begin{pmatrix} 0 & -i \\ i & 0 \end{pmatrix}$; (ii) $\begin{pmatrix} 1+i & 2+3i & 4-i \\ 2-i & 1+2i & 3+4i \\ 5-2i & 7+3i & 4-i \end{pmatrix}$;

(iii) $\begin{pmatrix} 0 & -i & 0 \\ i & 0 & -i \\ 0 & i & 0 \end{pmatrix}$; (iv) $\begin{pmatrix} 1 & 2-i & 1+3i \\ 2+i & 4 & 3i \\ 1-3i & -3i & 3 \end{pmatrix}$.

4. Calculate the inverses of the following matrices and comment on your results:

(i) $\begin{pmatrix} 1/3 & 2/3 & 2/3 \\ 2/3 & 1/3 & -2/3 \\ -2/3 & 2/3 & -1/3 \end{pmatrix}$; (ii) $\begin{pmatrix} \sqrt{3}/2 & -1/2 & 0 \\ 1/2 & \sqrt{3}/2 & 0 \\ 0 & 0 & 1 \end{pmatrix}$.

5. Solve the following sets of equations by a matrix method:

(i)
$$4x + 2y + z = 11$$
$$x - y + z = -4$$
$$x + y + z = 6$$

(ii)
$$x + y + z = 2$$
$$2x - y + z = 0$$
$$x + 2y - z = 4$$

(iii)
$$2x + 4y - 7z = 44$$
$$3x - 2y + z = -4$$
$$x + 3y - 2z = 19$$

(iv)
$$x + y + z = -1$$
$$3x - y + 2z = 4$$
$$2x - 5z = -5$$

(v)
$$-x - 2y - z = 3$$
$$x + 9y + 7z = -10$$
$$-3x + 4y - 2z = -2$$

6. Calculate the eigenvalues and eigenvectors of the following matrices:

(i) $\begin{pmatrix} 1 & 0 & -1 \\ 0 & 1 & 1 \\ -1 & 1 & 1 \end{pmatrix}$; (ii) $\begin{pmatrix} 4 & -4 & -2 \\ 1 & -1 & -2 \\ -1 & 2 & 3 \end{pmatrix}$; (iii) $\begin{pmatrix} 0 & 1 & 0 \\ 1 & 0 & \sqrt{3} \\ 0 & \sqrt{3} & 0 \end{pmatrix}$;

(iv) $\begin{pmatrix} 0 & i & 1 \\ -i & 1 & i \\ 1 & -i & 1 \end{pmatrix}$.

11

Differential Equations

Differential equations are equations that contain derivatives; for example

$$\frac{dy}{dx} + f(x,y) = 0 \tag{11.1}$$

They arise in many areas of chemistry and it is therefore important to know how to solve the more commonly occurring ones. They range in complexity from simple equations describing elementary kinetic processes, for example for first-order reactions

$$\frac{dx}{dt} = -kt \tag{11.2}$$

for successive first-order reactions

$$\frac{dx}{dt} = -k_2x + k_1Ae^{-k_1t} \tag{11.3}$$

for second-order reactions

$$\frac{dx}{dt} = k(a - x)(b - x) \tag{11.4}$$

through the equations describing harmonic and damped harmonic motion

$$\frac{d^2x}{dt^2} = -\omega^2x \tag{11.5}$$

$$\frac{d^2x}{dt^2} + b\frac{dx}{dt} + \omega^2x = 0 \tag{11.6}$$

to the Schrödinger equation in three dimensions

$$\frac{\partial^2\psi}{\partial x^2} + \frac{\partial^2\psi}{\partial y^2} + \frac{\partial^2\psi}{\partial z^2} + \frac{8\pi^2m(E - V)\psi}{h^2} = 0 \tag{11.7}$$

We can immediately classify differential equations into two categories. Equations 11.1 to 11.6 only involve functions of a single variable and are *ordinary differential equations*, whereas in equation 11.7, ψ is a function of three variables x, y and z. Such equations are called *partial differential equations* and further discussion of them will be deferred until the next chapter.

11.1 CLASSIFICATION OF ORDINARY DIFFERENTIAL EQUATIONS AND THEIR SOLUTIONS

Equations 11.1 to 11.4 only involve *first* derivatives whereas equations 11.5 and 11.6 contain second derivatives. We can classify differential equations by the index n of the highest derivative $d^n y/dx^n$ that occurs in the equation. This is the *order* of the equation and we see that equations 11.1 to 11.4 are *first order*, whereas equations 11.5 and 11.6 are *second order*. Equations of higher order do exist but we shall not be very interested in them.

A second classification is by *degree*, which is defined as the highest power of the highest derivative in the equation. In our examples, the highest derivative occurs to the first power so all of these equations are of *first degree*. The equation

$$\left(\frac{dy}{dx}\right)^2 + f(x,y) = 0 \qquad (11.8)$$

would be of second degree but first order. We must be careful to avoid confusion between the terms degree and order.

Since differential equations contain derivatives, their solution essentially involves integration. In general each integration introduces an arbitrary constant. The *general solution* of a differential equation of order n will contain n independent arbitrary constants. If we assign special values to these constants, we obtain a *particular solution*. In any chemical problem we shall generally use the given conditions to determine the arbitrary constants.

11.2 EQUATIONS OF FIRST ORDER AND FIRST DEGREE

These equations only contain dy/dx and a function of x and y and are of the general form of equation 11.1. The method of solution depends on the nature of the function f(x,y) and we shall discuss only the more important types.

11.2.1 Simple equations

If f(x,y) is a function of x alone, the solution of the problem simply involves integration. If

$$\frac{dy}{dx} = f(x) \qquad (11.9)$$

then

$$y = \int f(x)dx + c$$

where c is an arbitrary constant.

11.2.2 Variables separable

We can rearrange equation 11.4 as follows

$$k\,dt = \frac{dx}{(a - x)(b - x)} \qquad (11.10)$$

that is, we have rewritten it so that the left-hand side contains only terms involving t whereas the right-hand side contains only terms involving x so that we have separated the variables. Equations of this type are described as *variables separable* and can be solved by integrating both sides. Applying the methods of section 3.2.5 to equation 11.10 gives

$$kt = \int \frac{dx}{(a - x)(b - x)} = \frac{1}{(a - b)} \ln \frac{(a - x)}{(b - x)} + C \qquad (11.11)$$

C is usually obtained by assuming that at $t = 0$, $x = 0$.

In general, the variables-separable equation can be rewritten in the form

$$g(y) \frac{dy}{dx} = h(x) \qquad (11.12)$$

that is

$$g(y)dy = h(x)dx$$

which can be integrated to give

$$\int g(y)dy = \int h(x)dx \qquad (11.13)$$

Example

$$x \cos y - e^{-x} \sec y \frac{dy}{dx} = 0 \qquad (11.14)$$

Rearranging gives

$$\sec^2 y\, dy = x\, e^x\, dx$$

that is

$$\tan y = \int x\, e^x\, dx \qquad (11.15)$$

which can be integrated by parts (see section 3.2.4).

11.2.3 Homogeneous Equations

A function $f(x,y)$ is said to be homogeneous of degree n if

$$f(\lambda x, \lambda y) = \lambda^n f(x,y) \qquad (11.16)$$

For example, the function $x^4 - x^3 y$ is homogeneous and of degree 4 since

$$f(\lambda x, \lambda y) = (\lambda x)^4 - (\lambda x)^3 (\lambda y) = \lambda^4 (x^4 - x^3 y) = \lambda^4 f(x,y)$$

whereas the function $x^4 - x^3 + y^2$ is not homogeneous

$$f(\lambda x, \lambda y) = (\lambda x)^4 - (\lambda x)^3 + (\lambda y)^2 \neq \lambda^n f(x,y)$$

A *homogeneous first-order differential equation* is of the form

$$A(x,y)dx + B(x,y)dy = 0 \qquad (11.17)$$

where $A(x,y)$ and $B(x,y)$ are homogeneous functions of the same degree; that is

$$A(\lambda x, \lambda y) = \lambda^n A(x,y)$$

and

$$B(\lambda x, \lambda y) = \lambda^n B(x,y)$$

Such equations can often be reduced to the variables-separable type by the substitution $y = vx$.

Example

$$\frac{dy}{dx} = \frac{9x^2 + 2xy + 3y^2}{2x(x + y)} \qquad (11.18)$$

is homogeneous of degree two.

Applying the chain rule to $y = vx$ gives

$$\frac{dy}{dx} = x\frac{dv}{dx} + v$$

and eliminating y and dy/dx from equation 11.18 gives

$$x\frac{dv}{dx} = \frac{9 + v^2}{2 + 2v} \qquad (11.19)$$

which is now of the variables-separable type. Separation of the variables gives

$$\frac{dx}{x} = \frac{2(1 + v)}{9 + v^2}\,dv$$

which on integration by the methods of section 3.2.5 yields

$$\ln x = \ln(9 + v^2) + \frac{2}{3}\tan^{-1}\frac{v}{3} + C$$

The general solution is obtained by substituting for v to give

$$\ln x = \ln\left(9 + \frac{y^2}{x^2}\right) + \frac{2}{3}\tan^{-1}\frac{y}{3x} + C$$

11.2.4 Exact differential equations

In section 4.5 we discussed the exact differential and said that the differential

$$M(x,y)dx + N(x,y)dy \qquad (11.20)$$

is exact if

$$\frac{\partial M(x,y)}{\partial y} = \frac{\partial N(x,y)}{\partial x} \qquad (11.21)$$

The consequence of this is that some function $z = f(x,y)$ exists such that

$$\frac{\partial z}{\partial x} = M(x,y); \ \frac{\partial z}{\partial y} = N(x,y) \qquad (11.22)$$

If we have the differential equation

$$M(x,y)dx + N(x,y)dy = 0 \tag{11.23}$$

and the left-hand side is an exact differential dz, then dz is zero and f(x,y) is a constant. The solution of this equation is equivalent to the determination of the function f(x,y). Often this can be done by inspection; for example

$$(4x^3y^3 - 2xy)dx + (3x^4y^2 - x^2)dy = 0 \tag{11.24}$$

Here

$$\frac{\partial z}{\partial x} = 4x^3y^3 - 2xy, \quad \frac{\partial z}{\partial y} = 3x^4y^2 - x^2 \tag{11.25}$$

and we see at once that

$$z = x^4y^3 - x^2y \tag{11.26}$$

Thus the solution to the equation is

$$x^4y^3 - x^2y = C \tag{11.27}$$

We can proceed more formally as follows. Given

$$M(x,y)dx + N(x,y)dy = 0 \tag{11.28}$$

we are looking for a function z = f(x,y) such that

$$\frac{\partial z}{\partial x} = M(x,y) \quad \text{and} \quad \frac{\partial z}{\partial y} = N(x,y) \tag{11.29}$$

Let us integrate with respect to x

$$z(x,y) = \int M(x,y)dx + \phi(y) \tag{11.30}$$

since z is a function of two variables, the 'constant' of integration will be a function of y. To determine $\phi(y)$, we now consider the y derivative of z

$$N(x,y) = \frac{\partial z}{\partial y} = \frac{\partial}{\partial y}\left[\int M(x,y)dx + \phi(y)\right] \tag{11.31}$$

This enables us to find $\phi(y)$ and hence the function z.

Example

$$(y^2e^{xy^2} + 4x^3)dx + (2xye^{xy^2} - 3y^2)dy = 0 \tag{11.32}$$

$$z(x,y) = \int(y^2e^{xy^2} + 4x^3)dx + \phi(y)$$

$$= e^{xy^2} + x^4 + \phi(y) \tag{11.33}$$

But $\partial z/\partial y$ must be equal to $2xy\,e^{xy^2} - 3y^2$. From equation 11.33 $\partial z/\partial y = 2xy\,e^{xy^2} + (d\phi/dy)$ and hence $d\phi/dy$ must be equal to $-3y^2$ and $\phi = -y^3$. Thus

$$z(x,y) = \exp(xy^2) + x^4 - y^3 \tag{11.34}$$

and the general solution to equation 11.32 is

$$\exp(xy^2) + x^4 - y^3 = C \tag{11.35}$$

Differential equations occurring in practice are rarely exact but can often easily be transformed into exact equations by the use of integrating factors. For example, the equation

$$\frac{dy}{y} + \left(\frac{1}{x} - \frac{x}{y}\right)dx = 0 \qquad (11.36)$$

is not exact but multiplication by xy gives

$$x\,dy + (y - x^2)dx = 0 \qquad (11.37)$$

which is now exact and can be solved by inspection to give the general solution

$$\left(xy - \frac{x^3}{3}\right) = C \qquad (11.38)$$

In some cases the integrating factor can be found by inspection by trying a few simple cases, but rules do exist for more difficult cases.

11.2.5 Linear equations

A particularly important type of differential equation is the *linear equation*, which has the general form

$$\frac{dy}{dx} + P(x)y = Q(x) \qquad (11.39)$$

Equation 11.2 describing two consecutive first-order reactions is of this type. The standard technique for solving the linear equation is to find an integrating factor $u(x)$ that will transform $dy + P(x)y\,dx$ into an exact differential. Thus we require

$$u(x)dy + P(x)u(x)y\,dx \qquad (11.40)$$

to be an exact differential so that there is some function $z = f(x,y)$ such that

$$\frac{\partial z}{\partial x} = P(x)u(x)y \quad \text{and} \quad \frac{\partial z}{\partial y} = u(x) \qquad (11.41)$$

Applying the criterion for an exact differential we get

$$\frac{\partial u(x)}{\partial x} = \frac{\partial}{\partial y}\left[P(x)u(x)y\right] \qquad (11.42)$$

that is

$$\frac{\partial u(x)}{\partial x} = P(x)u(x)$$

Hence

$$\frac{1}{u}\frac{\partial u}{\partial x} = P(x)$$

$$\frac{d}{dx}\ln u(x) = P(x)$$

$$\ln u(x) = \int P(x)dx$$

and

$$u(x) = \exp(\int P(x)dx) \tag{11.43}$$

Thus the equation becomes

$$\exp(\int P(x)dx)\frac{dy}{dx} + P(x)y\exp(\int P(x)dx) = Q(x)\exp(\int P(x)dx) \tag{11.44}$$

The left-hand side is the differential of $y \exp(\int P(x)dx)$ and the equation becomes

$$\frac{d}{dx}\left[y\exp(\int P(x)dx)\right] = Q(x)\exp(\int P(x)dx) \tag{11.45}$$

which can be solved by integrating both sides to give

$$y\exp(\int P(x)dx) = \int Q(x)\exp(\int P(x)dx)dx \tag{11.46}$$

We shall now apply this technique to the differential equation for successive first-order reactions. Consider the process $A \xrightarrow{k_1} B \xrightarrow{k_2} C$ in which the concentrations of A, B and C at time t are a, b and c, respectively, and the rate constants for the two reactions are k_1 and k_2. The rate of disappearance of A is given by

$$\frac{da}{dt} = -k_1 a \tag{11.47}$$

which has the solution

$$a = a_0 e^{-k_1 t} \tag{11.48}$$

where a_0 is the concentration of A at time t = 0. The rate of change of the concentration of B is given by

$$\frac{db}{dt} = k_1 a - k_2 b = k_1 a_0 \exp(-k_1 t) - k_2 b \tag{11.49}$$

$$\frac{db}{dt} + k_2 b = k_1 a_0 \exp(-k_1 t)$$

Multiplying by the integrating factor $\exp(\int k_2 dt) = \exp(k_2 t)$ gives

$$\exp(k_2 t)\frac{db}{dt} + k_2 b\exp(k_2 t) = k_1 a_0 \exp(k_2 - k_1)t \tag{11.50}$$

which can be rewritten as

$$\frac{d}{dt}\left[b\exp(k_2 t)\right] = k_1 a_0 \exp\left[(k_2 - k_1)t\right] \tag{11.51}$$

Therefore

$$b\exp(k_2 t) = \frac{k_1 a_0}{k_2 - k_1}\exp\left[(k_2 - k_1)t\right] + C \tag{11.52}$$

and applying the initial condition that at t = 0, b = 0 leads to the solution

$$b = \frac{k_1 a_0}{k_2 - k_1}\left[\exp(-k_1 t) - \exp(-k_2 t)\right] \tag{11.53}$$

The equation

$$(x - 2)\frac{dy}{dx} = y + 2(x - 2)^3 \quad (11.54)$$

is linear as can be seen by rearranging it to give

$$\frac{dy}{dx} - \frac{y}{x - 2} = 2(x - 2)^2 \quad (11.55)$$

In this case the integrating factor is

$$\exp\left(\int - \frac{dx}{x - 2}\right) = e^{-\ln(x-2)} = \frac{1}{x - 2} \quad (11.56)$$

and the equation becomes

$$\left(\frac{1}{x - 2}\right)\frac{dy}{dx} - \frac{y}{(x - 2)^2} = 2(x - 2) \quad (11.57)$$

that is

$$\frac{d}{dx}\left(\frac{y}{x - 2}\right) = 2(x - 2)$$

Therefore

$$\frac{y}{x - 2} = (x - 2)^2 + C$$

and

$$y = (x - 2)^3 + C(x - 2) \quad (11.58)$$

Our work on first-order linear equations will form a foundation for the discussion of second-order linear equations.

11.3 FIRST-ORDER EQUATIONS OF HIGHER DEGREE

These are of little importance in chemistry and will not be discussed here.

11.4 LINEAR SECOND-ORDER DIFFERENTIAL EQUATIONS

These equations have the general form

$$\frac{d^2y}{dx^2} + p(x)\frac{dy}{dx} + q(x)y = f(x) \quad (11.59)$$

If $f(x) = 0$, the equation is termed *homogeneous*, whereas equations with $f(x) \neq 0$ are *inhomogeneous*. Here we shall be concerned only with the case in which $p(x)$ and $q(x)$ are constants, that is with linear equations and constant coefficients. The case of non-constant coefficients is more difficult and the reader is referred to more advanced texts, for example Stephenson (1973), chapter 22.

Before considering the solution of the second-order equation, let us look again at the first-order case. Consider the equations

$$\frac{dy}{dx} + ay = f(x) \qquad (11.60)$$

$$\frac{dy}{dx} + ay = 0 \qquad (11.61)$$

that is, the inhomogeneous and homogeneous cases.

Equation 11.60 has the solution

$$y = e^{-ax} \int f(x)e^{ax}\, dx + Ce^{-ax} \qquad (11.62)$$

whereas equation 11.61 has the solution

$$y = Ce^{-ax} \qquad (11.63)$$

Thus the solution to the inhomogeneous equation consists of the general solution to the homogeneous or *reduced equation* plus another term, which is a *particular solution* (the solution with C = 0) to the inhomogeneous equation. The general solution to the reduced equation is called the *complementary function*. This is also true for second-order equations so we can write

general solution = particular solution
+ complementary function

Thus the solution of a linear second-order inhomogeneous differential equation with constant coefficients involves two processes: the solution of the reduced equation and the determination of a particular integral.

11.4.1 Solution of the homogeneous equation

We consider first the equation

$$\frac{d^2y}{dx^2} + a\frac{dy}{dx} + by = 0 \qquad (11.64)$$

and introduce the symbol D to represent the differential operator d/dx. Thus we can rewrite the equation as

$$D^2y + aDy + by = 0 \qquad (11.65)$$

We can envisage factorising this by the methods of elementary algebra to give

$$(D - k_1)(D - k_2)y = 0 \qquad (11.66)$$

Remembering that D is an operator, expansion gives

$$D^2y - (k_1 + k_2)Dy + k_1k_2y = 0 \qquad (11.67)$$

and we see that k_1 and k_2 are the roots of the *auxiliary equation*

$$k^2 + ak + b = 0 \qquad (11.68)$$

The general solution to the homogeneous equation for $k_1 \neq k_2$

is

$$y = C_1 \exp(k_1 x) + C_2 \exp(k_2 x) \tag{11.69}$$

where C_1 and C_2 are arbitrary constants. This is a result that can be remembered easily and verified by substitution. However, the solution is obtained as follows. Let

$$(D - k_2)y = z \tag{11.70}$$

where z is some function of x. We can rewrite the original equation as

$$(D - k_1)z = 0 \tag{11.71}$$

that is

$$\frac{dz}{dx} - k_1 z = 0$$

which has the general solution

$$z = C \exp(k_1 x) \tag{11.72}$$

Thus equation 11.70 becomes

$$\frac{dy}{dx} - k_2 y = C \exp(k_1 x) \tag{11.73}$$

which is a first-order linear equation that can be solved by the integrating-factor method. Multiplying by the integrating factor $\exp(\int -k_2\, dx)$ gives, for $k_1 \neq k_2$

$$\exp(-k_2 x)\frac{dy}{dx} - k_2 \exp(-k_2 x)y = C \exp[(k_1 - k_2)x] \tag{11.74}$$

which yields on integration

$$y \exp(-k_2 x) = \frac{C \exp[(k_1 - k_2)x]}{k_1 - k_2} + D \tag{11.75}$$

that is

$$y = \frac{C}{k_1 - k_2} \exp(k_1 x) + D \exp(k_2 x)$$

which is of the form

$$y = C_1 \exp(k_1 x) + C_2 \exp(k_2 x) \tag{11.76}$$

If $k_1 = k_2$, equation 11.74 becomes

$$\exp(-k_2 x)\frac{dy}{dx} - k_2 \exp(-k_2 x)y = C \tag{11.77}$$

and integration gives

$$y \exp(-k_2 x) = Cx + D$$

that is

$$y = Cx \exp(k_2 x) + D \exp(k_2 x) \tag{11.78}$$

These results are compeltely general and cover the cases of k_1, k_2 real and complex

Example

$$\frac{d^2y}{dx^2} + 4\frac{dy}{dx} - 5y = 0$$

that is

$$D^2y + 4Dy - 5y = 0 \qquad (11.79)$$

can be factorised as

$$(D + 5)(D - 1)y = 0 \qquad (11.80)$$

and has the general solution

$$y = c_1e^{-5x} + c_2e^{x} \qquad (11.81)$$

However, if we have the equation

$$D^2y + 4Dy + 5y = 0 \qquad (11.82)$$

the roots of the auxiliary equation

$$k^2 + 4k + 5 = 0 \qquad (11.83)$$

are now complex, namely

$$k = \frac{-4 \pm \sqrt{(16 - 20)}}{2} = -2 \pm i \qquad (11.84)$$

and the general solution to equation 11.82 is

$$y = c_1e^{(-2+i)x} + c_2e^{(-2-i)x}$$

$$= e^{-2x}(c_1e^{ix} + c^2e^{-ix}) \qquad (11.85)$$

Recalling the Euler relation from section 7.5

$$e^{ix} = \cos x + i \sin x \qquad (11.86)$$

we see that the solution can be rewritten

$$y = e^{-2x}[(c_1 + c_2)\cos x + (c_1 - c_2)i \sin x] \qquad (11.87)$$

that is, the solution is of the form

$$y = e^{-2x}[d_1 \cos x + d_2 \sin x] \qquad (11.88)$$

where d_1 and d_2 are new arbitrary constants.

Summarising, we have three cases:

1. $k_1 \neq k_2$ (real)

   general solution $= c_1 \exp(k_1x) + c_2 \exp(k_2x)$

2. $k_1 = k_2 = k$ (real)

   general solution $= c_1xe^{kx} + c_2e^{kx}$

3. $k_1 \neq k_2$ (complex) $k_1 = \alpha + i\omega$

$k_2 = \alpha - i\omega$

general solution $y = e^{\alpha x}(c_1 \cos \omega x + c_2 \sin \omega x)$

Important physical applications of this type of equation include simple and damped harmonic motion and a.c. circuits.

(i) Simple harmonic motion

This is motion under a restoring force which is proportional to the displacement from the equilibrium position. The acceleration d^2x/dt^2 of a particle of mass m undergoing simple harmonic motion (S.H.M.) is related to the displacement from equilibrium by the equation

$$\frac{d^2x}{dt^2} = -\omega^2 x \qquad (11.89)$$

where $\omega^2 = k/m$ and k is called the *force* constant, that is

$$\frac{d^2x}{dt^2} + \omega^2 x = 0$$

which can be factorised to give

$$\left(\frac{d}{dt} + i\omega\right)\left(\frac{d}{dt} - i\omega\right)x = 0 \qquad (11.90)$$

This is an example of category 3 and the general solution is thus

$$x = e^0(c_1 \cos \omega t + c_2 \sin \omega t)$$

that is

$$x = c_1 \cos \omega t + c_2 \sin \omega t \qquad (11.91)$$

The parameters c_1 and c_2 can be chosen to fit initial conditions, for example at t = 0, x = a and dx/dt = 0 for a particle starting with velocity 0 at a displacement a from the origin to give

$$x = a \cos \omega t \qquad (11.92)$$

(ii) Damped harmonic motion

If, in addition to the restoring force $-\omega^2 x$, there is a damping force proportional to the velocity, we have the equation

$$\frac{d^2x}{dt^2} + 2b\frac{dx}{dt} + \omega^2 x = 0 \qquad (11.93)$$

This is a particularly interesting equation because there are different types of solution depending on the relative values of b and ω. The auxiliary equation is

$$k^2 + 2bk + \omega^2 = 0 \qquad (11.94)$$

and has the solution

$$k = -b \pm \surd(b^2 - \omega^2) \qquad (11.95)$$

There are three cases

A. $b \neq \omega$, $b > \omega$

In this case k_1 and k_2 are real and we have the solution

$$x = e^{-bt}\{c_1 \exp[\surd(b^2 - \omega^2)t] + c_2\exp[-\surd(b^2 - \omega^2)t]\} \qquad (11.96)$$

Since $b > \omega$, $\surd(b^2 - \omega^2) < b$ and therefore both terms decay exponentially with time t.

B. $b \neq \omega$, $b < \omega$

Here k_1 and k_2 are complex. If we denote $\surd(\omega^2 - b^2)$ by ω' the solution is

$$x = e^{-bt}(c_1 \cos \omega' t + c_2 \sin \omega' t) \qquad (11.97)$$

Using the formula for $\sin(A + B)$ we can rewrite $c_1 \cos \omega' t + c_2 \sin \omega' t$ as $\surd(c_1^2 + c_2^2)\sin(\omega' t + \delta)$, where δ is $\tan^{-1}(c_2/c_1)$; that is

$$x = e^{-bt}\surd(c_1^2 + c_2^2)\sin(\omega' t + \delta) \qquad (11.98)$$

Thus in this case we have the superposition of an exponential decay on an oscillatory function.

C. $b = \omega$

If b is equal to ω the general solution is

$$x = c_1 te^{-bt} + c_2 e^{-bt} \qquad (11.99)$$

and the motion is not oscillatory but is said to be *critically damped*.

These three types of behaviour are illustrated in figure 11.1 for the initial conditions $x = 1$, $dx/dt = 0$ at $t = 0$.

This approach can be applied to homogeneous linear differential equations with constant coefficients of higher order than two. If we have

$$D^n y + a_1 D^{n-1} y + \ldots a_{n-1} Dy + a_n y = 0 \qquad (11.100)$$

which can be factorised into

$$(D - k_1)(D - k_2) \ldots (D - k_n)y = 0 \qquad (11.101)$$

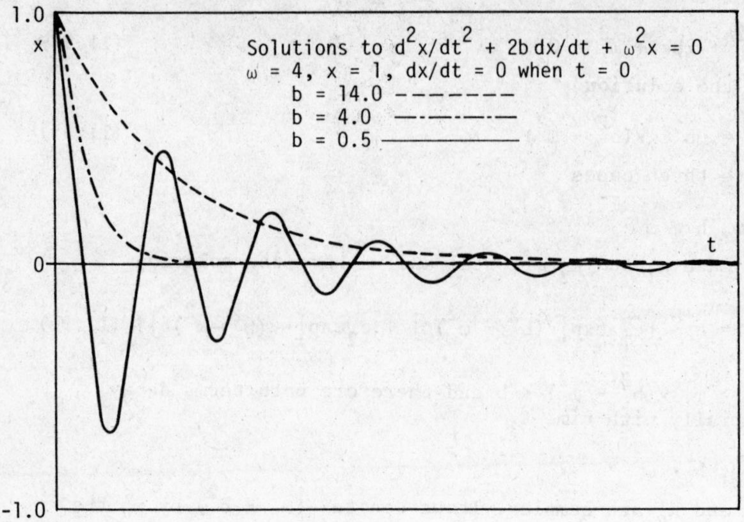

Figure 11.1

where all the k_i are distinct, the general solution is

$$y = \sum_{i=0}^{n} c_i \exp(k_i x) \qquad (11.102)$$

For repeated roots, for example one root k_i repeated g times, we have a term of the form

$$c_i(1 + d_1 x + d_2 x^2 + \ldots d_{g-1} x^{g-1}) \exp(k_i x) \qquad (11.103)$$

for the repeated root.

11.4.2 Solution of the inhomogeneous equation

The solution of this type of equation is more difficult and we shall only consider a method applicable to fairly straightforward cases. More powerful methods such as the D-operator method or the use of Laplace transforms can be found in more advanced texts. As we discussed at the beginning of this section, the general solution of an equation of this type can be expressed as the sum of the complementary function (the general solution of the reduced equation) and a particular integral. Our task therefore, is to find a particular integral. If, in the equation

$$\frac{d^2y}{dx^2} + a\frac{dy}{dx} + by = f(x) \qquad (11.104)$$

the function f(x) is a polynomial, an exponential or a combination of sines and cosines, a particular solution can be found fairly easily by the *method of undetermined coefficients*.

(i) f(x) is a polynomial

For example

$$(D^2 - 7D - 5)y = x^3 - 1 \tag{11.105}$$

The technique is to try the polynomial

$$px^3 + qx^2 + rx + s$$

and to determine coefficients p, q, r, s such that the polynomial will be a particular solution of the equation. Thus

$$D(px^3 + qx^2 + rx + s) = 3px^2 + 2qx + r$$

$$D^2(px^3 + qx^2 + rx + s) = 6px + 2q$$

Therefore

$$\begin{aligned}(D^2 - 7D - 5)(px^3 + qx^2 + rx + s)\\ = -5px^3 - x^2(21p + 5q) + x(6p - 14q - 5r)\\ + (2q - 7r - 5s)\end{aligned} \tag{11.106}$$

We now determine p, q, r and s by equating the right-hand sides of equations 11.105 and 11.106 to give simultaneous equations

$$\left.\begin{aligned} -5p &= 1\\ -21p - 5q &= 0\\ 6p - 14q - 5r &= C\\ 2q - 7r - 5s &= -1 \end{aligned}\right\} \tag{11.107}$$

which have the solution

$$p = -\frac{1}{5}, \quad q = \frac{21}{5}, \quad r = -\frac{324}{125}, \quad s = \frac{2603}{625}$$

If we have an equation of the type

$$D^2y + aDy = f(x) \tag{11.108}$$

we have to take a polynomial of one degree higher. For example, in the case of

$$(D^2 - 7D)y = x^3 - 1 \tag{11.109}$$

we would have to consider the polynomial

$$nx^4 + px^3 + qx^2 + rx + s$$

and apply the same technique to determine the coefficients. In this case, however, s will be indeterminate.

(ii) f(x) is an exponential

For the equation

$$(D^2 + aD + b)y = Me^{mx} \tag{11.110}$$

three cases exist:

(1) If e^{mx} does not occur in the complementary function, we take Ae^{mx} as the trial particular integral and determine A as before.

(2) If e^{mx} does occur in the complementary function, taking this for the trial particular integral would not add anything to the solution. In this case we try Axe^{mx}.

(3) If m is the double root of the auxiliary equation, the complementary function will be of the form $c_1e^{mx} + c_2xe^{mx}$ so in order to get a new contribution we have to consider Ax^2e^{mx} as our trial particular integral. For example

$$(D^2 + 4D + 4)y = 2e^{2x} \tag{11.111}$$

$$CF = c_1e^{-2x} + c_2xe^{-2x}$$

so we take Ae^{2x} as our trial particular integral. Thus we have

$$(D^2 + 4D + 4)Ae^{2x} = (4 + 8 + 4)Ae^{2x}$$

$$= 16Ae^{2x} \tag{11.112}$$

Equating the right-hand sides of equations 11.111 and 11.112 gives A = 1/8 and the general solution is then

$$y = c_1e^{-2x} + c_2xe^{-2x} + \frac{1}{8}e^{2x} \tag{11.113}$$

However, if we had considered

$$(D^2 + 4D + 4)y = 2e^{-2x} \tag{11.114}$$

taking Ae^{-2x} as our trial particular integral would have yielded zero for $(D^2 + 4D + 4)Ae^{-2x}$ because e^{-2x} is already contained in the complementary function. Instead we try Ax^2e^{-2x}, which gives

$$(D^2 + 4D + 4)Ax^2e^{-2x} = 2Ae^{-2x} \tag{11.115}$$

Thus A = 1 and the general solution is

$$y = c_1e^{-2x} + c_2xe^{-2x} + 2x^2e^{-2x} \tag{11.116}$$

(iii) f(x) is a combination of sines and cosines

If f(x) = P cos nx + Q sin nx we should try A cos nx + B sin nx unless cos nx and sin nx occur in the complementary function, in which case we should try x(A cos nx + B sin nx). For example

$$(D^2 + 1)y = 3\cos 3x - \sin 3x \tag{11.117}$$

The complementary function is $c_1\cos x + c_2\sin x$, so we can take A cos 3x + B sin 3x as our trial function

$$(D^2 + 1)(A \cos 3x + B \sin 3x) = -(8A \cos 3x + 8B \sin 3x) \quad (11.118)$$

Thus A = -3/8 and B = 1/8 and the general solution is

$$y = c_1 \cos x + c_2 \sin x - \frac{3}{8} \cos 3x + \frac{1}{8} \sin 3x \quad (111.19)$$

If, on the other hand, we have the equation

$$(D^2 + 1)y = 3 \cos x - \sin x \quad (11.120)$$

we would have to try x(A cos x + B sin x) as the trial function. Thus

$$(D^2 + 1)\left[x(A \cos x + B \sin x)\right] = -2A \sin x + 2B \cos x \quad (11.121)$$

Thus A = -3/2, B = -1/2 and the general solution is

$$y = c_1 \cos x + c_2 \sin x - x\left(\frac{3}{2} \cos x + \frac{1}{2} \sin x\right) \quad (11.122)$$

These methods can also be applied when f(x) is a combination of the types of function mentioned above. For example

$$\frac{d^2y}{dx^2} - 5\frac{dy}{dx} + 6y = 6x + \sin x \quad (11.123)$$

that is

$$(D - 2)(D - 3)y = 6x + \sin x$$

The complementary function is $c_1e^{-2x} + c_2e^{3x}$ and we can therefore take a trial particular integral of the form ax + b + c sin x + d cos x

$$(D^2 - 5D + 6)(ax + b + c \sin x + d \cos x)$$
$$= 5(c + d)\sin x + 5(d - c)\cos x + 6ax + (6b - 5c) \quad (11.124)$$

On comparing the right-hand sides of equations 11.123 and 11.124 we find that a = 1, b = 5/6, c = d = 1/10, and hence the general solution is

$$y = c_1e^{-2x} + c_2e^{3x} + x + \frac{5}{6} + \frac{1}{10}(\sin x + \cos x) \quad (11.125)$$

The equation

$$\frac{d^2x}{dt^2} + \frac{a\,dx}{dt} + bx = c \cos \alpha t \quad (11.126)$$

is of importance physically in the theory of forced oscillations in mechanical and electrical systems. Consider, for example, an atomic system of polarisability α in which an electric field **E** induces a dipole moment **μ** = α**E**. Classically we can consider an electron of charge $-e$ performing damped harmonic motion about an equilibrium position at which there is a charge $+e$, and subject the system to an alternating electric field of strength $\mathbf{E} = \mathbf{E}_0 \cos \omega t$. The classical equation of motion is

$$m \frac{d^2r}{dt^2} + b \frac{dr}{dt} + kr = -eE_0 \cos \omega t \tag{11.127}$$

From equation 11.97 we see that the complementary function is

$$\exp(-bt/2m) \left[c_1 \exp\left\{ \sqrt{\left[\left(\frac{b}{2m}\right)^2 - \left(\frac{k}{m}\right)^2\right]} t \right\} + c_2 \exp\left\{ -\sqrt{\left[\left(\frac{b}{2m}\right)^2 - \left(\frac{k}{m}\right)^2\right]} t \right\} \right] \tag{11.128}$$

(provided that $b/2m \neq k/m$). For the particular integral we look for a solution of the type $A \cos \omega t + B \sin \omega t$. Thus

$$\left(m\frac{d^2}{dt^2} + b \frac{d}{dt} + k \right) (A \cos \omega t + B \sin \omega t)$$
$$= (k - m\omega^2)(A \cos \omega t + B \sin \omega t) + b\omega(-A \sin \omega t + B \cos \omega t) \tag{11.129}$$

Comparing the coefficients of $\cos \omega t$ and $\sin \omega t$ with the right-hand side of equation 11.127 leads to

$$\left. \begin{aligned} A &= \frac{-eE_0(k - m\omega^2)}{(k - m\omega^2)^2 + b^2\omega^2} \\ B &= \frac{-eE_0 b\omega}{(k - m\omega^2)^2 + b^2\omega^2} \end{aligned} \right\} \tag{11.130}$$

When a reasonable time has elapsed, the contribution to the solution from equation 11.128 will be insignificant; that is the amplitude of the oscillation of the electron will have become constant and the value of r can reasonably be represented as

$$r = A \cos \omega t + B \sin \omega t \tag{11.131}$$

The induced dipole moment will be given by

$$\mu = er \tag{11.132}$$

and the polarisability α is obtained by dividing by E_0. For further details we refer the reader to Kauzmann (1957), page 568.

11.5 PROBLEMS FOR SOLUTION

1. Find the general solutions of the following differential equations:

(i) $x \dfrac{dy}{dx} = \tan y$; (ii) $\dfrac{dy}{dx} = \dfrac{2xy}{x^2 + 1}$;

(iii) $(1 + y)dx - (1 + x)dy = 0$; (iv) $(x^2 - y^2)\frac{dy}{dx} = xy$;

(v) $(2x - y)\frac{dy}{dx} = 2y - x$;

(vi) $2x(y \exp x^2 - 1)dx + \exp(x^2)dy = 0$;

(vii) $(6x^5y^3 + 4x^3y^5)dx + (3x^6y^2 + 5x^4y^4)dy = 0$

(viii) $\frac{dy}{dx} + \frac{y}{x} = x^2$; (ix) $\frac{dy}{dx} + 2xy = \exp(-x^2)$;

(x) $\frac{dy}{dx} + y \cot x = 5e^{\cos x}$; (xi) $x^3 \frac{dy}{dx} + (2 - 3x^2)y = x^3$.

2. In a certain culture of bacteria, the rate of increase is proportional to the number present at that time.

(i) If it is found that the number doubles in 4 hours, how many may be expected at the end of 12 hours?

(ii) If there are 10^4 at the end of 3 hours and 4×10^4 at the end of 5 hours, how many were there at the beginning?

3. For a second-order reaction $2A \rightarrow C + D$ the rate of reaction is given by

$$\frac{dx}{dt} = k(a - x)^2$$

where a is the initial concentration of A and x is the concentration of C (and D) at time t. Solve the differential equation to give x as a function of t. What is the half life $t_{1/2}$ such that the concentration of A has fallen to half the initial value when the time $t = t_{1/2}$?

4. ^{140}Ba decays to give ^{140}La, which subsequently decays to ^{140}Ce

$$^{140}Ba \rightarrow {}^{140}La + \beta \text{ (half life 12 days)}$$

$$^{140}La \rightarrow {}^{140}Ce \text{ (stable)} + \beta \text{ (half life 10 hours)}$$

Calculate the decay constants λ_{Ba} and λ_{La}. If the initial concentration of ^{140}Ba is 1000 units and the initial concentration of ^{140}La is zero, calculate the concentration of ^{140}Ba after 20 days, and the concentrations of ^{140}La after 10 hours and after 20 days.

(U.W.)

5. In a circuit containing inductance L and resistance R, the current i at time t is given by Helmholtz's equation

$$L\frac{di}{dt} + Ri = E(t)$$

where $E(t)$ is the electromotive force.

(i) Solve this for i when $E(t) = E_0$ (a constant) and the initial current is i_0.

(ii) Find i when $E(t)$ is given by

$$E(t) = \sin \omega t$$

where ω is a constant.

6. In the reversible second-order reaction

$$A + B \rightleftharpoons 2C$$

if the initial concentrations of A and B are 1 and 2, respectively, the rate of formation of C is given by

$$\frac{dx}{dt} = k_1(1 - x)(2 - x) - k_2x^2$$

where x is the concentration of C at time t and k_1 and k_2 are constants. Given that at $t = 0$, $x = 0$ and at equilibrium (that is, when $dx/dt = 0$), $x = 1/2$, derive a relation between time and concentration.

(U.W.)

7. The differential equation

$$\frac{dx}{dt} = k_1(a - x) - k_2x^2$$

in which k_1, k_2 and a are constants, describes the rate of a reversible reaction in which the forward reaction is first order and the backward reaction is second order. Given that at $t = 0$, $x = 0$, find t as a function of x.

8. In the irreversible third-order reaction

$$A + B + C \rightarrow D$$

the rate of formation of D is given by

$$\frac{dx}{dt} = k(a - x)(b - x)(c - x)$$

where x is the concentration of D at time t; a, b and c are the initial concentrations of A, B and C, and k is a constant. Given that $x = 0$ at $t = 0$, find t as a function of x.

9. Solve the differential equations:

(i) $\dfrac{d^2y}{dx^2} + \dfrac{dy}{dx} - 6y = 0$; (ii) $(D^2 - 2D - 3)y = 0$;

(iii) $(D^2 + 4)y = 0$; (iv) $(D^2 + 4D + 4)y = 0$;

(v) $(D^2 - 2D + 10)y = 0$; (vi) $\dfrac{d^2y}{dx^2} + 2\dfrac{dy}{dx} + 5y = 0$.

10. A spring with force constant $k = 48\ \mathrm{N\ m^{-1}}$ hangs vertically with its upper end fixed. A mass of 16 kg is attached to its lower end. After coming to rest the mass is pulled down 0.04 m and released. Derive a relationship between the displacement of the mass from the rest position and time.

11. If, in the above problem, the velocity at time t is v and the mass is subject to a retarding force of

(i) v/64 N and (ii) 64v N

derive relationships between displacement and time.

12. Find particular solutions of the differential equations:

(i) $(D^2 + 4)y = \cos 3x + 3 \sin 3x$;

(ii) $(D^2 + 4)y = \cos 2x + 3 \sin 2x$;

(iii) $(D^2 + 3D - 4)y = \sin 2x$;

(iv) $(2D^2 + 2D + 3)y = x^2 + 2x - 1$;

(v) $(D^2 + 3D)y = x^4 + 3x^2 - 1$;

(vi) $(D^2 - 3D + 2)y = 5e^{3x}$;

(vii) $(D^2 + 4D + 4)y = e^{-2x}$;

(viii) $(D^2 + 3D + 2)y = 3e^{-x}$.

13. Find *general* solutions of the following differential equations:

(i) $D^2y - Dy - 2y = e^{2x}$;

(ii) $5D^2y + 2Dy + y = 2x + 3$;

(iii) $D^2y - 4Dy - 5y = \cos x$;

(iv) $D^2y + 4Dy + 5y = 40 \sin 3x$;

(v) $D^2y - 2Dy + y = \cos x + \sin x$.

14. In a circuit in which a generator producing a voltage $E_0 \sin \alpha t$ is connected through a condenser of capacitance C, a wire of resistance R and a coil of inductance L in series, the charge q on the condenser at time t is given by the equation

$$L\frac{d^2q}{dt^2} + R\frac{dq}{dt} + \frac{q}{C} = E_0 \sin \alpha t$$

Derive an expression for the charge q as a function of time. Regard L, R, C, E_0 and α as constants.

(U.W.)

12

Partial Differential Equations

In the previous chapter as an example of partial differential equation, we referred to the Schrödinger equation

$$\frac{\partial^2\psi}{\partial x^2} + \frac{\partial^2\psi}{\partial y^2} + \frac{\partial^2\psi}{\partial z^2} + \frac{8\pi^2 m}{h^2}(E - V)\psi = 0 \qquad (12.1)$$

where $\psi(x,y,z)$ is the wavefunction, m is the mass of the particle, h is Planck's constant, E is the total energy and V is the potential energy. We consider the solution of partial differential equations in this chapter. These equations can be approached from a formal mathematical viewpoint but for the physical scientist this is not particularly useful. We consider here the method of *separation of variables*, which can often lead to physically useful solutions. We shall illustrate the method with the wave equation and then consider the Schrödinger equation.

12.1 THE WAVE EQUATION

The vibration of a string, for example, is described by the *wave equation*

$$v^2 \frac{\partial^2\psi}{\partial x^2} - \frac{\partial^2\psi}{\partial t^2} = 0 \qquad (12.2)$$

where x is the position along the x-axis, t is the time and ψ is the displacement of the string perpendicular to the x-axis. Let us consider a string of length ℓ when it is unstretched and assume that it is fixed at the points $x = 0$ and $x = \ell$ (figure 12.1) that is

$$\psi(0,t) = \psi(\ell,t) = 0, \quad \text{for} \quad t \geqslant 0 \qquad (12.3)$$

The constant v is given by

$$v = \sqrt{\left(\frac{T}{m}\right)}$$

where T is the tension and m is the mass per unit length. We shall also have to specify the shape of the string when it is released at time $t = 0$. Let this be defined by a function $f(x)$

$$\psi(x,0) = f(x), \quad \text{for} \quad 0 \leqslant x \leqslant \ell \qquad (12.4)$$

We also have to specify the value at $t = 0$ of the derivative of

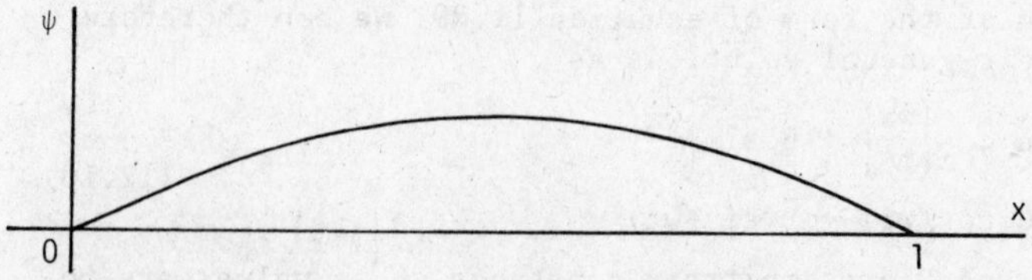

Figure 12.1

ψ with respect to t. Let this be g(x)

$$\left[\frac{\partial\psi}{\partial t}(x,t)\right]_{t=0} = g(x), \quad \text{for} \quad 0 \leqslant x \leqslant \ell \tag{12.5}$$

These are the *boundary conditions*, which will enable us to give a specific solution for a particular set of initial conditions.

The technique of separation of variables assumes that we can write the solution $\psi(x,t)$ as a product of two functions of a single variable, say X(x) and T(t); that is

$$\psi(x,t) = X(x)T(t) \tag{12.6}$$

and uses this assumption to reduce the partial differential equation to two ordinary differential equations, which, hopefully, can be solved by standard techniques. Substituting equation 12.6 into equation 12.2 gives

$$v^2 T(t)\,\frac{\partial^2 X(x)}{\partial x^2} - X(x)\,\frac{\partial^2 T(t)}{\partial t^2} = 0$$

that is

$$v^2\,\frac{1}{X(x)}\,\frac{\partial^2 X(x)}{\partial x^2} = \frac{1}{T(t)}\,\frac{\partial^2 T(t)}{\partial t^2} \tag{12.7}$$

In this equation the left-hand side depends only on x and the right-hand side only on t. Since x and t are independent of each other, each side of this equation must be equal to a constant so we can write

$$\left.\begin{aligned} v^2\,\frac{1}{X(x)}\,\frac{\partial^2 X(x)}{\partial x^2} &= -w^2 \\ \frac{1}{T(t)}\,\frac{\partial^2 T(t)}{\partial t^2} &= -w^2 \end{aligned}\right\} \tag{12.8}$$

where $-w^2$ is the *separation constant*. Thus we have two ordinary differential equations

$$\left.\begin{aligned} v^2\,\frac{1}{X(x)}\,\frac{d^2 X(x)}{dx^2} &= -w^2 \\ \frac{1}{T(x)}\,\frac{d^2 T(t)}{dt^2} &= -w^2 \end{aligned}\right\} \tag{12.9}$$

which are both of the form of equation 11.89. We can therefore write down their general solutions as

$$X(x) = A\cos\left(\frac{wx}{v}\right) + B\sin\left(\frac{wx}{v}\right)$$
$$T(t) = C\cos(wt) + D\sin(wt) \qquad (12.10)$$

where A, B, C and D are arbitrary constants whose values are to be determined from the boundary conditions. The function $\psi(x,t)$ is then given by

$$\psi(x,t) = \left[A\cos\frac{wx}{v} + B\sin\frac{wx}{v}\right]\left[(\cos wt + D\sin wt)\right] \qquad (12.11)$$

The condition that $\psi(0,t) = 0$ gives

$$0 = \left[A\cos 0 + B\sin 0\right]\left[C\cos wt + D\sin wt\right]$$

so $A = 0$. Similarly requiring that $\psi(\ell,t) = 0$ gives

$$0 = B\sin\left(\frac{w\ell}{v}\right)\left[C\cos wt + D\sin wt\right]$$

Since $B = 0$ would give the trivial solution $\psi(x,t) = 0$, we require $\sin(w\ell/v)$ to be zero and hence

$$\frac{w\ell}{v} = n\pi$$

where $n = 1, 2, 3 \ldots$

Thus we have

$$\psi(x,t) = \sin\left(\frac{n\pi x}{\ell}\right)\left[C'\cos wt + D'\sin wt)\right] \qquad (12.12)$$

where $C' = BC$, $D' = BD$. Since n can have an infinite number of values, there is an infinite number of solutions

$$\psi_n(x,t) = \sin\left(\frac{n\pi x}{\ell}\right)\left[C_n\cos wt + D_n\sin wt\right] \qquad (12.13)$$

which satisfy the boundary conditions of equations 12.3. Any linear combination of these functions is also a solution and the problem is now to choose the constants C_n and D_n in such a way as to satisfy the boundary conditions of equations 12.4 and 12.5. When $t = 0$

$$\psi(x,0) = \sum_{r=1}^{\infty}\sin\left(\frac{r\pi x}{\ell}\right)\left[C_r\cos 0 + D_r\sin 0\right]$$

that is

$$\psi(x,0) = \sum_{r=1}^{\infty} C_r\sin\left(\frac{r\pi x}{\ell}\right) = f(x) \qquad (12.14)$$

from equation 12.4. So in order to determine the coefficients C_r we require the Fourier expansion of f(x) in the interval $0 \leqslant x \leqslant \ell$. Similarly the condition of equation 12.5 leads to the following expression for the value of the derivative $\partial\psi/\partial t$ at $t = 0$

$$\left[\frac{\partial\psi(x,t)}{\partial t}\right]_{t=0} = \sum_{r=1}^{\infty} (-C_r \sin wt + D_r \cos wt)\, w \sin\left(\frac{\pi rx}{\ell}\right)\Bigg|_{t=0}$$

$$= \sum_{r=1}^{\infty} D_r w \sin\left(\frac{\pi rx}{\ell}\right) = \frac{\pi v}{\ell}\sum_{r=1}^{\infty} rD_r \sin\left(\frac{\pi rx}{\ell}\right) \qquad (12.15)$$

But this is equal to g(x) so we also require the Fourier expansion

$$g(x) = \frac{\pi v}{\ell}\sum_{r=1}^{\infty} rD_r \sin\left(\frac{\pi rx}{\ell}\right) \qquad (12.16)$$

for the interval $0 \leqslant x \leqslant \ell$. Using the technique of chapter 8, but taking care to change the variable to allow for the interval being from 0 to ℓ, gives the following values for the coefficients C_r and D_r

$$C_r = \frac{2}{\ell}\int_0^{\ell} f(x)\sin\left(\frac{\pi rx}{\ell}\right)dx$$

$$D_r = \frac{2}{r\pi v}\int_0^{\ell} g(x)\sin\left(\frac{\pi rx}{\ell}\right)dx \qquad (12.17)$$

12.2 THE SCHRÖDINGER EQUATION

The potential for a three-dimensional harmonic oscillator is

$$V = \frac{1}{2}k_x x^2 + \frac{1}{2}k_y y^2 + \frac{1}{2}k_z z^2 \qquad (12.18)$$

and the Schrödinger equation for this problem is

$$\frac{\partial^2\psi}{\partial x^2} + \frac{\partial^2\psi}{\partial y^2} + \frac{\partial^2\psi}{\partial z^2} + \frac{8\pi^2 m}{h^2}\left[E - \frac{1}{2}k_x x^2 - \frac{1}{2}k_y y^2 - \frac{1}{2}k_z z^2\right]\psi = 0 \qquad (12.19)$$

Using the separation of variables approach we write the wavefunction $\psi(x,y,z)$ in product form

$$\psi(x,y,z) = X(x)Y(y)Z(z)$$

and substitute into equation 12.19 to give

$$Y(y)Z(z)\frac{\partial^2 X}{\partial x^2} + X(x)Z(z)\frac{\partial^2 Y}{\partial y^2} + X(x)Y(y)\frac{\partial^2 Z}{\partial z^2}$$

$$+ \frac{8\pi^2 m}{h^2}\left[E - \frac{1}{2}k_x x^2 - \frac{1}{2}k_y y^2 - \frac{1}{2}k_z z^2\right]X(x)Y(y)Z(z) = 0$$

Division by $\psi(x,y,z)$ gives

$$\frac{1}{X(x)}\frac{\partial^2 X(x)}{\partial x^2} + \frac{1}{Y(y)}\frac{\partial^2 Y(y)}{\partial y^2} + \frac{1}{Z(z)}\frac{\partial^2 Z(z)}{\partial z^2}$$

$$+ \frac{8\pi^2 m}{h^2}\left[E - \frac{1}{2}k_x x^2 - \frac{1}{2}k_y y^2 - \frac{1}{2}k_z z^2\right] = 0 \qquad (12.21)$$

If we introduce the separation constants E_x, E_y, E_z such that

$$E = E_x + E_y + E_z \qquad (12.22)$$

we can separate equation 12.21 into three one-dimensional equations

$$\left.\begin{aligned} &\frac{1}{X(x)}\frac{d^2 X(x)}{dx^2} + \frac{8\pi^2 m}{h^2}\left[E_x - \frac{1}{2}k_x x^2\right] = 0 \\ &\frac{1}{Y(y)}\frac{d^2 Y(y)}{dy^2} + \frac{8\pi^2 m}{h^2}\left[E_y - \frac{1}{2}k_y y^2\right] = 0 \\ &\frac{1}{Z(z)}\frac{d^2 Z(z)}{dz^2} + \frac{8\pi^2 m}{h^2}\left[E_z - \frac{1}{2}k_z z^2\right] = 0 \end{aligned}\right\} \qquad (12.23)$$

In this example we have carried out the separation in cartesian co-ordinates, but this may not necessarily always be the best co-ordinate system. As mentioned in section 4.4.3, it is better to use spherical polar co-ordinates in the case of the hydrogen atom, where the potential is of the form $1/\sqrt{(x^2 + y^2 + z^2)}$. The Schrödinger equation in polar co-ordinates for the hydrogen atom is

$$\frac{1}{r^2}\frac{\partial}{\partial r}\left(r^2\frac{\partial\psi}{\partial r}\right) + \frac{1}{r^2 \sin\theta}\frac{\partial}{\partial\theta}\left(\sin\theta\frac{\partial\psi}{\partial\theta}\right) + \frac{1}{r^2\sin^2\theta}\frac{\partial^2\psi}{\partial\phi^2}$$

$$+ \frac{8\pi^2\mu}{h^2}\left[E + \frac{e^2}{4\pi\varepsilon_0 r}\right]\psi = 0 \qquad (12.24)$$

where e is the electronic charge and ε_0 is the permittivity of free space. We write the wavefunction in product form

$$\psi(r,\theta,\phi) = R(r)\Theta(\theta)\Phi(\phi) \qquad (12.25)$$

and proceed as before to substitute this into the original equation 12.24 to give

$$\Theta(\theta)\Phi(\phi)\frac{1}{r^2}\left[\frac{\partial}{\partial r}\left(r^2\frac{\partial R}{\partial r}\right)\right] + \frac{R(r)\Phi(\phi)}{r^2\sin\theta}\frac{\partial}{\partial\theta}\left(\sin\theta\frac{\partial\Theta}{\partial\theta}\right)$$

$$+ \frac{R(r)\Theta(\theta)}{r^2\sin^2\theta}\frac{\partial^2\Phi}{\partial\phi^2} + \frac{8\pi^2\mu}{h^2}\left[E + \frac{e^2}{4\pi\varepsilon_0 r}\right]R(r)\Theta(\theta)\Phi(\phi) = 0 \qquad (12.26)$$

which can be rearranged to yield

$$\frac{\sin^2\theta}{R(r)}\frac{\partial}{\partial r}\left(r^2\frac{\partial R}{\partial r}\right) + \frac{\sin\theta}{\Theta(\theta)}\frac{\partial}{\partial\theta}\left(\sin\theta\frac{\partial\Theta}{\partial\theta}\right) + \frac{1}{\Phi(\phi)}\frac{\partial^2\Phi}{\partial\phi^2}$$

$$+ r^2\sin^2\theta\,\frac{8\pi^2\mu}{h^2}\left[E + \frac{e^2}{4\pi\varepsilon_0 r}\right] = 0 \qquad (12.27)$$

At this stage we can separate to give two equations

$$\frac{1}{\Phi(\phi)}\frac{d^2\Phi}{d\phi^2} = -m^2 \qquad (12.28)$$

and

$$\frac{\sin^2\theta}{R(r)}\frac{\partial}{\partial r}\left(r^2\frac{\partial R}{\partial r}\right) + \frac{\sin\theta}{\Theta(\theta)}\frac{\partial}{\partial\theta}\left(\sin\theta\frac{\partial\Theta}{\partial\theta}\right)$$

$$+ r^2\sin^2\theta\,\frac{8\pi^2\mu}{h^2}\left[E + \frac{e^2}{4\pi\varepsilon_0 r}\right] - m^2 = 0 \qquad (12.29)$$

where the separation constant is $-m^2$. Rearrangement gives

$$\frac{1}{R(r)}\frac{\partial}{\partial r}\left(r^2\frac{\partial R}{\partial r}\right) + \frac{1}{\Theta(\theta)\sin\theta}\frac{\partial}{\partial\theta}\left(\sin\theta\frac{\partial\Theta}{\partial\theta}\right)$$

$$+ \frac{8\pi^2\mu r^2}{h^2}\left[E + \frac{e^2}{4\pi\varepsilon_0 r}\right] - \frac{m^2}{\sin^2\theta} = 0 \qquad (12.30)$$

which can also be separated to give

$$\frac{1}{\Theta(\theta)\sin\theta}\frac{d}{d\theta}\left(\sin\theta\frac{d\Theta}{d\theta}\right) - \frac{m^2}{\sin^2\theta} = -\beta \qquad (12.31)$$

and

$$\frac{1}{R(r)}\frac{d}{dr}\left(r^2\frac{dR}{dr}\right) - \beta + \frac{8\pi^2\mu r^2}{h^2}\left[E + \frac{e^2}{4\pi\varepsilon_0 r}\right] = 0 \qquad (12.32)$$

Thus the separation of variables technique results in the resolution of the partial differential equation 12.24 in three dimensions into the following ordinary differential equations

$$\frac{d^2\Phi(\phi)}{d\phi^2} = -m^2\Phi(\phi) \qquad (12.33)$$

$$\frac{1}{\sin\theta}\frac{d}{d\theta}\left(\sin\theta\frac{d\Theta(\theta)}{d\theta}\right) + \beta\,\Theta(\theta) - \frac{m^2\Theta(\theta)}{\sin^2\theta} = 0 \qquad (12.34)$$

$$\frac{1}{r^2}\frac{d}{dr}\left(r^2\frac{dR(r)}{dr}\right) - \beta\frac{R(r)}{r^2} + \frac{8\pi^2\mu}{h^2}\left[E + \frac{e^2}{4\pi\varepsilon_0 r}\right]R(r) = 0$$

$$(12.35)$$

The first of these is a standard form and has the general solution

$$\Phi(\phi) = C_1 \exp(im\phi) + C_2 \exp(-im\phi) \tag{12.36}$$

The others are linear equations with non-constant coefficients, which are not amenable to solution by the methods of chapter 11.

12.3 PROBLEMS FOR SOLUTION

1. The conduction of heat in a one-dimensional system is described by the equation

$$\frac{\partial^2 u}{\partial x^2} = \frac{1}{k}\frac{\partial u}{\partial t}$$

where $u(x,t)$ is the temperature at time t at a point x from the origin and k is a constant. Find the general solution $u(x,t)$, which decreases exponentially with t and satisfies the boundary conditions

$$u(0,t) = u(\ell,t) = 0, \quad t \geqslant 0$$

2. Laplace's equation in two dimensions is

$$\frac{\partial^2 \psi}{\partial x^2} + \frac{\partial^2 \psi}{\partial y^2} = 0$$

Find the general solution that satisfies the boundary conditions

$$\begin{aligned} \psi(x,y) = 0, \quad \text{when} \quad & x = 0,\ 0 \leqslant y \leqslant b \\ & x = a,\ 0 \leqslant y \leqslant b \\ & y = b,\ 0 \leqslant x \leqslant a \end{aligned}$$

3. In polar co-ordinates, Laplace's equation in two dimensions is

$$\frac{\partial^2 \psi}{\partial r^2} + \frac{1}{r}\frac{\partial \psi}{\partial r} + \frac{1}{r^2}\frac{\partial^2 \psi}{\partial \theta^2} = 0$$

Separate this equation into two ordinary differential equations.

4. The Schrödinger equation for a particle in a three-dimensional box such that

$$\begin{aligned} V = 0 \quad \text{for} \quad & 0 \leqslant x \leqslant a \\ & 0 \leqslant y \leqslant b \\ & 0 \leqslant z \leqslant c \end{aligned}$$

and $V = \infty$ otherwise, is

$$\frac{\partial^2 \psi}{\partial x^2} + \frac{\partial^2 \psi}{\partial y^2} + \frac{\partial^2 \psi}{\partial z^2} + \frac{8\pi^2 m}{h^2}\left[E - V\right]\psi = 0$$

where E is the energy of the particle, m is the mass and h is Planck's constant. Solve this equation for the two cases:

(i) $a = b = c$; (ii) $a \neq b \neq c$.

5. The Schrödinger equation for the three-dimensional harmonic oscillator can be written in terms of the cylindrical co-ordinates

$$x = \rho \cos \theta$$

$$y = \rho \sin \theta$$

$$z = z$$

thus

$$\frac{1}{\rho}\frac{\partial}{\partial \rho}\left(\rho \frac{\partial \psi}{\partial \rho}\right) + \frac{1}{\rho^2}\frac{\partial^2 \psi}{\partial \theta^2} + \frac{\partial^2 \psi}{\partial z^2} + \frac{8\pi^2 m}{h^2}$$

$$\times\left[E - 2\pi^2 m(\nu_x^2 \rho^2 \cos^2 \theta + \nu_y^2 \rho^2 \sin^2 \theta + \nu_z^2 z^2)\right]\psi = 0$$

Show that the equation is separable in this co-ordinate system if $\nu_x = \nu_y$

13

Numerical Methods

So far we have been almost entirely concerned with problems that have exact analytical solutions. The only exception was in the case of infinite series where we had to consider the question of convergence. In our numerical work we have used small numbers so that the arithmetic has been easy. However, problems in real life are not always so easy. For example, in chapter 3 we indicated that many functions cannot be integrated analytically. For such problems it is necessary to adopt numerical methods. Numerical analysis is a large subject and in this chapter we can only give a brief introduction to a few numerical procedures. We concentrate on the ideas behind the methods and ignore error analysis. The particular methods discussed are not necessarily those that would be used in practice for serious computation. For a thorough discussion the student should consult a text on numerical analysis such as McCracken and Dorn, 1964.

13.1 NEWTON'S METHOD FOR THE SOLUTION OF NONLINEAR EQUATIONS

In section 1.1.2(ii) we gave an explicit formula for the roots of the quadratic equation $ax^2 + bx + c = 0$. There are methods for the exact solution of cubic and quartic equations but they are cumbersome. There is no general method for finding the values of x for which a function $f(x) = 0$. Sketching the curve of the function using the methods of section 2.6.3 will give a rough idea of the location of the roots. If we find two values of x, x_1 and x_1' for which $f(x)$ has opposite signs, we know that there must be at least one root between x_1 and x_1' (figure 13.1).

One way of locating a root more accurately would be to bisect the interval $x_1 \leqslant x \leqslant x_1'$ by x_2 and select the pair of values (x_1,x_2) or (x_2,x_1') for which $f(x)$ has opposite signs. This process can be continued until the root has been obtained to the required degree of accuracy. This *bisection method* is, however, slow to converge.

Having found the approximate location of the root, *Newton's method* usually gives fairly rapid convergence. If there is a root in the region of $x = x_1$ at $x = x_1 + h$, where h is a small quantity, we can expand the function about x_1 by a Taylor series in powers of h

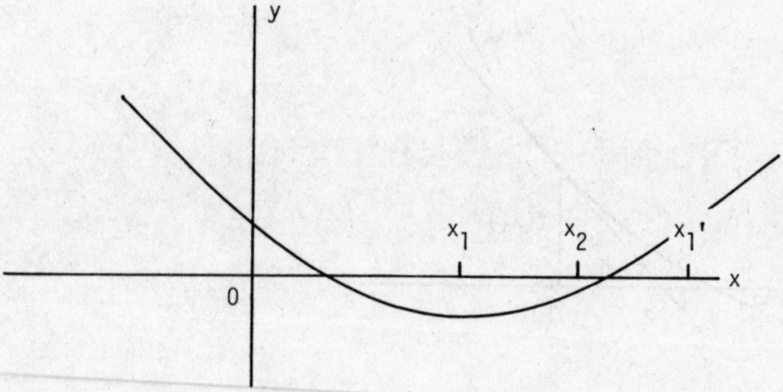

Figure 13.1

$$f(x_1 + h) = f(x_1) + hf'(x)\Big|_{x=x_1} + \frac{h^2}{2!} f''(x)\Big|_{x=x_1}$$

$$+ \frac{h^3}{3!} f'''(x)\Big|_{x=x_1} + \ldots \tag{13.1}$$

However, since $x = x_1 + h$ is a root, $f(x_1 + h) = 0$ so we can write

$$0 = f(x_1) + hf'(x)\Big|_{x=x_1} + \frac{h^2}{2!} f''(x)\Big|_{x=x_1} + \ldots \tag{13.2}$$

Neglecting powers of h larger than the first gives us an approximate expression for h

$$h \approx -\frac{f(x_1)}{f'(x)\big|_{x=x_1}} \tag{13.3}$$

so a better approximation x_2 to the root is given by *Newton's formula*

$$x_2 = x_1 - \frac{f(x_1)}{f'(x)\big|_{x=x_1}} \tag{13.4}$$

We illustrate this graphically in figure 13.2. The derivative at x_1, $f'(x)\big|_{x=x_1}$ is given by $f(x_1)/(x_1 - x_2)$ as shown in the figure.

The cubic equation $x^3 - 4x + 1 = 0$ occurs in the Hückel molecular-orbital theory of fulvene. If $x = 1/3$, $f(x) = -8/27$ and if $x = 1/4$, $f(x) = 1/64$, so $x = 0.25$ would appear to be a good starting value for x. Applying Newton's method gives

$$x_2 = 0.25 - \frac{1/64}{(-61/16)} \doteq \frac{31}{122} = 0.2541$$

Since $f(x_2) = 0.00006$ no further refinement is necessary for most purposes. We could equally well have started from $x_1 = 1/3$ to give

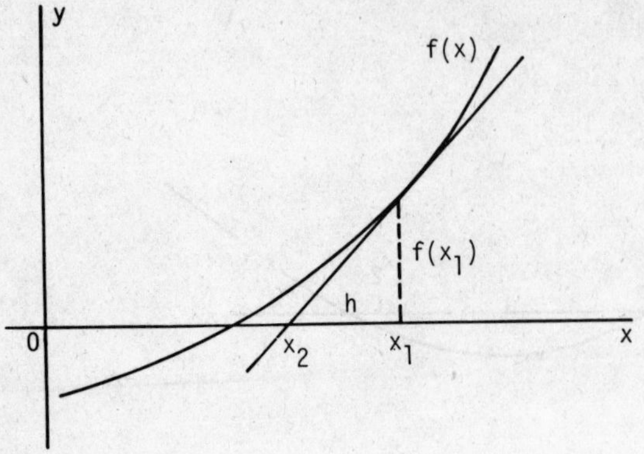

Figure 13.2

$$x_2 = \frac{1}{3} - \frac{(-8/27)}{(-11/3)} = \frac{25}{99} = 0.25253$$

Here a further application of Newton's formula may be necessary.

$$x_3 = 0.25253 - \left(\frac{0.0006}{-3.8087}\right) = 0.2541$$

The method has to be used with caution, however, since in certain circumstances the result diverges or oscillates. Figures 13.3 and 13.4 illustrate two possible cases.

13.2 NUMERICAL INTEGRATION OR QUADRATURE

In cases where the integral $\int f(x)dx$ cannot be evaluated analytically, it is often possible to evaluate the definite integral $\int_a^b f(x)dx$ numerically by replacing it by another

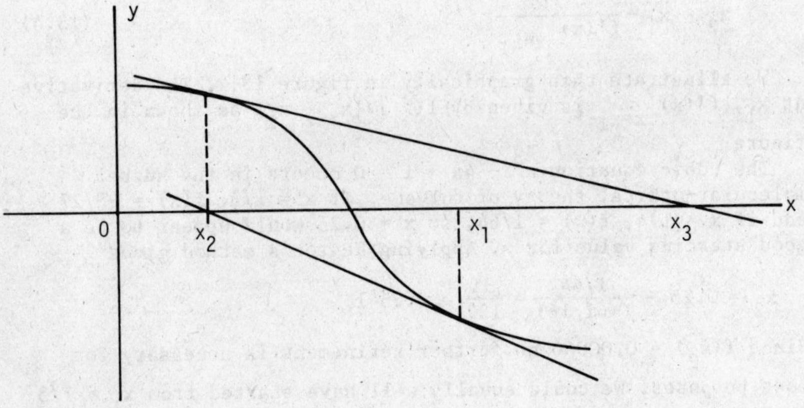

Figure 13.3

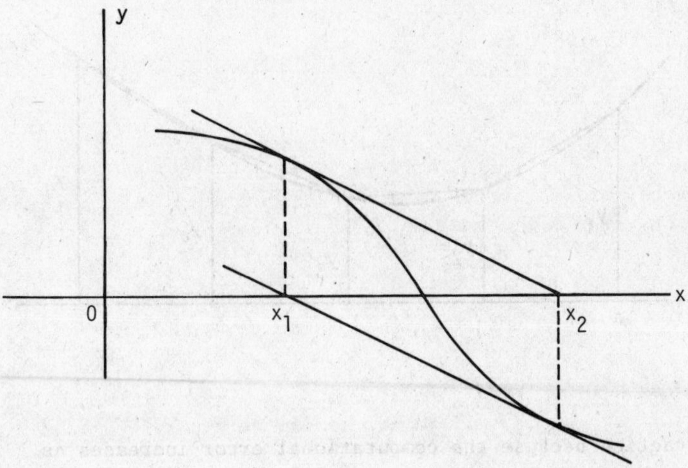

Figure 13.4

integral $\int_a^b \phi(x)dx$ which can be readily calculated. We outline three methods but make no attempt at error analysis. For such an analysis the reader should consult a text on numerical analysis such as McCracken and Dorn, 1964.

13.2.1 Trapezoidal rule

The simplest approach to the calculation of the definite integral $\int_a^b f(x)dx$ is to find an approximate method for the calculation of the area under the curve of $y = f(x)$ between $x = a$ and $x = b$. This can be done to a first approximation by representing the curve by a straight line. The integral is then given by the area of a trapezium, $\frac{1}{2}(b - a)[f(b) + f(a)]$. A better approximation is obtained by dividing the interval $a \leqslant x \leqslant b$ into n equal sub-intervals of length h such that it is not too gross an approximation to represent the curve by a straight line in each sub-interval (figure 13.5). The area under the curve in the interval between x_{i-1} and x_i is given approximately by the area of the trapezium of base h and heights y_i and y_{i+1}, that is $(h/2)(y_i + y_{i+1})$. The total area is thus given approximately by

$$A \approx \frac{h}{2}\left[(y_1 + y_2) + (y_2 + y_3) + \ldots + (y_n + y_{n+1})\right]$$

so

$$\int_a^b f(x)dx \approx \frac{h}{2}\left[y_1 + 2y_2 + 2y_3 + \ldots + 2y_n + y_{n+1}\right] \qquad (13.5)$$

This would be expected to approximate more closely to the true value as n increases. However, this is only true to a certain

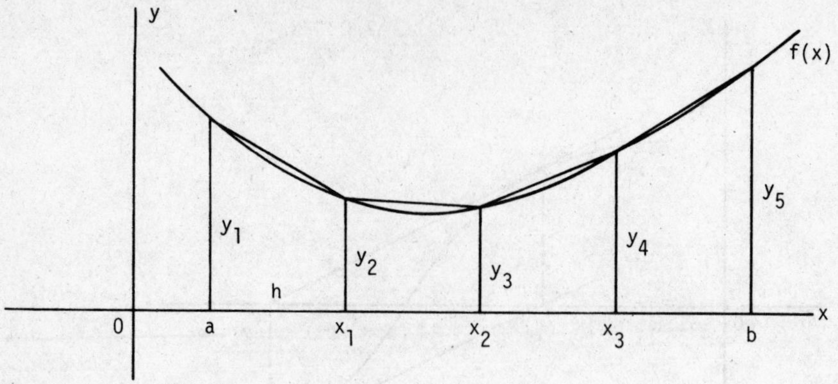

Figure 13.5

extent in practice because the computational error increases as n increases.

13.2.2 Simpson's rule

It is possible to achieve a more accurate result with the same number of intervals by using *Simpson's rule*. Let us consider the simple case where the interval $a \leqslant x \leqslant b$ is divided into two subintervals by the point x_1. The trapezoidal rule gives

$$\int_a^b f(x)dx \approx \frac{h}{2}\left[y_1 + 2y_2 + y_3\right] \tag{13.6}$$

However, let us expand $f(x)$ about the point $x = x_1$ in a Taylor series. To do this we introduce a new variable y defined by $x = x_1 + y$ and thus

$$\begin{aligned}\int_a^b f(x)dx &= \int_{x_1-h}^{x_1+h} f(x)dx = \int_{-h}^{h} f(x_1 + y)dy \\ &= \int_{-h}^{h} \Big[f(x_1) + yf'(x)\big|_{x=x_1} + \frac{y^2}{2} f''(x)\big|_{x=x_1} \\ &\quad + \frac{y^3}{3!} f'''(x)\big|_{x=x_1} \ldots\Big]dy\end{aligned} \tag{13.7}$$

Performing the integration gives

$$\begin{aligned}\int_a^b f(x)dx &= \Big[yf(x_1) + \frac{y^2}{2} f'(x)\big|_{x=x_1} + \frac{y^3}{3!} f''(x)\big|_{x=x_1} \\ &\quad + \frac{y^4}{4!} f'''(x)\big|_{x=x_1} + \ldots\Big]_{-h}^{h} \\ &= 2hf(x_1) + \frac{2h^3}{3!} f''(x)\big|_{x=x_1} + \frac{2h^5}{5!} f''''(x)\big|_{x=x_1} \\ &\quad + \ldots\end{aligned} \tag{13.8}$$

We shall neglect terms in h^5 and replace the derivative $f''(x)\big|_{x=x_1}$ by considering the Taylor series of $f(x_1 + h)$ and $f(x_1 - h)$

$$f(x_1 + h) = f(x_1) + hf'(x)\big|_{x=x_1} + \frac{h^2}{2!} f''(x)\big|_{x=x_1} + \ldots \tag{13.9}$$

$$f(x_1 - h) = f(x_1) - hf'(x)\big|_{x=x_1} + \frac{h^2}{2!} f''(x)\big|_{x=x_1} - \ldots \tag{13.10}$$

Thus adding equations 13.9 and 13.10 gives

$$f(x_1 + h) + f(x_1 - h) = 2\left[f(x_1) + \frac{h^2}{2!} f''(x)\big|_{x=x_1} + \frac{h^4}{4!} f''''(x)\big|_{x=x_1} + \ldots\right] \tag{13.11}$$

If we neglect terms in h^4 and higher powers of h, we can eliminate $f''(x)\big|_{x=x_1}$ between equations 13.11 and 13.8 to give

$$\int_a^b f(x)dx \approx 2h\left[f(x_1) + \frac{h^2}{3!}\left(\frac{f(x_1 + h) + f(x_1 - h) - 2f(x_1)}{h^2}\right)\right]$$

$$\approx \frac{h}{3}\left[f(x_1 - h) + 4f(x_1) + f(x_1 + h)\right]$$

that is

$$\int_a^b f(x)dx \approx \frac{h}{3}\left[y_1 + 4y_2 + y_3\right] \tag{13.12}$$

If we divide the interval $a \leqslant x \leqslant b$ into an even number n of intervals of length h, the definite integral is given approximately by

$$\int_a^b f(x)dx \approx \frac{h}{3}\left[y_1 + 4y_2 + 2y_3 + 4y_4 + \ldots 2y_{n-1} + 4y_n + y_{n+1}\right] \tag{13.13}$$

Let us compare the exact result with the results of using the trapezoidal rule and Simpson's rule for the integral

$$\int_0^1 \frac{dx}{1 + x^2}$$

The exact result is

$$\int_0^1 \frac{dx}{1 + x^2} = \tan^{-1} x\Big|_0^1 = \frac{\pi}{4} = 0.7854$$

Using the trapezoidal rule with four equal intervals gives

$$\int_0^1 \frac{dx}{1+x^2} = \frac{0.25}{2}\left[1 + 2 \times \frac{1}{1 + 1/16} + 2 \times \frac{1}{1 + 1/4} + 2 \times \frac{1}{1 + 9/16} + \frac{1}{2}\right]$$

$$= 0.125\,[1 + 32/17 + 8/5 + 32/25 + 1/2]$$

$$= 0.7828$$

whereas Simpson's rule gives

$$\int_0^1 \frac{dx}{1+x^2} = \frac{0.25}{3}\left[1 + 4 \times \frac{16}{17} + 2 \times \frac{4}{5} + 4 \times \frac{16}{25} + \frac{1}{2}\right] = 0.7854$$

We can demonstrate the superiority of Simpson's rule by performing the calculation with just two intervals

$$\int_0^1 \frac{dx}{1+x^2} = \frac{0.5}{3}\left[1 + 4 \times \frac{4}{5} + \frac{1}{2}\right] = 0.7833$$

13.2.3 Newton-Cotes formulae

The trapezoidal rule and Simpson's rule are two examples of *Newton-Cotes formulae* in which the integral $\int_a^b f(x)dx$ is obtained by calculating the integral of a polynomial $\phi_n(x)$ of degree n such that for a set of *equidistant points* x_i, $i = 0, 1, \ldots n$, the polynomial $\phi_n(x)$ has the same values as $f(x)$; that is

$$\phi_n(x_i) = f(x_i), \quad i = 0, 1 \ldots n \tag{13.14}$$

In the trapezoidal rule $f(x)$ is represented by a straight line whereas in Simpson's rule it is represented by parabola.

13.2.4 Gaussian quadrature

Both the trapezoidal and Simpson's rules depend on dividing the interval $a \leqslant x \leqslant b$ into subintervals of equal length. This is probably the most convenient method for computation by hand but for machine computation it is unnecessarily restrictive. In *Gauss's method* the definite integral is given by

$$\int_a^b f(x)dx \approx \sum_{i=0}^{n} c_i f(x_i) \tag{13.15}$$

where both c_i and x_i are varied to minimise the error. It is usual to change the variable of integration to a new variable w so that the range of integration is from $w = -1$ to $w = +1$. The required transformation is

$$x = \frac{(a+b)}{2} + \frac{(b-a)}{2}w \tag{13.16}$$

Since

$$dx = \frac{(b - a)}{2} dw \tag{13.17}$$

the integral becomes

$$\int_a^b f(x)dx = \frac{(b - a)}{2} \int_{-1}^{1} F(w)dw \approx \frac{(b - a)}{2} \sum_{i=0}^{n} d_i F(w_i) \tag{13.18}$$

For the interval $-1 \leqslant w \leqslant 1$, the required values of w_i are given by the (n + 1) real roots of the Legendre polynomial or degree (n + 1), $P_{n+1}(w)$. The set of numbers d_i are known as *weights*, and tabulations with the appropriate values of w_i can be found in various texts.

Gaussian quadrature requires a smaller number of points than Simpson's rule in order to achieve comparable accuracy. For n intervals of order h, the error in Gaussian quadrature is of the order h^{2n+1} whereas for the Newton-Cotes method it is of the order of h^n or h^{n+1}.

13.3 NUMERICAL SOLUTION OF ORDINARY DIFFERENTIAL EQUATIONS

In chapter 11 we discussed several types of differential equations that could be solved analytically. Other equations such as 12.34 and 12.35 can be solved analytically but only with some difficulty. However, there are many equations that cannot be solved analytically and we have to use numerical methods.

The problem is, given a derivative as a function of x and y

$$\frac{dy}{dx} = f(x,y) \tag{13.19}$$

and an initial set of values, that is $y(x_0) = y_0$, how do we obtain y as a function of x

$$y = F(x)? \tag{13.20}$$

We consider here first-order equations because we can always express higher-order equations in terms of simultaneous first-order equations. If we have the equation

$$\frac{d^2y}{dx^2} = g\left(\frac{dy}{dx}, y, x\right) \tag{13.21}$$

we can rewrite this in terms of a new function z = dy/dx

$$\left.\begin{aligned} \frac{dz}{dx} &= g(z,y,x) \\ \frac{dy}{dx} &= z \end{aligned}\right\} \tag{13.22}$$

This is in fact what we did in equations 11.70 to 11.73 for the second-order linear equation.

Two classes of method commonly used are the predictor-corrector methods and the Runge-Kutta methods. Computer programs are readily available for both of these classes. However, it is useful to start by considering a Taylor-series solution.

13.3.1 Taylor-series solution

Given $dy/dx = f(x,y)$ and a pair of values (x_0,y_0), we can expand $y = F(x)$ about $x = x_0$ in a Taylor series

$$y = y_0 + \left(\frac{dy}{dx}\right)_{x=x_0}(x - x_0) + \left(\frac{d^2y}{dx^2}\right)_{x=x_0}\frac{(x - x_0)^2}{2!}$$

$$+ \left(\frac{d^3y}{dx^3}\right)_{x=x_0}\frac{(x - x_0)^3}{3!} + \ldots \tag{13.23}$$

Thus we can calculate the value of y, y_1 at the point $x = x_1$ and can then repeat the process to calculate the value of y, y_2 at $x = x_2$ further along the x-axis. If we take equal increments h along the x-axis, $h = x_{m+1} - x_m$, we obtain

$$y_{m+1} = y_m + h\left(\frac{dy}{dx}\right)_{x=x_m} + \frac{h^2}{2!}\left(\frac{d^2y}{dx^2}\right)_{x=x_m} + \frac{h^3}{3!}\left(\frac{d^3y}{dx^3}\right)_{x=x_m} + \ldots \tag{13.24}$$

Provided that we can evaluate the higher derivatives, this should give us a solution to any desired degree of accuracy by the inclusion of more terms. However, successively higher derivatives become more difficult to evaluate and the method is generally not practicable. It does, though, give us a criterion for judging the success of other methods because we can say to what power of h a method agrees with the Taylor-series expansion.

13.3.2 The Runge-Kutta method

This is a one-step method which obtains the value y_{m+1} from the preceding point (x_m,y_m). In order to discuss the Runge-Kutta method we have to start with a relatively crude method, *Euler's method*. If the derivative of y at the point (x_m,y_m) is $dy/dx = f(x_m,y_m)$, a crude value for y_{m+1} at the point $x_{m+1} = x_m + h$ would be

$$y_{m+1} = y_m + hf(x_m,y_m) \tag{13.25}$$

The value of y_{m+1} includes the first term in the Taylor-series expansion. The error is illustrated in figure 13.6 and can be

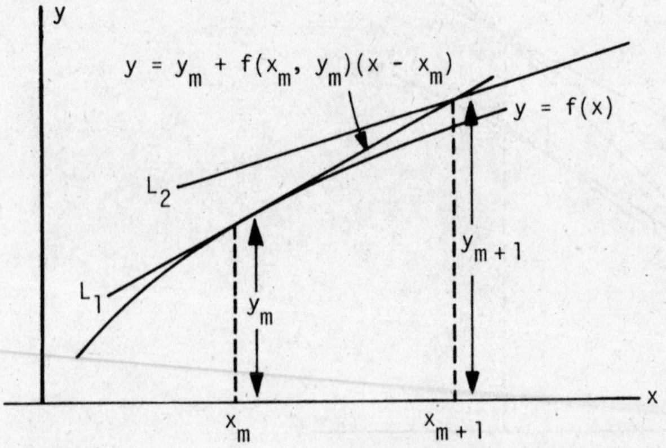

Figure 13.6

seen to be considerable. It is easy to see that in repeating the process to obtain y_{m+2}, y_{m+3}, etc., the errors will rapidly increase.

A better estimate of y_{m+1} is given by the *improved Euler method*. We obtain the point (x_{m+1}, y') where $y' = y_m + f(x_m, y_m)(x_{m+1} - x_m)$ as above and then calculate the slope of the curve at this point using the differential equation. This is $f(x_{m+1}, y')$ and is shown in the figure 13.6 by the line L_2. A better value for y at $x = x_{m+1}$ is given by proceeding from (x_m, y_m) along a line L' whose slope is the average of the slopes of L_1 and L_2 (figure 13.7); that is

$$y_{m+1} = y_m + (x_{m+1} - x_m)\frac{1}{2}[f(x_m, y_m) + f(x_{m+1}, y')] \qquad (13.26)$$

It can be shown by comparison with the Taylor-series solution that the modified Euler method includes terms up to h^2. Let us illustrate this by taking a simple example that can be solved exactly. The equation

$$\frac{dy}{dx} = y \qquad (13.27)$$

has the exact solution $y = e^x$ for the initial conditions $y(0) = 1$. The Euler method gives

$$y(h) = y(0) + hf(0, y) = 1 + h \qquad (13.28)$$

whereas the improved Euler method gives

$$y(h) = y(0) + h\frac{1}{2}[f(0, y_0) + f(h, 1 + h)]$$

$$= 1 + \frac{h}{2}[1 + (1 + h)] = 1 + h + \frac{h^2}{2} \qquad (13.29)$$

These are the expansions of e^h to first and second order in h, respectively.

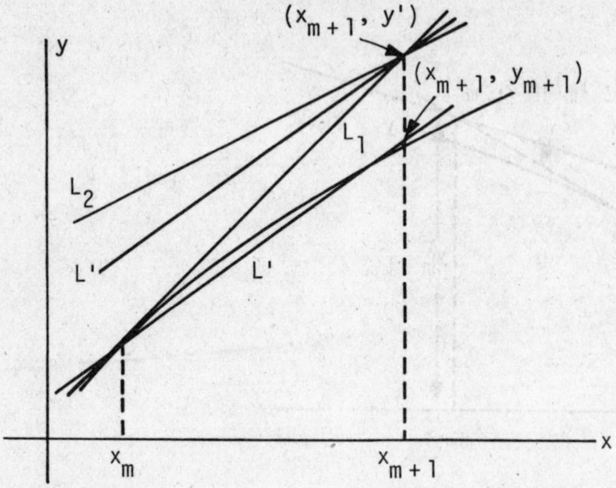

Figure 13.7

The improved Eüler method is one example of a second-order *Runge-Kutta method*. The most commonly used Runge-Kutta method is the fourth-order formula, which is often simply referred to as the Runge-Kutta method. In this method y_{m+1} is given by the equation

$$y_{m+1} = y_m + \frac{h}{6}(k_1 + 2k_2 + 2k_3 + k_4) \tag{13.30}$$

where $k_1 = f(x_m, y_m)$

$$k_2 = f\left(x_m + \frac{h}{2}, y_m + \frac{hk_1}{2}\right)$$

$$k_3 = f\left(x_m + \frac{h}{2}, y_m + \frac{hk_2}{2}\right)$$

$$k_4 = f(x_m + h, y_m + hk_3)$$

Applying this to our example

$$\frac{dy}{dx} = y, \; y(0) = 1$$

we obtain $k_1 = h$, $k_2 = 1 + h/2$, $k_3 = 1 + h/2 + h^2/4$, $k_4 = 1 + h^2/2 + h^3/4$ and

$$y(h) = 1 + h + \frac{h^2}{2} + \frac{h^3}{6} + \frac{h^4}{24} \tag{13.31}$$

Thus the fourth-order Runge-Kutta method includes terms up to h^4. It is interesting to note the if $f(x,y)$ is a function of x alone, $F(x)$, then

$$y(x) = \int_{x_0}^{x} F(x)dx \tag{13.32}$$

and application of the fourth-order Runge-Kutta equations gives precisely the same result as integration by Simpson's rule.

13.3.3 Predictor-corrector methods

Runge-Kutta methods are one-step processes in that the point (x_{m+1}, y_{m+1}) is calculated in terms of the previous point (x_m, y_m) and makes no use of points such as (x_{m-1}, y_{m-1}) calculated previously. Also the fourth-order equations 13.30 require four evaluations of the function f(x,y), which may be very time-consuming. Once a few steps have been taken, a *predictor-corrector method* may be more appropriate. We illustrate with a second-order method. Suppose we have calculated two points y_{m-1} and y_m. We could *predict* as a first guess $y_{m+1}^{(0)}$ that y_{m+1} would be given by

$$y_{m+1}^{(0)} = y_{m-1} + 2hf(x_m, y_m) \tag{13.33}$$

This is illustrated in figure 13.8. L_1 is the tangent at (x_m, y_m) and L is a line of the same slope passing through (x_{m-1}, y_{m-1}). Using (x_{m-1}, y_{m-1}) as a starting point gives a better estimate of y_{m+1} than the Euler method, which uses (x_m, y_m). A still better estimate of y_{m+1}, $y_{m+1}^{(1)}$ can be obtained by analogy with the Euler method by proceeding from (x_m, y_m) along a line whose slope is the average of the slope of L_1 and the tangent L_2 at $(x_{m+1}, y_{m+1}^{(0)})$. Let this be a line L' which has a slope of

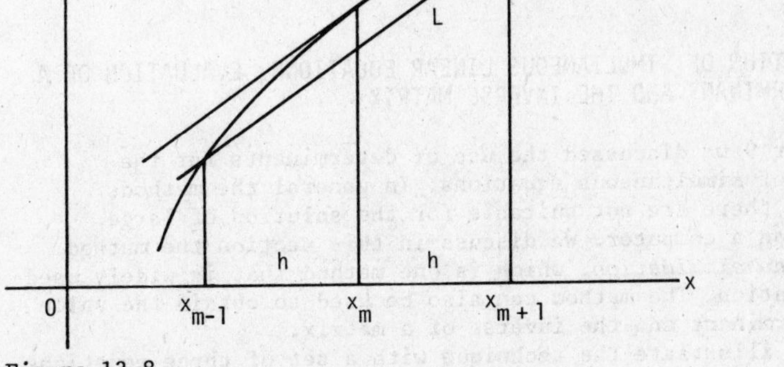

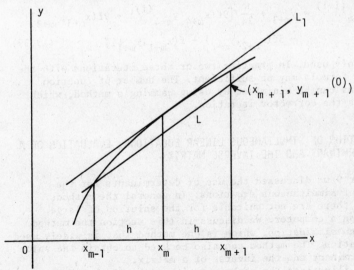

Figure 13.8

$$\frac{1}{2}[f(x_m,y_m) + f(x_{m+1},y_{m+1}^{(0)})] \qquad (13.34)$$

Thus our corrected value $y_{m+1}^{(1)}$ is

$$y_{m+1}^{(1)} = y_m + \frac{h}{2}[f(x_m,y_m) + f(x_{m+1},y_{m+1}^{(0)})] \qquad (13.35)$$

This corrected value can then be used in place of $y_{m+1}^{(0)}$ in equation 13.34 to give a further improved value $y_{m+1}^{(2)}$

$$y_{m+1}^{(2)} = y_m + \frac{h}{2}[f(x_m,y_m) + f(x_{m+1},y_{m+1}^{(1)})] \qquad (13.36)$$

and the process repeated until two successive values $y_{m+1}^{(i)}$ and $y_{m+1}^{(i+1)}$ differ by less than some positive value ε.

$$|y_{m+1}^{(i+1)} - y_{m+1}^{(i)}| < \varepsilon \qquad (13.37)$$

Equation 13.33 is the *predictor formula* and equation 13.35 is the *corrector formula*. Having obtained y_{m+1} to the required degree of accuracy, we then use y_{m+1} and y_m in the predictor formula to obtain $y_{m+2}^{(0)}$ and iterate with the corrector formula.

In computational examples the Adams-Bashforth predictor

$$y_{m+4}^{(0)} = y_{m+3} + \frac{h}{24}[55f(x_{m+3},y_{m+3}) - 59f(x_{m+2},y_{m+2}) + 37f(x_{m+1},y_{m+1}) - 9f(x_m,y_m)] \qquad (13.38)$$

and the Adams-Moulton corrector

$$y_{m+4}^{(i+1)} = y_{m+3} + \frac{h}{24}[9f(x_{m+4},y_{m+4}^{(i)}) + 9f(x_{m+3},y_{m+3}) - 5f(x_{m+2},y_{m+2}) + f(x_{m+1},y_{m+1})] \qquad (13.39)$$

are commonly used. In practice two or three iterations with the corrector formula may be sufficient. The number of function evaluations can be minimised by using Hamming's method, which eliminates the corrector iteration.

13.4 SOLUTION OF SIMULTANEOUS LINEAR EQUATIONS, EVALUATION OF A DETERMINANT AND THE INVERSE MATRIX

In chapter 9 we discussed the use of determinants for the solution of simultaneous equations. In general the methods described there are not suitable for the solution of large problems on a computer. We discuss in this section the method of *gaussian elimination*, which is one method that is widely used in computation. The method can also be used to obtain the value of a determinant and the inverse of a matrix.

Let us illustrate the technique with a set of three equations with three unknowns

$$a_{11}x + a_{12}y + a_{13}z = b_1 \tag{13.40}$$

$$a_{21}x + a_{22}y + a_{23}z = b_2 \tag{13.41}$$

$$a_{31}x + a_{32}y + a_{33}z = b_3 \tag{13.42}$$

We first of all eliminate x from equations 13.41 and 13.42 by multiplying equation 13.40 by a_{21}/a_{11} or a_{31}/a_{11}, respectively, and substracting the result from equation 13.41 or 13.42. Thus we obtain

$$a_{11}x + a_{12}y + a_{13}z = b_1 \tag{13.43}$$

$$a_{22}'y + a_{23}'z = b_2' \tag{13.44}$$

$$a_{32}'y + a_{33}'z = b_3' \tag{13.45}$$

where

$$a_{22}' = a_{22} - a_{12} \times \frac{a_{21}}{a_{11}}; \quad a_{23}' = a_{23} - a_{13} \times \frac{a_{21}}{a_{11}};$$

$$b_2' = b_2 - b_1 \times \frac{a_{21}}{a_{11}}$$

and

$$a_{32}' = a_{32} - a_{12} \times \frac{a_{31}}{a_{11}}; \quad a_{33}' = a_{33} - a_{13} \times \frac{a_{31}}{a_{11}};$$

$$b_3' = b_3 - b_1 \frac{a_{31}}{a_{11}}$$

We can now eliminate y from the third equation by multiplying equation 13.44 by a_{32}'/a_{22}' and subtracting the result from equation 13.45 to give

$$a_{11}x_1 + a_{12}y + a_{13}z = b_1 \tag{13.46}$$

$$a_{22}'y + a_{23}'z = b_2' \tag{13.47}$$

$$a_{33}''z = b_3'' \tag{13.48}$$

where

$$a_{33}'' = a_{33}' - a_{23}' \times \frac{a_{32}'}{a_{22}'}; \quad b_3'' = b_3' - b_2' \times \frac{a_{32}'}{a_{22}'}$$

The solution is now readily obtained by *back substituting* $z = b_3''/a_{33}''$ into equation 13.47 to give y and then obtaining x from equation 13.46. The results are

$$z = \frac{b_3''}{a_{33}''}; \quad y = \frac{b_2' - a_{23}'z}{a_{22}'}; \quad x = \frac{b_1 - a_{12}y - a_{13}z}{a_{11}} \qquad (13.49)$$

This is simply a systematic way of solving the equations by the elementary method of elimination. It is clearly applicable to larger systems of equations and a computer program for this can easily be written.

However, for large systems of equations, many arithmetical operations are involved and rounding errors can rapidly accumulate and render the final result inaccurate. In particular each elimination involves multiplication by a quantity of the type $m_{ij} = a_{ij}/a_{jj}$. In order to minimise rounding errors these multipliers should all be less than unity in magnitude. This is readily done by interchanging the order of the equations so that a_{jj} is numerically the largest of the coefficients a_{ij} with $i \geqslant j$ in column j. Thus in our example we should order the equations so that $|a_{11}|$ is larger than $|a_{21}|$ or $|a_{31}|$. For the second stage we should order the second and third equations so that $|a_{22}'| \geqslant |a_{32}'|$. This process is called *pivoting*. It is also possible to rearrange the columns but the gain in accuracy is not usually sufficient to offset the extra computation required.

Another refinement that can improve accuracy is *scaling* but there is no standard way of doing this. One approach is to divide each row by the element with the largest modulus in that row. An alternative is to divide each row by a quantity d_i given by

$$d_i = \left(\sum_{j=1}^{n} a_{ij}^2 \right) \qquad (13.50)$$

One also has to look out for ill-conditioning. This is present when small changes in the b_i result in large changes in x, y, z.

The application of gaussian elimination transforms a determinant into one in which the only non-zero elements are in the *upper triangle*. Thus applying the method to a third-order determinant gives

$$\begin{vmatrix} a_{11} & a_{12} & a_{13} \\ a_{21} & a_{22} & a_{23} \\ a_{31} & a_{32} & a_{33} \end{vmatrix} = \begin{vmatrix} a_{11} & a_{12} & a_{13} \\ 0 & a_{22}' & a_{23}' \\ 0 & 0 & a_{33}'' \end{vmatrix} \qquad (13.51)$$

The value of such a determinant is simply the product of the diagonal elements $a_{11}a_{22}'a_{33}''$. In order to avoid rounding errors it is necessary to use pivoting. Each interchange of two rows will introduce a sign change so care must be taken to keep count of such interchanges.

To calculate the inverse of the matrix **A**, we require a matrix such that

$$\mathbf{AX} = \mathbf{1} \tag{13.52}$$

where **1** is the unit matrix. The first column of **X** will be such that

$$\begin{pmatrix} a_{11} & a_{12} & a_{13} & \cdots \\ a_{21} & a_{22} & a_{23} & \cdots \\ a_{31} & a_{32} & a_{33} & \cdots \\ \vdots & \vdots & \vdots & \end{pmatrix} \begin{pmatrix} x_{11} \\ x_{21} \\ x_{31} \\ \vdots \end{pmatrix} = \begin{pmatrix} 1 \\ 0 \\ 0 \\ \vdots \end{pmatrix} \tag{13.53}$$

Thus we can obtain the column vector $\{\mathbf{X}_1\}$ by solving the simultaneous equations 13.53 by the method of gaussian elimination. We can obtain all the columns of **X** by taking successive columns from **1** on the right-hand side of equation 13.53.

Compact methods in which the matrix **A** is expressed as the product of a lower triangle matrix **L** and an upper triangle matrix **U**

$$\mathbf{A} = \mathbf{LU} \tag{13.54}$$

are also widely used.

13.5 PROBLEMS FOR SOLUTION

1. Using Newton's method find the real roots of the following equations to three decimal places:

(i) $x^4 - 8x^3 + 23x^2 + 16x - 50 = 0$;

(ii) $4x^3 - x^2 + 16x - 5 = 0$

(iii) $\theta = \tan\theta$ for $\pi < 0 < 2\pi$;

(iv) $x^3 - 3x + 7 = 0$

(v) $\exp(2x) - 2 - 3x = 0$;

(vi) $\ln x - x + 2 = 0$.

2. Evaluate the following integrals using the trapezoidal rule and Simpson's rule with four intervals.

(i) $\int_0^1 \frac{dx}{\sqrt{(1 + x^2)}}$; (ii) $\int_3^2 \frac{dx}{\sqrt{(x^2 - 1)}}$;

(iii) $\int_0^{\pi/2} \sqrt{(2 + \sin x)}dx$; (iv) $\int_0^{\pi/2} \frac{dx}{\sqrt{(1 - \frac{1}{2}\sin^2 x)}}$ (the elliptic integral);

(v) $\int_0^1 \frac{dx}{\sqrt{(1 + x^3)}}$; (vi) $\int_0^1 (1 + x^2)^{1/3}dx$.

3. Evaluate the integral $\int_0^4 \exp(-x^2)dx$ by Simpson's rule with intervals of h = 1 and h = 0.5. Compare your result with the exact result

$$\int_0^\infty \exp(-x^2)dx = \sqrt{\pi}/2.$$

4. Obtain numerical solutions to the following differential equations by the improved Euler method and by the second-order predictor-corrector method. The initial value of y, the step size h and the final value of y to be calculated are indicated. Compare your results with the analytical solution.

(i) $dy/dx = 1 - 3x$; $y(0) = 1$, $h = 0.5$, continue to $y(5)$;

(ii) $dy/dx = \exp(-x) - y$; $y(0) = 0$, $h = 0.1$, continue to $y(0.5)$

(iii) $dy/dx = (y/x) + 2x^2 \exp(x)$; $y(0.2) = 0$, $h = 0.2$, continue to $y(3)$;

(iv) $dy/dx = \cos x - y$; $y(0) = 0.5$, $h = 0.5$, continue to $y(5)$.

5. Solve the following sets of simultaneous equations by gaussian elimination:

(i)
$$5x + 7y + 6z + 5u = a_1$$
$$7x + 10y + 8z + 7u = a_2$$
$$6x + 8y + 10z + 9u = a_3$$
$$5x + 7y + 9z + 10u = a_4$$

for the values of a_i given by

	a_1	a_2	a_3	a_4
(a)	23	32	33	31
(b)	23.1	31.9	32.9	31.1

(ii)
$$x + y - z + w = 0$$
$$3x - y + 2z + 3w = 7$$
$$x + 2y - 2z - w = -1$$
$$3z + w = 9$$

6. Evaluate the following determinants by reducing them to upper-triangle form. Calculate the inverse of the corresponding matrix.

(i) $\begin{vmatrix} 0 & 0 & 1 & 1 \\ 1 & 2 & 0 & -1 \\ -1 & -2 & -1 & 1 \\ 3 & 6 & 2 & -3 \end{vmatrix}$; (ii) $\begin{vmatrix} 1 & 3 & 6 & 10 \\ 9 & 2 & 7 & 4 \\ 3 & 2 & 0 & 4 \\ 7 & 2 & 5 & 11 \end{vmatrix}$

14

Elementary Statistics and Error Analysis

In this chapter we give an introduction to the ideas commonly used in analysing experimental data and in assessing the accuracy of the results. The statistical analysis of experimental data is a large subject and we can only give a brief outline of the more common techniques. For further details the reader should consult some of the references given in the bibliography.

14.1 ERRORS

Errors are always present in experimental measurements however carefully they are made. In general the results of a series of measurements of the same experimental quantity will differ and it is important to be able to estimate its value and the accuracy of the estimate. Errors can arise from various sources. *Accidental errors* due to the observer are revealed by repeated observations. Successive readings appear to be randomly distributed and no apparent order can be discerned. Random errors also occur through sample variation. *Systematic errors* are due to the instrument or the way in which the measurement has been set up. Such errors will be revealed by making comparison with another set of measurements made on a different instrument or by a different method and can be compensated for by calibration. There may also be a systematic *personal error* or *bias*, which would be revealed in measurements made on the same instrument by someone else. Random errors also arise through *noise*, which is due to fluctuations at the atomic and molecular level. It is the random errors we seek to analyse by statistical methods.

We should distinguish between *accuracy*, which is the closeness of a set of measurements to the 'actual' or 'true' value, and *precision*, which is the closeness with which the measurements agree with one another.

14.2 FREQUENCY DISTRIBUTIONS

Here we consider how we can effectively present the results we obtain from a set of measurements x_i and give a quantitative measure of the scatter. Merely to list them in the order in which they are obtained is not very illuminating. Suppose we make ten measurements T_i of a temperature and obtain the following results in degrees Kelvin: 298.2, 298.1, 297.7, 297.8, 297.9, 298.1, 297.9,

298.0, 297.9, 298.0. One method is to make a table in which we list the values in ascending order and record the *frequency* of each observed value. The frequency is the number of times each particular value occurs.

Table 14.1

Temperature/K	297.7	297.8	297.9	298.0	298.1	298.2
Frequency	1	1	3	2	2	1

In this case we could conveniently do this in terms of intervals of 0.1 in the temperature. However, if we had, say, 100 readings quoted to two decimal places, we might wish to classify them into *classes* with *class limits* given by 297.70 to 297.79, 297.80 to 297.89, etc. The *class width* is the difference between the first number specifying one class and the first number specifying the next and is 0.1 in this case. The actual choice of class width depends on the nature of the data.

We can display the results graphically in a *histogram* in which we represent the frequency of each class by a rectangle whose base is equal to the class width and whose height is equal to the frequency as in figure 14.1.

If we ranked 100 readings into classes of width 0.05, the histogram might look like figure 14.2.

As the number of readings increases and the class width decreases, the *envelope* of the histogram approaches more closely to a continuous curve, called the *frequency-distribution curve*, as in figure 14.3. In this curve the area under the curve between observations x_i and x_{i+1} represents the proportion of observations in this range. If we divide f_i, the frequency of an observation, by n, the total number of observations, we obtain the *relative*

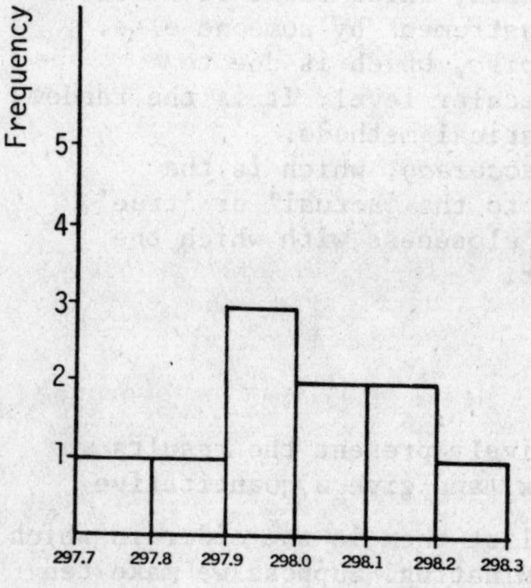

Figure 14.1

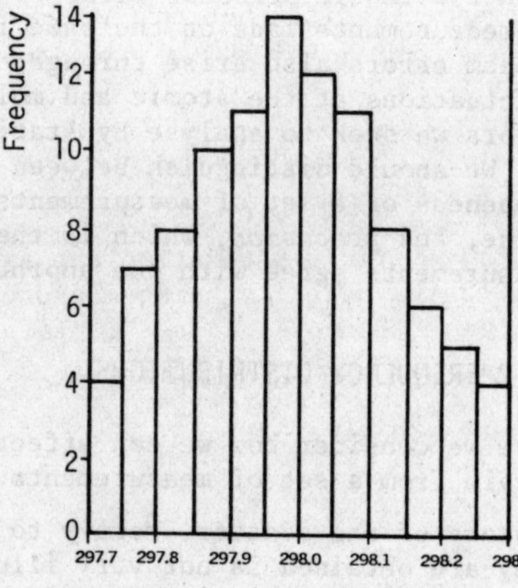

Figure 14.2

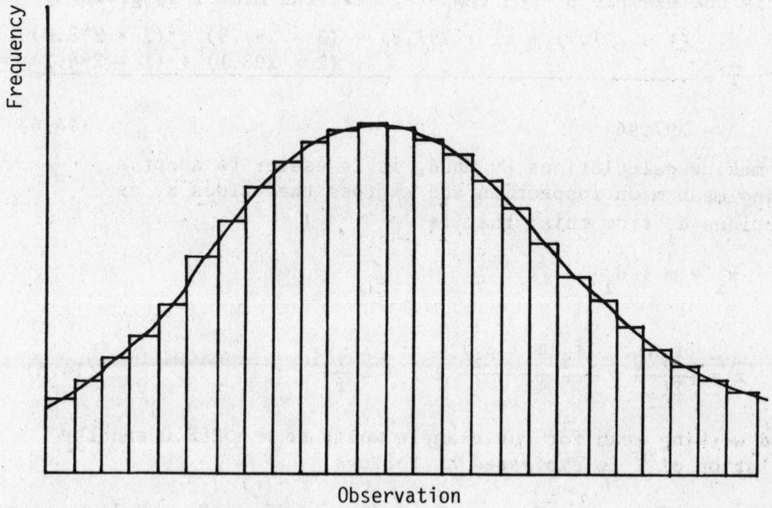

Figure 14.3

frequency or *probability* of that observation. The probability of obtaining an observation in the range between x_i and x_{i+1} is given by the area under the probability distribution curve for that range.

In section 3.6.7 we gave the distribution function for speeds of molecules in a gas as

$$\frac{dN}{N_0} = 4\pi\left(\frac{m}{2\pi kT}\right)^{3/2} \exp\left(-\frac{mc^2}{2kT}\right)c^2\ dc \qquad (14.1)$$

which gives the proportion of molecules having speeds between c and c + dc or the frequency of occurrences of a speed in this range.

Several important statistical quantities are used to describe the frequency distribution. An important concept is the *mean*, $\bar{x}$, which is simply the sum of all the observations x_i divided by the number n

$$\bar{x} = \frac{\sum_{i=1}^{n} x_i}{n} \qquad (14.2)$$

For a symmetric distribution the mean tells us the most probable value of the quantity being measured. If we classify the observations into k classes containing observation x_i with frequency f_i, we can simplify the calculation by summing over the k classes to give

$$\bar{x} = \frac{\sum_{i=1}^{k} f_i x_i}{\sum_{i=1}^{k} f_i} = \frac{\sum_{i=1}^{k} f_i x_i}{n} \qquad (14.3)$$

Thus in our example of ten temperatures, the mean $\overline{T}$ is given by

$$\overline{T} = \frac{(1 \times 297.7) + (1 \times 297.8) + (3 \times 297.9) + (2 \times 298.0) + (2 \times 298.1) + (1 \times 298.2)}{10}$$

$$= 297.96 \qquad (14.4)$$

When making calculations by hand, it is easier to adopt a *working mean* m on inspection and express the values x_i as deviations d_i from this; that is

$$x_i = m + d_i$$

so

$$\bar{x} = \frac{\Sigma f_i x_i}{\Sigma f_i} = \frac{\Sigma f_i (m + d_i)}{\Sigma f_i} = m + \frac{\Sigma f_i d_i}{\Sigma f_i} \qquad (14.5)$$

A good working mean for our example would be m = 298.0 and the calculation of $\overline{T}$ is expressed as follows

$$\overline{T} = 298.0 + \frac{1}{10}\Big[(1 \times -0.3) + (1 \times -0.2) + (3 \times -0.1) + (2 \times 0.0) + (2 \times 0.1) + (1 \times 0.2)\Big]$$

$$= 298.0 + \frac{1}{10}(-0.4) = 297.96 \qquad (14.6)$$

We can also define a *relative frequency* r_i of an observation x_i by

$$r_i = \frac{f_i}{\Sigma f_i} = \frac{f_i}{n} \qquad (14.7)$$

Since the sum of the frequencies is equal to n, the sum of the relative frequencies is equal to unity.

If we have a continuous distribution in which $f(x_i)$ gives the frequency of x lying between x_i and $x_i + dx$, the mean is given by the formula of equation 3.127; that is

$$\bar{x} = \frac{\int_{x_a}^{x_b} f(x)x \, dx}{\int_{x_a}^{x_b} f(x) dx} \qquad (14.8)$$

where x_a and x_b are the minimum and maximum values of x, respectively. If the frequency function is properly *normalised* the integral in the denominator will be equal to unity.

If there are some observations that are abnormally high or abnormally low they will distort the mean and in such cases the *median* is a better statistic. If there are 2n + 1 observations the median is the value x_{n+1}. If there is an even number 2n, then the median is the mean of x_n and x_{n+1}. The median of the above set of temperatures is 297.95. In this case the mean and the median are close to each other.

The maximum frequency or the maximum on the frequency-distribution curve is known as the *mode*.

The mean, median and mode tell us something about the centre of the frequency distribution, but don't give any information about the width of the distribution. A crude measure is the *range*, which is the difference between the maximum and minimum values. In our example this is 0.5. In general the range is not terribly meaningful and may even be infinite as in the case of the distribution of molecular speeds. A more satisfactory measure is the *interquartile range*, which is obtained by finding the values of x_i, $x_{0.25}$ and $x_{0.75}$ such that 25 per cent and 75 per cent of the distribution lies below them (figure 14.4). Thus 50 per cent of the distribution lies in the interquartile range between $x_{0.25}$ and $x_{0.75}$. However, even this measure is relatively crude.

The *mean deviation*, which is the mean of the moduli of the differences d_i between x_i and the mean $\bar{x}$ gives a quantitative measure of the scatter

$$\text{mean deviation} = \frac{\sum_i f_i |d_i|}{n} = \frac{\sum_i f_i |\bar{x} - x_i|}{n} \tag{14.9}$$

where each observation x_i occurs f_i times. It is necessary to take the moduli of the deviations; otherwise zero would be obtained. The mean deviation for our example is given by

$$\frac{1}{10}\left[(1 \times 0.26) + (1 \times 0.16) + (3 \times 0.06) + (2 \times 0.04) + (2 \times 0.14) + (1 \times 0.24)\right] = 0.12 \tag{14.10}$$

The most widely used measures of scatter are the *standard*

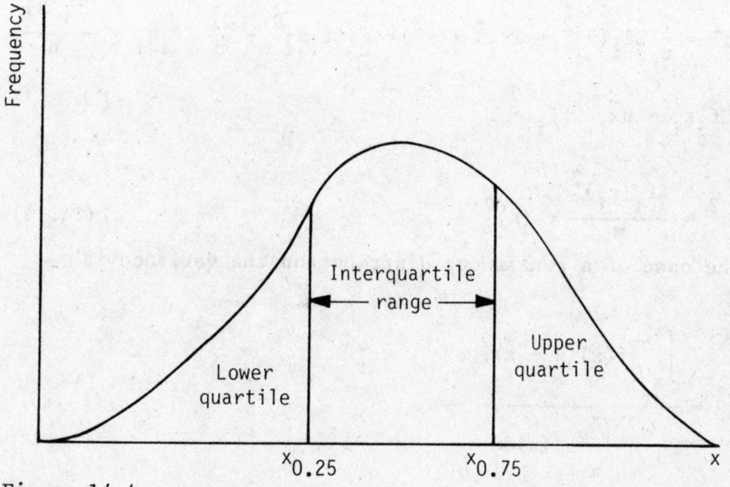

Figure 14.4

deviation σ and the *variance* σ^2. The variance is the mean of the squares of the deviations d_i of the observations x_i from the mean $\bar{x}$

$$\sigma^2 = \frac{\Sigma f_i d_i^2}{n} = \frac{\Sigma f_i (x_i - \bar{x})^2}{n} \tag{14.11}$$

The significance of the standard deviation will become clearer later.

The variance of our ten observations is given by

$$\sigma^2 = \frac{1}{10}\{[1 \times (0.26)^2] + [1 \times (0.16)^2] + [3 \times (0.06)^2] + [2 \times (0.04)^2] + [2 \times (0.14)^2] + [1 \times (0.24)^2]$$
$$= 0.024 \tag{14.12}$$

and the standard deviation is 0.15.

The calculation of the variance by hand can be made easier by using the working mean m. If each value of x_i is written as $x_i = m + (x_i - m)$ the variance is given by

$$\sigma^2 = \frac{1}{n}\Sigma f_i (x_i - \bar{x})^2 = \frac{1}{n}\Sigma f_i [(m - \bar{x}) + (x_i - m)]^2$$
$$= \frac{1}{n}\Sigma f_i [(x_i - m)^2 + 2(x_i - m)(m - \bar{x}) + (m - \bar{x})^2]$$
$$= \frac{1}{n}\Sigma f_i (x_i - m)^2 + \frac{2(m - \bar{x})}{n}\Sigma f_i (x_i - m) + (m - \bar{x})^2 \frac{\Sigma f_i}{n}$$
$$= \frac{1}{n}\Sigma f_i (x_i - m)^2 + 2(m - \bar{x})\left(\bar{x} - \frac{m\Sigma f_i}{n}\right) + (m - \bar{x})^2$$
$$= \frac{1}{n}\Sigma f_i (x_i - m)^2 - (m - \bar{x})^2 \tag{14.13}$$

An alternative expression can be obtained by expanding the square $(x_i - \bar{x})^2$ in equation 14.11 to give

$$\sigma^2 = \frac{1}{n}\Sigma f_i (x_i^2 - 2x_i\bar{x} + \bar{x}^2) = \frac{1}{n}\Sigma f_i x_i^2 - \frac{2\bar{x}}{n}\Sigma f_i x_i + \frac{\Sigma f_i (\bar{x})^2}{n}$$

But

$$\Sigma f_i x_i = n\bar{x}, \quad \Sigma f_i = n$$

so

$$\sigma^2 = \frac{\Sigma f_i (x_i)^2}{n} - (\bar{x})^2 \tag{14.14}$$

In the case of a continuous distribution the variance is given by

$$\sigma^2 = \frac{\int_{x_a}^{x_b} f(x)(x - \bar{x})^2 \, dx}{\int_{x_a}^{x_b} f(x)dx} \tag{14.15}$$

14.3 THE NORMAL DISTRIBUTION

Since we are concerned with random errors, the most important frequency distribution for our purposes is the *normal* or *gaussian distribution*. The *gaussian law of error* states that random errors are distributed according to the normal distribution. Two other distributions that are important in other contexts are the binomial and the Poisson distributions.

If we made an infinite number of observations we would find that the frequency distribution y would be given by the function

$$y = \frac{1}{\sigma\sqrt{(2\pi)}} \exp\left[-\frac{(x-\bar{x})^2}{2\sigma^2}\right] \qquad (14.16)$$

where $\bar{x}$ is the 'true' mean and σ is the standard deviation. This is symmetrical about the mean and a graph of this function is shown in figure 14.5. The mean $\bar{x}$ is the value of x having the highest frequency and represents the 'true' value of the quantity being measured.

This function is properly normalised so that

$$\int_{-\infty}^{\infty} y\,dx = 1 \qquad (14.17)$$

The area under the curve between $x = x_1$ and $x = x_2$ gives the probability of an observation x having a value between x_1 and x_2. This is given by the definite integral

$$\int_{x_1}^{x_2} y\,dx = \int_{x_1}^{x_2} \frac{1}{\sigma\sqrt{2\pi}} \exp\left[-\frac{(x-\bar{x})^2}{2\sigma^2}\right] \qquad (14.18)$$

This is related to the *error function* erf(T), which is defined by

$$\mathrm{erf}(T) = \frac{2}{\sqrt{\pi}} \int_0^T \exp(-t^2)\,dt \qquad (14.19)$$

for which values are tabulated. The integral in equation 14.18 can be expressed in terms of this by the change of variable

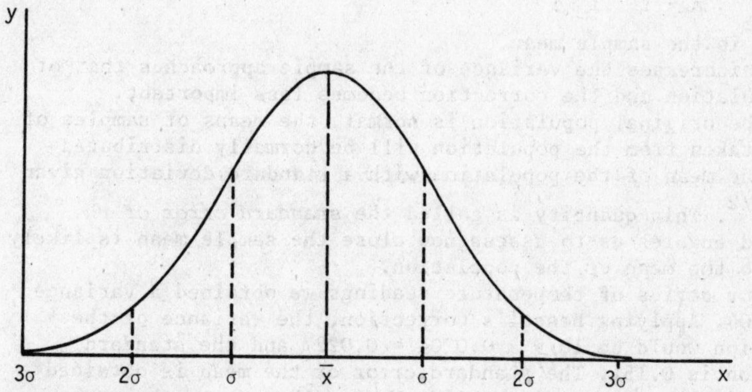

Figure 14.5

$(x - \bar{x})/\sigma = t$. Thus

$$\int_{x_1}^{x_2} y\,dx = \int_{t_1}^{t_2} \frac{1}{\sqrt{(2\pi)}} \exp(-\tfrac{1}{2}t^2)dt \qquad (14.20)$$

where $t_1 = (x_1 - \bar{x})/\sigma$ and $t_2 = (x_2 - \bar{x})/\sigma$. This can be expressed as the sum of two integrals as follows

$$\int_{x_1}^{x_2} y\,dx = \int_0^{t_2} \frac{1}{\sqrt{(2\pi)}} \exp(-\tfrac{1}{2}t^2)dt - \int_0^{t_1} \frac{1}{\sqrt{(2\pi)}} \exp(-\tfrac{1}{2}t^2)dt$$

$$= \int_0^{\sqrt{2}t_2} \frac{1}{\sqrt{(2\pi)}} \exp(-t^2)dt - \int_0^{\sqrt{2}t_1} \frac{1}{\sqrt{(2\pi)}} \exp(-t^2)dt \qquad (14.21)$$

The meaning of the standard deviation now becomes clearer because approximately 68 per cent of the distribution lies between $\bar{x} - \sigma$ and $\bar{x} + \sigma$. For $\bar{x} \pm 2\sigma$ the proportion is approximately 95 per cent and for $\bar{x} \pm 3\sigma$ it rises to 99.7 per cent. Thus the distribution lies almost entirely between $\bar{x} \pm 3\sigma$ although it theoretically stretches to $\pm\infty$.

14.4 SAMPLING

The normal distribution is based on an infinite number of observations. However, we are only able to make a finite number of observations and are thus concerned with a *sample* from the total *population*. Our set of temperature measurements is a sample from the infinite number theoretically possible. Because we only have a sample, the mean that we calculate will in general differ from the mean of the population and the standard deviation will also be different from that of the population. The variance σ^2 of an infinite population can, however, be estimated from a sample of n observations by the use of *Bessel's correction*

$$\sigma^2 = \frac{1}{n - 1} \Sigma f_i(x_i - \bar{x})^2 \qquad (14.22)$$

where $\bar{x}$ is the sample mean.

As n increases the variance of the sample approaches that of the population and the correction becomes less important.

If the original population is normal, the means of samples of size n taken from the population will be normally distributed about the mean of the population with a standard deviation given by $\sigma/n^{1/2}$. This quantity is called the *standard error of the mean* and enables us to assess how close the sample mean is likely to be to the mean of the population.

In our series of temperature readings we obtained a variance of 0.0204. Applying Bessel's correction, the variance of the population would be 10/9 × 0.0204 = 0.0227 and the standard deviation is 0.151. The standard error of the mean is obtained by dividing by $\sqrt{10}$ to give 0.048. We can thus quote the average temperature as 297.96 ± 0.048 (10 measurements). By this we mean that if we made a much larger number of measurements of the temperature, the mean would lie between 297.96 - 0.048 and 297.96 + 0.048 with a probability of 0.68. Since the probabilities depend on the number of measurements on which the standard error of the mean is based it is important to quote this number.

14.5 THE METHOD OF LEAST SQUARES AND CURVE FITTING

We are usually more interested in finding the most accurate representation of the variation of some observable y with respect to a variable x than in the measurement of a single quantity. In this section we consider the application of statistical ideas to the fitting of a function to a set of experimental data.

14.5.1 Principle of least squares

The *principle of least squares* states that for a normal distribution the most probable value X of any observed quantity is such that the sum of the squares of the deviations of the observations x_i from the value X is a minimum. Thus we require the sum $\Sigma(X - x_i)^2$ to be a minimum.

We can use this principle to show that the most probable value is the mean $\bar{x}$ as we asserted in section 14.2. We wish to minimise the sum $\sum_{i=1}^{n} (X - x_i)^2$. Let us rewrite this in terms of the mean $\bar{x}$

$$\sum_{i=1}^{n} (X - x_i)^2 = \sum_{i=1}^{n} [(X - \bar{x}) + (\bar{x} - x_i)]^2$$

$$= \Sigma(X - \bar{x})^2 + 2\Sigma(X - \bar{x})(\bar{x} - x_i) + \Sigma(\bar{x} - x_i)^2$$

$$= n(X - \bar{x})^2 + 2(X - \bar{x})\Sigma(\bar{x} - x_i) + \Sigma(\bar{x} - x_i)^2$$

Since the sum of deviations from the mean, $\Sigma(\bar{x} - x_i)$ is zero we have

$$\sum_{i=1}^{n} (X - x_i)^2 = n(X - \bar{x})^2 + \Sigma(\bar{x} - x_i)^2 \qquad (14.23)$$

which will be a minimum if $(X - \bar{x})$ is zero. Thus the most probable value of X is equal to the mean $\bar{x}$.

We can easily extend this to the case in which each observation x_i occurs with a frequency f_i. In this case we wish to minimise $\Sigma f_i(X - x_i)^2$. The mean is now

$$\bar{x} = \frac{\Sigma f_i x_i}{\Sigma f_i}$$

and the sum of the squares of the deviations from X can be written as

$$\Sigma f_i (X - x_i)^2 = \Sigma f_i (x_i - \bar{x})^2 + (X - \bar{x})^2 \Sigma f_i \qquad (14.24)$$

which is a minimum for $X = \bar{x}$.

The frequencies f_i are often also called *weights*. In some cases it may be desirable to assign weights to observations for reasons other than frequency. For example they may not all be of the same accuracy. In this case one can assign a weight equal to the reciprocal of the variance for that observation.

14.5.2 Fitting of data to a linear function

In a particular experiment we may expect a measured quantity y to depend linearly on some variable x; that is

$$y = mx + b \qquad (14.25)$$

A common application is in reaction kinetics, where the logarithm of the rate constant k is proportional to the reciprocal of the temperature T

$$\ln k = \ln A - \left(\frac{E}{R}\right)\frac{1}{T} \qquad (14.26)$$

where E is the activation energy and R is the gas constant. In the first instance we suppose that the variable x, which is the reciprocal of temperature, can be measured accurately but y, the logarithm of the rate constant, will be subject to experimental error. In general a plot of the observed values of y, $y_{i(obs)}$, against x will show some scatter and the drawing of a straight line involves an element of guess work (figure 14.6).

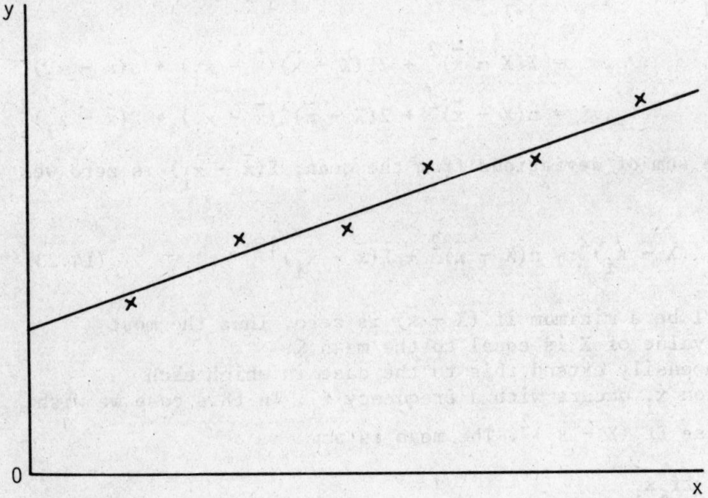

Figure 14.6

However, we can determine values of m and b that give the 'best' fit to the data by *regression analysis* or *least-squares analysis*. For these best values of m and b, equation 14.25 will predict a value of y, $y_{i(exp)} = mx_i + b$ for $x = x_i$. We use the principle of least squares to find m and b such that the sum $\Sigma(y_{i(obs)} - y_{i(exp)})^2$ is a minimum. Thus we require $S = \Sigma_i(y_{i(obs)} - mx_i - b)^2$ to be a minimum. The conditions for this to be the case are that the partial derivatives $\partial S/\partial m$ and $\partial S/\partial b$ are zero and the second derivatives $\partial^2 S/\partial m^2$ and $\partial^2 S/\partial b^2$ are positive. The first derivatives are

$$\frac{\partial S}{\partial m} = -\Sigma 2x_i(y_{i(obs)} - mx_i - b) = 0 \qquad (14.27)$$

and

$$\frac{\partial S}{\partial b} = -\Sigma 2(y_{i(obs)} - mx_i - b) = 0 \qquad (14.28)$$

The second derivatives are $2\Sigma x_i^2$ and 2, respectively, so the values of m and b satisfying equations 14.27 and 14.28 lead to a minimum in S. Rearranging these equations gives the *normal equations*

$$m\Sigma x_i^2 - 2\Sigma x_i y_{i(obs)} + b\Sigma x_i = 0 \qquad (14.29)$$

and

$$\Sigma y_{i(obs)} - m\Sigma x_i + nb = 0 \qquad (14.30)$$

which can be solved for m and b to give

$$m = \frac{n\Sigma x_i y_{i(obs)} - \Sigma x_i \Sigma y_{i(obs)}}{n\Sigma(x_i^2) - (\Sigma x_i)^2} \qquad (14.31)$$

and

$$b = \frac{\Sigma x_i \Sigma x_i y_{i(obs)} - \Sigma(x_i^2)\Sigma y_{i(obs)}}{(\Sigma x_i)^2 - n\Sigma(x_i^2)} \qquad (14.32)$$

The constant m is known as the *regression coefficient*. These values of m and b give the straight line y = mx + b that best fits the data.

Let us find the best straight line for the variation of ln k with 1/T from the data in table 14.2.

Table 14.2

y_i(ln k)	2.42	2.18	2.05	1.82	1.57	1.43
x_i(1/T)	0.0020	0.0022	0.0024	0.0026	0.0028	0.0030

$\Sigma x_i y_i = 0.027974$; $\Sigma y_i = 11.47$; $\Sigma x_i = 0.015$;

$\Sigma(x_i^2) = 0.0000382$; $(\Sigma x_i)^2 = 0.000225$

Therefore

$$m = \frac{(6 \times 0.027974) - (0.015 \times 11.47)}{(6 \times 0.0000382) - 0.000225} = -1001.4$$

and

$$b = \frac{(0.015 \times 0.027974) - (0.0000382 \times 11.47)}{0.000225 - (6 \times 0.0000382)} = 4.415$$

Thus the best linear relation or *line of regression* of (ln k) on (1/T) is

$$\ln k = -1001.4 \left(\frac{1}{T}\right) + 4.415 \qquad (14.33)$$

and is shown in figure 14.7.

The line of regression obtained in this way passes through the point $(\bar{x},\bar{y})$, where $\bar{x}$ and $\bar{y}$ are the means of x and y, respectively. We can also express the equation of the line in terms of $(\bar{x},\bar{y})$ as follows

$$y - \bar{y} = m(x - \bar{x})$$

where

$$m = \frac{\Sigma(x_i - \bar{x})(y_i - \bar{y})}{\Sigma(x_i - \bar{x})^2} \qquad (14.34)$$

This form may be more convenient for calculation by hand.

The accuracy of the regression is given by quoting variances for the regression coefficients. If the data are fitted to the equation

$$y = mx + b$$

the variances for m and b, α_m^2 and α_b^2 are given by

$$\alpha_m^2 = \frac{n\sigma^2}{n\Sigma(x_i)^2 - (\Sigma x_i)^2}; \quad \alpha_b^2 = \frac{\sigma^2\Sigma(x_i^2)}{n\Sigma(x_i)^2 - (\Sigma x_i)^2} \qquad (14.35)$$

where σ^2 is the variance of y, which is given by

$$\sigma^2 = \frac{\Sigma(y_i - mx_i - b)^2}{n - 2}$$

The factor (n - 2) appears because two degrees of freedom have been used in the determination of σ^2. The variance $\alpha^2(y_0)$ for any estimated point y_0 is given by

$$\alpha^2(y_0) = \sigma^2\left[\frac{1}{n} + \frac{(x_0 - \bar{x})^2}{\sum_{i=1}^{n}(x_i - \bar{x})^2}\right] \qquad (14.36)$$

In our example, $\sigma^2 = 0.00117$, so

$$\alpha_m = \left(\frac{6 \times 0.00117}{6 \times 0.0000382 - 0.000225}\right)^{1/2} = 40.9$$

and

$$\alpha_b = \left(\frac{0.00117 \times 0.0000382}{6 \times 0.0000382 - 0.000225}\right)^{1/2} = 0.103$$

We can therefore write our result as

$$y = (-1001.4 \pm 40.9)x + (4.415 \pm 0.103) \tag{14.37}$$

If the data are fitted to the equation

$$y - \bar{y} = m(x - \bar{x})$$

the standard error in m, α_m, is given by

$$\alpha_m^2 = \frac{\sigma^2}{\sum_i (x_i - \bar{x})^2} \tag{14.38}$$

So far we have considered the case in which only the values of y are subject to error. Often both x and y are subject to error and the analysis presented above is not sufficient. In such cases we have also to determine the line of regression of x on y by regarding the values of x as subject to error and the values of y as being accurate. This will give an equation

$$x = m'y + b' \tag{14.39}$$

where the coefficients m' and b' are given by interchanging x and y in equations 14.31 and 14.32 to give

$$m' = \frac{n\Sigma x_{i(obs)} y_i - \Sigma x_{i(obs)} \Sigma y_i}{n\Sigma(y_i^2) - (\Sigma y_i)^2} \tag{14.40}$$

$$b' = \frac{\Sigma y_i \Sigma x_{i(obs)} y_i - \Sigma(y_i^2)\Sigma x_{i(obs)}}{(\Sigma y_i)^2 - n\Sigma(y_i^2)} \tag{14.41}$$

The line obtained will in general be different from the line y = mx + b obtained by the regression of y on x. In our example $(\Sigma y_i)^2 = 131.56$ and $\Sigma(y_i^2) = 22.6335$ and we obtain

$$m' = \frac{(6 \times 0.027974) - (0.015 \times 11.47)}{(6 \times 22.6335) - 131.56} = -0.00099$$

and

$$b' = \frac{(11.47 \times 0.027974) - (22.6335 \times 0.015)}{131.56 - (6 \times 22.6335)} = 0.004395$$

Thus (1/T) = -0.00099 (ln k) + 0.004395, which can be rearranged to give

$$\ln k = -1008.32 \left(\frac{1}{T}\right) + 4.43 \tag{14.42}$$

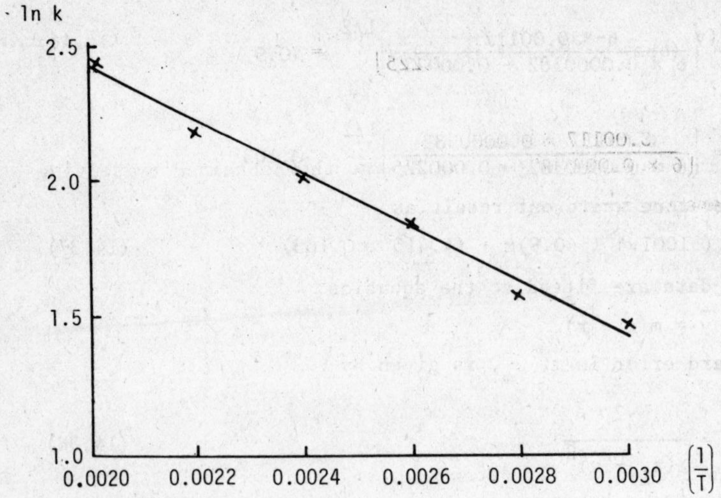

Figure 14.7

The 'best' straight line would then be the line passing through the point $(\bar{x},\bar{y})$ and bisecting the acute angle between the two lines. The difference between equations 14.33 and 14.42 is too small to illustrate on a graph.

14.5.3 Fitting of data to other functions

The method discussed above can be extended to the determination of the best function of the type

$$y = a_0 + a_1x + a_2x^2 + \ldots + a_mx^m \tag{14.43}$$

where we seek to determine the (m + 1) constants a_0, a_1 ... a_m such that the sum of squares

$$S = \Sigma\left[y_{i(\text{obs})} - (a_0 + a_1x + \ldots a_mx^m)\right]^2 \tag{14.44}$$

is a minimum. This is known as *curvilinear regression*. In the case of the quadratic function

$$y = a_0 + a_1x + a_2x^2 \tag{14.45}$$

we require the sum

$$S = \sum_{i=1}^{n} (y_{i(\text{obs})} - a_0 - a_1x_i - a_2x_i^2)^2$$

to be a minimum. Thus the derivatives $\partial S/\partial a_0$, $\partial S/\partial a_1$ and $\partial S/\partial a_2$ have to be zero, leading to the equations

$$\sum_i (y_{i(\text{obs})} - a_0 - a_1x_i - a_2x_i^2) = 0$$

$$\sum_i x_i(y_{i(obs)} - a_0 - a_1x_i - a_2x_i^2) = 0 \tag{14.46}$$

$$\sum_i x_i^2(y_{i(obs)} - a_0 - a_1x_i - a_2x_i^2) = 0$$

The optimum values of a_0, a_1 and a_2 are then obtained by solving the normal equations

$$\left.\begin{aligned} &\sum_i y_{i(obs)} - na_0 - a_1\sum_i x_i - a_2\sum_i x_i^2 = 0 \\ &\sum_i x_iy_{i(obs)} - a_0\sum_i x_i - a_1\sum_i x_i^2 - a_2\sum_i x_i^3 = 0 \\ &\sum_i x_i^2y_{i(obs)} - a_0\sum_i x_i^2 - a_1\sum_i x_i^3 - a_2\sum_i x_i^4 = 0 \end{aligned}\right\} \tag{14.47}$$

The method can be readily extended to higher polynomials and to combinations of other functions as long as they are of the form of a linear combination in which the parameters to be optimised are the coefficients a_i; that is

$$y = \sum_i a_if_i(x) \tag{14.48}$$

For functions of this type, the determination of the coefficients a_i only involves the solution of simultaneous equations. If the parameters to be optimised occur in the functions $f_i(x)$ themselves, the optimisation becomes much more difficult.

14.6 SIGNIFICANCE TESTS

14.6.1 Significance levels

It is important to be able to decide in a quantitative way whether the outcome of an experiment is statistically significant. For example, under certain conditions a chemical reaction may have a mean yield of $\bar{x}_0$. Suppose we change the reaction conditions and observe for a series of n experiments under the new conditions that the new yield is $\bar{x}_1$. We now have to decide whether this change in yield is *significant*; that is can we attribute it to the change in reaction conditions, or does it merely arise because we have taken a small sample from a large population? We do this by calculating the *probability* p that for a series of n yields obtained under the original conditions, we would obtain a mean yield as good as or better than $\bar{x}_1$. If p is larger than 0.1 (that is, there is better than a one in ten chance of obtaining $\bar{x}_1$ under the old conditions), then conventionally we say the result is *not significant*. The generally accepted convention in interpretating significance is given in table 14.3. Thus a result is generally regarded as being significant if there is less than a one in twenty probability of it occurring in a sample from the original population.

Table 14.3

probability	conclusion
$p \geqslant 0.1$	not significant
$0.1 > p \geqslant 0.05$	possibly significant but doubtful
$0.05 > p \geqslant 0.01$	significant
$0.01 > p \geqslant 0.001$	highly significant
$0.001 > p$	very highly significant

Before considering significance tests in detail we should define the term *degrees of freedom*. A set of n observations has n degrees of freedom. However, each time we calculate a parameter such as the mean or the variance from a set of data we use up one degree of freedom. So if we calculate the mean of n observations, the variance will have $\phi = n - 1$ degrees of freedom.

There are many significance tests but we confine our attention to three. We first consider the problem we outlined above: given a sample having a mean $\bar{x}_1$, what is the probability of it being drawn from the original population having a mean $\bar{x}_0$? There are two tests for this known as the *u-test* and *Student's t-test* depending on whether the variance of the population is known or not. Another problem is to decide whether a given sample of data is drawn from a normal (or other distribution). This can be determined using the χ^2*-test*. These tests require the use of statistical tables such as those listed in the bibliography.

14.6.2 The u-test

This test is used to determine whether the population from which our new sample of n-observations with mean $\bar{x}_1$ is drawn is the same as the original normal population with mean $\bar{x}_0$ and variance σ^2. We calculate the parameter u given by

$$u = \frac{(\bar{x}_1 - \bar{x}_0)}{SE(\bar{x}_1)} = \frac{\bar{x}_1 - \bar{x}_0}{(\sigma/\sqrt{n})} \qquad (14.49)$$

where $SE(\bar{x}_1)$ is the standard error of the mean $\bar{x}_1$. This is the transformation necessary to express a normal distribution of observed mean values $\bar{x}_1$ with standard error $(\sigma/\sqrt{n})$ about the mean value $\bar{x}_0$ in terms of the standard gaussian function $(1/\sqrt{2\pi})$ $\exp(-u^2/2)$ of equation 14.20. We can determine the probability of u exceeding u_1 from *standard normal distribution tables* of the integral $(1/\sqrt{2\pi}) \int_{u_1}^{\infty} \exp(-\frac{1}{2}u^2)du$. This gives us the probability of $\bar{x}_1$ differing from $\bar{x}_0$ by at least as much as the given amount.

Under the original conditions a given chemical reaction has a mean yield of 32 g with a standard deviation of 1.2 g. The conditions are changed and the yields from five experiments are 32.1, 33.0, 35.6, 33.9 and 34.8 g. We wish to determine whether there has been a significant increase in the yield. The new mean is given by

$$\bar{x}_1 = \frac{1}{5}\left[32.1 + 33.0 + 35.6 + 33.9 + 34.8\right] = 33.88 \text{ g}$$

Thus

$$u = \frac{(32 - 33.88)}{(1.2/\sqrt{5})} = -3.5 \tag{14.50}$$

Standard normal tables show that the probability that $u \geqslant 3.5$ is 0.000233. (Since the distribution is symmetrical there is an equal probability that $u \leqslant -3.5$ in this case). The increase in yield in this case is very highly significant.

If the yields under the new conditions are 31.0, 31.7, 32.2, 33.4 and 34.2 g the new mean is 32.5 and the value of u is given by

$$u = -\frac{0.50}{(1.2/\sqrt{5})} = -0.932 \tag{14.51}$$

Examination of the tables shows that the probability of $|u| \geqslant 0.93$ is 0.176 so in this case the increase in yield is not significant.

We can calculate the limits within which we expect the true value of the mean yield $\bar{x}$ under the new conditions to lie from the value of the mean $\bar{x}_1$ of our sample and its standard error $\sigma/\sqrt{n}$. We express our results in terms of *confidence limits*. We determine the limits $\Delta(\bar{x}_1)$ such that there is, for example, a 0.1 probability, or *risk*, that the true mean $\bar{x}$ will lie outside the range between $\bar{x}_1 - \Delta(\bar{x}_1)$ and $\bar{x}_1 + \Delta(\bar{x}_1)$. These limits are the 90 per cent confidence limits. In general, if the risk of the true mean lying outside the confidence limits is α, the limits are the $100(1 - \alpha)$ per cent confidence limits. The risk α can usually be divided into two parts such that there is a risk $\alpha/2$ that the mean $\bar{x}$ will lie above the upper limit and a risk $\alpha/2$ that it will lie below the lower limit. We can determine from standard normal tables the value of u, $u_{\alpha/2}$ for which there is a probability $\alpha/2$ of u exceeding $u_{\alpha/2}$. For a normal distribution there is also a probability $\alpha/2$ that u is less than $-u_{\alpha/2}$. Thus there is a probability $\alpha/2$ that the sample mean $\bar{x}_1$ will exceed $\bar{x}_{1+}$ where $\bar{x}_{1+}$ is given by

$$u_{\alpha/2} = \frac{\bar{x}_{1+} - \bar{x}}{(\sigma/\sqrt{n})} \tag{14.52}$$

Similarly there is a probability $\alpha/2$ that the mean of the sample will be less than $\bar{x}_{1-}$ given by

$$-u_{\alpha/2} = \frac{\bar{x}_{1-} - \bar{x}}{(\sigma/\sqrt{n})} \qquad (14.53)$$

From these relations we deduce that there is a probability α that the sample mean $\bar{x}_1$ lies outside the limits

$$\bar{x} \pm u_{\alpha/2}(\sigma/\sqrt{n}) \qquad (14.54)$$

If $\bar{x}_1$ is used to estimate $\bar{x}$ then there is a probability α that $\bar{x}$ will lie outside the limits

$$\bar{x}_1 \pm u_{\alpha/2}(\sigma/\sqrt{n}) \qquad (14.55)$$

If we are interested in the 90 per cent confidence limits for the yield under the first set of new conditions we deduce that there is a 10 per cent probability that the new average mean will lie outside the limits

$$\bar{x}_1 \pm u_{0.05}(\sigma/\sqrt{n}) = 33.88 \pm 1.64 \times \frac{1.2}{\sqrt{5}} = 33.88 \pm 0.88 \qquad (14.56)$$

where $u_{0.05}$ is the value of u such that 5 per cent of the distribution lies above it. Thus there is a 5 per cent probability of the new mean yield being less than 33.00 g and a 5 per cent probability of it being higher than 34.76 g.

14.6.3 Student's t-test

Student's t-test is used when the standard deviation σ of the original population is not known. In such cases we calculate the parameter t given by

$$t = \frac{\bar{x}_1 - \bar{x}_0}{SE(\bar{x}_1)} = \frac{\bar{x}_1 - \bar{x}_0}{(\sigma_1/\sqrt{n})} \qquad (14.57)$$

where σ_1 is the standard deviation for our sample of n observations and $SE(\bar{x}_1)$ is the standard error of the mean. Since t is based on the standard deviation of a limited sample, its distribution will be different from the normal distribution. Statistical tables contain tabulations for various degrees of freedom of values of t that will be exceeded in *absolute value* with given probabilities. If we are just interested in one end of the distribution, that is the probability that $t > t_0$ or $t < -t_0$, we have to divide the values in the tables by 2.

In our first set of improved yields with mean $\bar{x}_1 = 33.88$, the standard deviation σ_1 is given by

$$\sigma_1 = \left\{\frac{1}{5}\left[(1.78)^2 + (0.88)^2 + (1.72)^2 + (0.02)^2 + (0.62)^2\right]\right\}^{1/2}$$
$$= 1.207$$

Thus

$$t = \frac{33.88 - 32.0}{(1.207/\sqrt{5})} = 3.482$$

For four degrees of freedom $|t|$ will exceed 2.78 with 5 per cent probability and 3.75 with 2 per cent probability. Thus the probabilities of t lying above 2.78 and 3.75 are 2.5 per cent and 1 per cent respectively, and the result is significant.

The standard deviation σ_2 for the second set with mean $\bar{x}_2$ = 32.5 is given by

$$\sigma_2 = \left\{\frac{1}{5}\left[(1.5)^2 + (0.8)^2 + (0.3)^2 + (0.9)^2 + (1.71)^2\right]\right\}^{1/2}$$
$$= 1.156$$

In this case

$$t = \frac{32.5 - 32.0}{(1.156/\sqrt{5})} = 0.967$$

This result is not significant because t will exceed 0.74 with 25 per cent probability and 1.53 with 10 per cent probability.

As in the case of the u-test, we can assign confidence limits to the mean. To obtain 90 per cent confidence limits for the yield under the first set of conditions we write

$$\begin{aligned}\bar{x} &= \bar{x}_1 \pm t_{0.05(\phi=4)} \times SE(\bar{x}_1) \\ &= \bar{x}_1 \pm t_{0.05(\phi=4)}\left(\frac{\sigma_1}{\sqrt{n}}\right)\end{aligned} \tag{14.58}$$

where $t_{0.05(\phi=4)}$ is the value of t that cuts off an area of 5 per cent in *one tail* of the distribution. Since the tables give the value t whose absolute value is exceeded with probability α, we require the value corresponding to 10 per cent. For four degrees of freedom this is 2.13. Thus

$$\bar{x} = 33.88 \pm 2.13\left(\frac{1.207}{\sqrt{5}}\right) = 33.88 \pm 1.15 \tag{14.59}$$

In this case there is a 5 per cent probability of the yield being less than 32.73 g and 5 per cent probability of its being higher than 35.03 g.

14.6.4 The χ^2-test

If we wish to know if a set of observations corresponds to a random sample drawn from a normal distribution, we can use the χ^2-test. We first of all classify the data into r classes and determine the frequencies $f_{i(obs)}$ for each class. From the mean $\bar{x}$ and the variance σ^2 of the data we can calculate the frequencies $f_{i(exp)}$ that would be expected for a normal distribution. We can then compute the quantity χ^2 given by

$$\chi^2 = \sum_{i=1}^{r} \frac{(f_{i(obs)} - f_{i(exp)})^2}{f_{i(exp)}} \tag{14.60}$$

In doing this we have used up three degrees of freedom by calculating the mean and variance and by making the sums of the observed and expected frequencies equal. Thus the number of degrees of freedom will be r - 3. Tables of the χ^2-distribution give the probability that for a given number of degrees of freedom a given value of χ^2 will be exceeded.

Let us apply the χ^2-test to the data given in table 14.4. The mean $\bar{x}$ is 12.52 and the standard deviation σ is 0.193. We obtain

Table 14.4

Class	Observed frequency $f_{i(obs)}$	u	Expected frequency $f_{i(exp)}$	$\frac{(f_{i(obs)} - f_{i(exp)})^2}{f_{i(exp)}}$
12.0	0	-2.18	1.02	1.02
12.1	2	-1.66	2.38	0.06
12.2	4	-1.44	5.50	0.41
12.3	7	-0.62	9.84	0.82
12.4	10	-0.10	13.48	0.90
12.5	17		13.92	0.68
12.6	13	0.41	11.53	0.19
12.7	9	0.93	7.18	0.46
12.8	4	1.45	3.52	0.07
12.9	3	1.97	1.18	2.81
13.0	1	2.49	0.45	0.67

the expected frequencies $f_{i(exp)}$ for the class x_i from the standard normal distribution tables by taking $u = (x_i - \bar{x})/\sigma$. Summing the numbers in the fifth column gives $\chi^2 = 8.08$. We have eight degrees of freedom and examination of χ^2-tables shows that χ^2 will exceed 7.34 with 50 per cent probability and 13.36 with 10 per cent probability. Thus the result is not significant and we conclude that the sample is drawn from a normal distribution.

This test is not restricted to normal distributions but can be used to test whether any series of observed frequencies $f_{i(obs)}$ conforms to an expected pattern $f_{i(exp)}$.

14.7 PROBLEMS FOR SOLUTION

1. Calculate the mean, median, variance and standard deviation for each of the following sets of data. Assuming each set is drawn from a normal distribution, calculate the standard error of the mean:

(i) 15.6, 15.9, 15.4, 15.6, 15.5, 15.7, 15.5, 15.3, 15.6, 15.8.

(ii)

Class	20.0	20.2	20.4	20.6	20.8	21.0	21.2
Frequency	1	3	4	7	10	12	9

Class	21.4	21.6	21.8	22.0
Frequency	6	4	3	1

(iii)

Class	0	5	10	15	20	25	30	35	40	45	50
Frequency	1	4	7	11	13	17	22	29	31	35	40

Class	55	60	65	70	75	80	85	90	95	100
Frequency	33	27	21	11	7	4	2	1	1	0

2. What proportion of the normal distribution lies above:

(i) $\bar{x} + 0.5\sigma$; (ii) $\bar{x} + 1.5\sigma$; (iii) $\bar{x} + 2.5\sigma$?

3. What values of x define the interquartile range for a normal distribution?

4. Determine the best straight-line relationship for the following data assuming that only y is subject to error. Quote standard errors for the regression coefficients:

(i)

x	0	0.5	1.0	1.5	2.0	2.5	3.0	3.5	4.0	4.5	5.0
y	1.1	1.45	1.9	2.1	2.7	3.4	4.2	4.4	5.1	5.6	5.9

(ii)

x	1	2	3	4	5	6	7	8
y	100.3	201.7	295.7	403.6	497.1	611.3	703.1	788.9

x	9	10
y	906.3	1019.1

5. Determine the best straight-line relationship for the following data assuming that both x and y are subject to error:

x	0.1	1.9	4.1	6.2	7.9	10.1	12.0	13.9	16.1
y	0.5	10.2	20.3	29.5	41.0	50.7	59.3	72.1	78.7

x	17.8	19.9
y	91.3	98.9

6. Use the method of least squares to find the function $y = ax^2 + bx + c$ that gives the best fit to the following data, assuming that only y is subject to error:

x	0	1	2	3	4	5	6	7	8
y	1.2	2.1	4.8	10.2	16.5	27.0	37.3	49.3	66.1

x	9	10
y	83.0	100.7

7. Apply the χ^2-test to establish whether the data in questions 1(ii) and 1(iii) are drawn from normal distributions.

8. Under particular reaction conditions, compound A is obtained with 78.5 per cent purity. The standard deviation is 2.7 per cent. In ten experiments under new conditions the following percentage purities were obtained: 81.2, 80.1, 79.7, 82.3, 83.1, 80.2, 84.3, 78.6, 85.2, 81.7.

Has there been any significant change in the purity of the product? Calculate the 95 per cent confidence limits for the mean purity under the new conditions. Would your conclusion be the same if you did not know the standard deviation under the original conditions?

Bibliography

GENERAL

W. J. Moore, *Physical Chemistry*, Longman, London (5th edn, 1972)
L. Pauling and E. B. Wilson, *Introduction to Quantum Mechanics*, McGraw-Hill, New York (1935)
W. Kauzmann, *Quantum Chemistry*, Academic Press, New York (1957).
P. W. Atkins, *Molecular Quantum Mechanics*, Clarendon Press, Oxford (1970)
H. Goldstein, *Classical Mechanics*, Addison-Wesley, Reading, Mass. (1950)

GENERAL MATHEMATICAL TEXT

G. Stephenson, *Mathematical Methods for Science Students*, Longman, London (2nd edn,1973)

MATHEMATICAL TABLES

H. B. Dwight, *Tables of Integrals and Other Mathematical Data*, Macmillan, New York (4th edn, 1961)
M. Abramovitz and I. A. Stegun, *Handbook of Mathematical Functions*, Dover, New York (1965)

CHAPTER 5

S. Simons, *Vector Analysis for Mathematicians, Scientists and Engineers*, Pergamon, Oxford (2nd edn, 1970)

CHAPTER 6

J. A. Green, *Sequences and Series*, Routledge & Kegan Paul, London (1958)

CHAPTER 7

W. Ledermann, *Complex Numbers*, Routledge & Kegan Paul, London (1960)

CHAPTER 8

I. N. Sneddon, *Fourier Series*, Routledge & Kegan Paul, London (1961)

P. D. Robinson, *Fourier and Laplace Transforms*, Routledge & Kegan Paul, London (1968)

CHAPTER 10

G. Stephenson, *An Introduction to Matrices, Sets and Groups*, Longman, London (1965)

CHAPTER 12

G. Stephenson, *An Introduction to Partial Differential Equations for Science Students*, Longman, London (2nd edn, 1970)

CHAPTER 13

D. D. McCracken and W. S. Dorn, *Numerical Methods and Fortran Programming*, Wiley, New York (1964)

CHAPTER 14

Biometrika Tables for Statisticians, Biometrika Trustees, University College, London

R. A. Fisher and F. Yates, *Statistical Tables for Biological, Agricultural and Medical Research*, Oliver & Boyd, Edinburgh (6th edn, 1963)

J. Murdoch and J. A. Barnes, *Statistical Tables*, Macmillan, London (2nd edn, 1970)

O. L. Davies and P. L. Goldsmith, *Statistical Methods in Research and Production*, Oliver & Boyd, Edinburgh (4th edn, 1972)

C. J. Brooks, I. G. Betteley and S. M. Loxston, *Mathematics and Statistics*, Wiley, London (1966), chapters 9-16

J. Topping, *Errors of Observation and Their Treatment*, Chapman & Hall, London (3rd edn, 1962)

E. S. Swinbourne, *Analysis of Kinetic Data*, Nelson, London (1971)

Solutions to Problems

CHAPTER 1

1. (i) $-\frac{3}{8}$, (ii) $-\frac{3}{8}$, (iii) $\frac{3}{4}$;
2. (i) y versus x^2, (ii) y versus $x^{1/2}$, (iii) ln x versus t, (iv) ln k versus $u^{1/2}$, (v) ln y versus ln k;
3. (i) $(3 \pm \sqrt{41})/4$, (ii) $(-2 \pm \sqrt{31})/3$, (iii) no real solutions;
4. (i) All x except $x = \pm 1/\sqrt{3}$, (ii) $x < 1$ and $x > 3$, (iii) all x except −3, 1, 2;
5. (i)-(iii) odd, (iv) even, (v) odd;
6. $1/\sqrt{2}$, $1/\sqrt{2}$, 1/2, $\sqrt{3}/2$, 1/2, $\sqrt{3}$;
9. (i) $\frac{1}{2}\sin 6A$, (ii) $\frac{1}{2}(\cos 5A - \cos 9A)$, (iii) $\frac{1}{2}(\cos 9A + \cos A)$;
10. $\frac{1}{2}\{\cos[2\pi(\nu_k + \nu)t] + \cos 2\pi(\nu_k - \nu)t\}$;
11. $2a_0 \cos(2\pi x/\lambda)\cos(2\pi\nu t)$;
12. 12.182, 0.13534, 40.447, 4.54×10^{-5};
13. 2, −6, 0.5, 4, −1, −3, 6;
14. 0.6309, 1.4307, 2.8074;
15. 2.303;
16. $\pi/6$, $\pi/3$; $\pi/4$, 1.266, 2.837, 3.9176.

CHAPTER 2

1. (i) 0, (ii) 1;
2. (i) yes, (ii) no;
3. (i) 2x, (ii) $3x^2$, (iii) $4x - 3$, (iv) $-1/(1 + x)^2$;
4. (i) 1/3, (ii) −74/5;
5. (i) $21x^2 + 8x$, (ii) $(2/3)x^{-2/3}$, (iii) $-(3/8)x^{-7/4}$, (iv) $8x^3 + 7x^2$, (v) $30x^4 - 60x^3 + 20x - 21$, (vi) $4x^3$, (vii) $3x^{1/2}(\sqrt{x} + 2)(\sqrt{x} - 1) + x(2\sqrt{x} + 1)$, (viii) $1/(x + 1)^2$, (ix) $6x(1 - 3x^2)$, (x) $(x^2 - 4x + 2)/(x - 2)^2$, (xi) $-40(1 - 5x)^7$, (xii) $x^{-1/2}(1 - x)^{-3/2}$, (xiii) $-8nx(1 - 2x^2)^{2n-1}$, (xiv) $3\cos 3x - 3\sin 3x$, (xv) $3\sin x \cos x(\sin x - \cos x)$, (xvi) $3x^2[\cos x^3 - \sin x^3]$, (xvii) $-5\,\mathrm{cosec}^2(5x + 1)$, (xviii) $-4x\,\mathrm{cosec}\,2x^2 \cot 2x^2$, (xix) $5\exp(5x)$, (xx) $-2\exp(5 - 2x)$, (xxi) $1/x$,

(xxii) $-\tan x$, (xxiii) $3x^2/(x^3 + 3)$,
(xxiv) $\ln(\sin x) + x \cot x$, (xxv) $-\sin x \exp(\cos x)$,
(xxvi) $\ln 3 \times 3^x$, (xxvii) $\ln 2 \times \sec x \tan x \times 2^{\sec x}$,
(xxviii) $x^{-1/2} \exp(\surd x)$;

6. 0;
7. (i) $x = 3$, minimum; $x = -1/3$, maximum, (ii) $x = 1$, maximum; $x = -1$, minimum, (iii) approx. $x = -0.5$, minimum; approx. $x = 0.7$, maximum; approx. $x = 2.9$, minimum;
11. (i) $4/\surd(1 - 16x^2)$, (ii) $a/(a^2 + x^2)$, (iii) $4x/\{(x^2 - 1)\surd[(x^2 - 1)^2 - (x^2 + 1)^2]\}$; (iv) $-1/[\surd(9 - x^2)]$;
13. (i) $-(6x + 7y)/(7x + 18y)$, (ii) $[2x - 4x(x^2 + y^2)]/[4y(x^2 + y^2) + 2y]$, (iii) $(3y - 3x^2)/(3y^2 - 3x)$;
14. (i) $\left[\dfrac{x(x+1)(x-2)}{(x^2+1)(2x+3)}\right]^{1/2} \dfrac{1}{2}\left[\dfrac{1}{x} + \dfrac{1}{x+1} + \dfrac{1}{x-2} - \dfrac{2x}{x^2+1} - \dfrac{2}{2x+3}\right]$,

    (ii) $(\sin x)^{\tan x}[(\sec^2 x)\ln(\sin x) + 1]$,

    (iii) $\dfrac{x(x^2+1)^{1/2}}{(x+1)^{2/3}}\left[\dfrac{1}{x} + \dfrac{x}{x^2+1} - \dfrac{2}{3(x+1)}\right]$.

CHAPTER 3

1. (i) $0.08x^5$, (ii) $(4/3)x^3 - (5/2)x^2 + x$, (iii) $-2.5x^{-0.4}$, (iv) $\ln(x + 3)$, (v) $\ln(x^2 + 4)$, (vi) $(2/3)(ax + b)^{3/2}/a$, (vii) $1/3 \exp(3x - 1)$, (viii) $1/16(x^2 + 1)^8$, (ix) $1/2 \exp(x^2)$, (x) $1/3 \sin 3x + 3 \cos 3x$, (xi) $1/4 \sin^4 x$, (xii) $\ln(1 + \tan x)$, (xiii) $(ax + b)/2a + [\sin 2(ax + b)]/4a$, (xiv) $\sin x - (1/3)\sin^3 x$, (xv) $x/8 - (\sin 4x)/32$, (xvi) $-2 \cot 2x$, (xvii) $-(1/11) \cos 11x/2 - (1/5) \cos 5x/2$;
2. (i) $1/4 \sin^{-1} 2x + 1/2x\surd(1 - 4x^2)$, (ii) $\ln(\tan x)$, (iii) $1/2 \tan^{-1}[2 \tan(1/2x)]$, (iv) $1/3 \sin x^3$, (v) $-(1/6)\ln(1 - 2x^3)$, (vi) $-2 \cos \surd x$, (vii) $-(1/2)\ln(1 + 2 \cos x)$, (viii) $1/2(\ln x)^2$;
3. (i) $\sin x - x \cos x$, (ii) $x^3 \sin x + 3x^2 \cos x - 6x \sin x - 6 \cos x$, (iii) $1/2x^2 \ln x - 1/2x$, (iv) $1/4x^4 \ln x - (1/16)x^4$, (v) $e^x(0.4 \sin 2x + 0.2 \cos 2x)$, (vi) $x \tan^{-1} x - (1/2)\ln(1 + x^2)$, (vii) $x/b - a \ln(a + bx)/b^2$,

(viii) $x - 2\ln(2x + 3)$, (ix) $(1/3)x^3 + (1/2)x^2 + x + \ln(x - 1)$, (x) $\ln(1 - x) + 3/(1 - x)$, (xi) $x + (5/3)\ln(x - 2) - (2/3)\ln(x + 1)$, (xii) $(1/2)x^2 - 2x + 2\ln(x + 1) - \ln(x - 1)$, (xiii) $-(3/2)\ln x + (5/3)\ln(x - 1) - (1/6)\ln(x + 2)$, (xiv) $(1/5)[(3/2)\ln(x^2 + 4) - \tan^{-1}(1/2x) - 3\ln(1 - x)]$, (xv) $(1/\sqrt{8})\tan^{-1}[(x + 3)/\sqrt{8}]$, (xvi) $(1/\sqrt{13})\tan^{-1}(2x + 1)/\sqrt{13}$, (xvii) $\cosh^{-1}(x - 2)/\sqrt{2}$, (xviii) $\sqrt{(x^2 + 2x - 1)} + \cosh^{-1}(x + 1)/\sqrt{2}$, (xix) $2\sin^{-1}(x/\sqrt{2}) + (1/2)\ln\sqrt{(2 - x^2)}$, (xx) $-\cosh^{-1}[(2x + 1)/x]$, (xxi) $-(1/2)x(1 - x^2)^{1/2} + (1/2)\sin^{-1} x$, (xxii) $-2\sqrt{(1 - x)} + (2/3)(1 - x)^{3/2}$;

4. (i) $2/35$, (ii) $(16/55)(1 + 1/\sqrt{2})$. (iii) $-(7/8) + 1/\sqrt{2}$, (iv) $2 + 2\ln(5/3)$;
6. 0;
7. (i) $\pi,0$, (ii) $0,0$, (iii) $\pi,0$;
8. 4/27;
9. 57π;
10. $4(5^{5/2} - 2^{5/2})/5$
11. $(4/3)\pi a^2 b$;
12. $\pi^2/2$;
13. $(1/p)\sin pt$, $(m/4p^2)(1 - \cos 2pT)$;
14. $(\pi/6,1/2)$;
15. (a) $(1/RT)\ln(V_2/V_1)$, (b) $k/(1 - \gamma)[V_2^{1-\gamma} - V_1^{1-\gamma}]$;
16. (5/2,0);
17. (a) 45M/2, (b) 45M/7;
18. (a) $2/\pi$, (b) 1/2;
19. $(8kT/\pi m)^{1/2}$;
20. $4V_0^2/\pi g$.

CHAPTER 4

1. (i) $-2x\sin(x^2 + y^2)$, $-2y\sin(x^2 + y^2)$, (ii) $(y^3 - x^2y)/(x^2 + y^2)^2$, $(x^3 - xy^2)/(x^2 + y^2)^2$, (iii) a/y^2, $-2ax/y^3$;
2. (i) $\exp(x + y)[\cos(x - y) + \sin(x - y)]$, (ii) $\exp(x + y)[\sin(x - y) - \cos(x - y)]$, (iii) $2\cos(x - y)\exp(x + y)$, (iv) $2\sin(x - y)\exp(x + y)$, (v) $-2\cos(x - y)\exp(x + y)$;
4. (i) $[(1/y) - (z/x^2)]\{\ln[(x/y) + (y/z) + (z/x)] + 1\}$, (ii) $[(-x/y^2) + (1/z)]\{\ln[(x/y) + (y/z) + (z/x)] + 1\}$, (iii) $[(-y/z^2) + (1/x)]\{\ln[(x/y) + (y/z) + (z/x)] + 1\}$;
5. $5x^4$;
6. -3;

7. (i) $(1/y)dx - (x/y^2)dy$, (ii) $(2xy + y^3)dx + (x^2 + 3xy^2)dy$, (iii) $y\exp(xy)dx + x\exp(xy)dy$;
10. (i) $(\partial f/\partial u) + y(\partial f/\partial v)$, (ii) $-(\partial f/\partial u) + x(\partial f/\partial v)$;
14. $\frac{ih}{2\pi}\left[\sin\phi\frac{\partial}{\partial\theta} + \cot\theta\cos\phi\frac{\partial}{\partial\phi}\right]$,

$-\frac{ih}{2\pi}\left[\cos\phi\frac{\partial}{\partial\theta} - \cot\theta\sin\phi\frac{\partial}{\partial\phi}\right]$;

16. (i) $-(6x + 7y)/(7x + 18y)$, (ii) $[2x - 4x(x^2 + y^2)]/[4y(x^2 + y^2) + 2y]$, (iii) $(3y - 3x^2)/(3y^2 - 3x)$, (iv) $\cot x \cot y$, (v) $-(mx^{m-1}y^n - \ln a \times a^{x+y})/(nx^m y^{n-1} - \ln a \times a^{x+y})$;
17. (i) R/V_0P, $-\frac{1}{V_0}\left[\frac{R/(V - b)}{2a/V^3 - RT/(V - b)^2}\right]$;
18. (i) exact, (ii) inexact, (iii) inexact, (iv) exact;
19. 4096/3, (ii) 128/3, (iii) $11e^3 - 3e$, (iv) 4/3, 3/2.

CHAPTER 5

1. (i) $3\mathbf{i} + \mathbf{j} - 3\mathbf{k}$, $\mathbf{i} - 7\mathbf{j} + \mathbf{k}$, -8, $10\mathbf{i} + 3\mathbf{j} + 11\mathbf{k}$, -7, $\cos^{-1}(-8/7\sqrt{6})$; (ii) $3\mathbf{i} - 2\mathbf{j} - 2\mathbf{k}$, $\mathbf{i} - 4\mathbf{j}$, 0, $4\mathbf{i} + \mathbf{j} + 5\mathbf{k}$, 11, $\pi/2$; (iii) $3\mathbf{i} - 2\mathbf{j} + 2\mathbf{k}$, $-\mathbf{i} - 4\mathbf{j}$, 0, $-4\mathbf{i} + \mathbf{j} + 7\mathbf{k}$, 5, $\pi/2$; (iv) $3\mathbf{i} + 3\mathbf{j} + 3\mathbf{k}$, $-\mathbf{i} - \mathbf{j} - \mathbf{k}$, 6, 0, -9, 0; (v) $5\mathbf{i} - \mathbf{j} - \mathbf{k}$, $3\mathbf{i} - 3\mathbf{j} + 3\mathbf{k}$, 0, $3\mathbf{i} + 9\mathbf{j} + 6\mathbf{k}$, 15, $\pi/2$; (vi) $4\mathbf{i} + 3\mathbf{j} - 4\mathbf{k}$, $2\mathbf{i} - \mathbf{j} + 2\mathbf{k}$, 2, $-\mathbf{i} + 8\mathbf{j} + 5\mathbf{k}$, -3, $\cos^{-1}(2/154)$;
2. (i) $2/\sqrt{14}$, $3/\sqrt{14}$, $-1/\sqrt{14}$; (ii) $1/\sqrt{6}$, $2/\sqrt{6}$, $1/\sqrt{6}$; (iii) $1/\sqrt{26}$, $3/\sqrt{26}$, $-4/\sqrt{26}$; (iv) $3/\sqrt{14}$, $-1/\sqrt{14}$, $2/\sqrt{14}$;
3. $\mathbf{i} + 5\mathbf{j} + \mathbf{k}$, $\sqrt{542}/2$;
4. 14, $6\mathbf{i} + 2\mathbf{j} + 10\mathbf{k}$;
5. (i) 0, $19\mathbf{i} + 17\mathbf{j} - 20\mathbf{k}$; (ii) 0, $-24\mathbf{i} - 6\mathbf{j} + 12\mathbf{k}$; (iii) -4, $4\mathbf{i} + 2\mathbf{j} + 4\mathbf{k}$;
11. (i) $(4t + 3)\mathbf{i} + (6t^2 + 4)\mathbf{j} + 2\mathbf{k}$, $4\mathbf{i} + 12t\mathbf{j}$; (ii) $3\cos t\,\mathbf{i} - (2\sin 2t + 1)\mathbf{j} + 2t\mathbf{k}$; $-3\sin t\,\mathbf{i} - 4\cos 2t\,\mathbf{j} + 2\mathbf{k}$;
12. $m[(2t^3 + 2t + 1)\mathbf{i} - 3t^2(t + 1)\mathbf{j} - 3(2t^2 - 2t - 1)\mathbf{k}]$;
13. (i) $-\frac{2A[x\mathbf{i} + y\mathbf{j} + z\mathbf{k}]}{(x^2 + y^2 + z^2)^2}$, (ii) $2a(x\mathbf{i} + y\mathbf{j} + z\mathbf{k})$, (iii) $[2ax + b(y + z)]\mathbf{i} + [2ay + b(x + z)]\mathbf{j} + [2az + b(x + y)]\mathbf{k}$;
14. (i) 0, $2(y - z)\mathbf{i} + 2(z - x)\mathbf{j} + 2(x - y)\mathbf{k}$; (ii) $2y + 2 + xy + 2xz$, $xz\mathbf{i} - (yz + z^2)\mathbf{j} + (2x - 1)\mathbf{k}$; (iii) $3 + 2z - 3z^2$, $-2y\mathbf{i} - 6x\mathbf{j} + (2x - 2)\mathbf{k}$.

CHAPTER 6

1. 250500;

2. $n(n + 1)ax/2$;
3. $(2^{20} - 1)/2^{19}$;
4. 55944;
5. If $\exp(-h\nu/kT) < 1$, the sum is $1/[\exp(h\nu/kT) - 1]$;
7. (i) divergent, (ii) divergent, (iii) divergent, (iv) divergent, (v) convergent, (vi) divergent, (vii) convergent, (viii) divergent;
8. (i) divergent, (ii) absolutely convergent, (iii) divergent, (iv) conditionally convergent;
9. (i) $|x| < 1$, (ii) $|x| < 1$, (iii) $|x| < 2$, (iv) $|x| < 1$;
10. (i) $x + \frac{x^3}{3!} + \frac{x^5}{5!} + \ldots$, for all x;
(ii) $x + \frac{x^2}{2} + \frac{x^3}{3} + \ldots$, for $|x| < 1$ and $x = -1$;
(iii) $\frac{2x^2}{2!} - \frac{8x^4}{4!} + \frac{32x^6}{6!} + \ldots$, for all x;
(iv) $1 + \frac{x}{2} - \frac{1}{4}\frac{x^2}{2!} + \frac{3}{8}\frac{x^3}{3!} - \frac{15}{16}\frac{x^4}{4!} + \ldots$, for $|x| < 1$;
(v) $1 - \frac{3}{2}x + \frac{15}{4}\frac{x^2}{2!} - \frac{3 \times 5 \times 7}{8}\frac{x^3}{5!} + \ldots$, for $|x| < 1$;
(vi) $\frac{\pi}{2} - x - \frac{x^3}{2 \times 3} - \frac{1 \times 3x^5}{2 \times 4 \times 5} - \ldots$, for $|x| < 1$, $0 < \cos^{-1} x < \pi$;
(vii) $x + \frac{x^3}{3} + \frac{2x^5}{15} + \frac{17x^7}{315} + \ldots$, for $|x| < \frac{\pi}{2}$;
11. 1, $\cos\theta$, $\frac{1}{2}(3\cos^2\theta - 1)$, $\frac{1}{2}(5\cos^3\theta - 3\cos\theta)$ $\frac{1}{8}(35\cos^4\theta - 30\cos^2\theta + 3)$; $\frac{1}{8}(63\cos^5\theta - 70\cos^3\theta + 15\cos\theta)$.

CHAPTER 7

1. (i) $13 - 3i$, $13 + 3i$; (ii) $41 - 13i$, $41 + 13i$; (iii) $-9 - 38i$, $-9 + 38i$; (iv) $14 - \sqrt{2}i$, $14 + \sqrt{2}i$; (v) 5, 5; (vi) $(22 + 59i)/61$, $(22 - 59i)/61$; (vii) $-(3/2) - (5i/2)$, $-(3/2) + (5i/2)$; (viii) $-(1/5) - (2\sqrt{6}i/5)$, $-(1/5) + (2\sqrt{6}i/5)$; (ix) $-95 + 59i$, $-95 - 59i$;
2. (i) 5, $\cos^{-1}(4/5)$; (ii) 13, $\cos^{-1}(5/13)$; (iii) 2, $\pi/3$; (iv) 1, $\pi/2$; (v) $\sqrt{5}/2$, $\cos^{-1}(2/\sqrt{5})$; (vi) $\sqrt{10}$, $\cos^{-1}(3/\sqrt{10})$;
3. (i) $1.938 + 0.495i$, (ii) $-(3/2) + (3\sqrt{3}/2)i$, (iii) $4 + 3i$, (iv) $\sqrt{2} - \sqrt{2}i$;
4. (i) $3i/2$, $3\sqrt{3} - 3i$; (ii) $(1/3) - (i/\sqrt{3})$, $6\cos(\pi/12) + 6i\sin(\pi/12)$;
5. $\cos\theta(4\sin\theta - 8\sin^3\theta)$, $8\cos^4\theta - 8\cos^2\theta + 1$, $5\sin\theta - 20\sin^3\theta + 16\sin^5\theta$, $16\cos^5\theta - 20\cos^3\theta + 5\cos\theta$;
11. (i) $(1/\sqrt{2}) + (i/\sqrt{2})$, (ii) $-(1/\sqrt{2}) + (i/\sqrt{2})$, (iii) $-(1/\sqrt{2}) - (i/\sqrt{2})$, (iv) $(1/\sqrt{2}) - (i/\sqrt{2})$, (v) i, (iv) $-i$;

12. $2^{1/3}$, $2^{1/3}(-(1/2) + (\sqrt{3}/2)i)$, $2^{1/3}(-(1/2) - (\sqrt{3}/2)i)$;

13. $13^{1/8}(0.989 + 0.146i)$, $13^{1/8}(-0.146 + 0.989i)$, $13^{1/8}(-0.989 - 0.146i)$, $13^{1/8}(0.146 - 0.989i)$;

14. $\psi_0 = N_0(\chi_0 + \chi_1 + \chi_2 + \chi_3 + \chi_4 + \chi_5)$

$$\psi_1 = N_1[\chi_0 + \tfrac{1}{2}\chi_1 - \tfrac{1}{2}\chi_2 - \chi_3 - \tfrac{1}{2}\chi_4 + \tfrac{1}{2}\chi_5 + (i\sqrt{3}/2)(\chi_1 + \chi_2 - \chi_4 - \chi_5)]$$

$$\psi_{-1} = N_{-1}[\chi_0 + \tfrac{1}{2}\chi_1 - \tfrac{1}{2}\chi_2 - \chi_3 - \tfrac{1}{2}\chi_4 + \tfrac{1}{2}\chi_5 - (i\sqrt{3}/2)(\chi_1 + \chi_2 - \chi_4 - \chi_5)]$$

$$\psi_2 = N_2[\chi_0 - \tfrac{1}{2}\chi_1 - \tfrac{1}{2}\chi_2 + \chi_3 - \tfrac{1}{2}\chi_4 - \tfrac{1}{2}\chi_5 + (i\sqrt{3}/2)(\chi_1 - \chi_2 + \chi_4 - \chi_5)]$$

$$\psi_{-2} = N_{-2}[\chi_0 - \tfrac{1}{2}\chi_1 - \tfrac{1}{2}\chi_2 + \chi_3 - \tfrac{1}{2}\chi_4 - \tfrac{1}{2}\chi_5 - (i\sqrt{3}/2)(\chi_1 - \chi_2 + \chi_4 - \chi_5)]$$

$$\psi_3 = N_3(\chi_0 - \chi_1 + \chi_2 - \chi_3 + \chi_4 - \chi_5).$$

CHAPTER 8

3. $\dfrac{\pi}{4} - \sum_{r \text{ even}} \dfrac{\sin rx}{r}$;

4. $\dfrac{2}{\pi}\left[\sum_{r \text{ odd}}\left(\dfrac{\pi^2}{r} - \dfrac{4}{r^3}\right)\sin rx - \pi^2 \sum_{r \text{ even}} \dfrac{\sin rx}{r}\right]$;

6. $\dfrac{1}{2} + \sum_{k=1}^{\infty}\left(\dfrac{4}{k^2\pi^2}\right)\cos(k\pi x)$;

7. $\dfrac{1}{2} + \dfrac{2}{\pi}\left[\sum_{k=1,5,9\ldots} \dfrac{1}{k}\cos(kx/a) - \sum_{k=3,7,11\ldots} \dfrac{1}{k}\cos(kx/a)\right]$;

8. $\dfrac{1}{\pi} + \sum_{r \text{ even}} \dfrac{2}{\pi(r^2 - 1)}(-1)^{(r/2)+1}\cos rx.$

CHAPTER 9

1. (i) -12, (ii) -59, (iii) 176, (iv) 732;
4. (i) 2, 5, 17, (ii) 7.0867, 0.4567 ± 1.8218i, (iii) 0.6852, -8.4111, 5.7259;
6. (i) $x = 1$, $y = 2$, $z = 3$; (ii) $x = 6/7$, $y = 10/7$, $z = -2/7$; (iii) $x = 2$, $y = 3$, $z = -4$; (iv) $x = -5$, $y = 7$, $z = 2$;
7. (i) $x = (1/3) - \lambda$, $y = \lambda$, $z = 1/3$; (ii) $x = 3/8$, $y = 3/8$; $z = 1/2$; (iii) no solution;
8. (i) No solution for $k = 1, 2$, there are no values of k for which there is more than one solution;
9. Determinant of coefficients of x, y, z is zero; $k = 2$, $x = (12 - 7z)/11$, $y = (2 + 19z)/11$;

10. (i) $x = (2 - 3k - 5k^2)/(1 + k^3)$, $y = (3 + 5k + 2k^2)/(1 + k^3)$, $z = (5 + 2k - 3k^2)/(1 + k^3)$; (ii) $x = 5 - z$, $y = 3 - z$;
11. (i) yes, (ii) no;
12. $c = 1$: $x = -z$, $y = 0$; $c = 2$: $x = 0$, $y = -z$;
13. (i) $x = -7z/11$, $y = 19z/11$; (ii) $x = -11z/10$, $y = 13z/10$; (iii) no solution.

CHAPTER 10

1. (i) $\begin{pmatrix} 3 & 2 & 1 \\ 2 & 9 & 9 \\ 5 & 5 & 3 \end{pmatrix}$, $\begin{pmatrix} -1 & -4 & 3 \\ 4 & 5 & 1 \\ -5 & 3 & 3 \end{pmatrix}$, $\begin{pmatrix} 13 & 3 & -5 \\ 24 & 28 & 25 \\ 11 & 11 & 16 \end{pmatrix}$, $\begin{pmatrix} 11 & 15 & 16 \\ 5 & 31 & 20 \\ 8 & 2 & 15 \end{pmatrix}$,

$\begin{pmatrix} 1 & 3 & 0 \\ -1 & 7 & 4 \\ 2 & 5 & 3 \end{pmatrix}$, $\begin{pmatrix} 2 & -1 & 5 \\ 3 & 2 & 1 \\ -1 & 4 & 0 \end{pmatrix}$, $\begin{pmatrix} 11 & 5 & 8 \\ 15 & 31 & 2 \\ 16 & 20 & 15 \end{pmatrix}$, $\frac{1}{34}\begin{pmatrix} 1 & 11 & -19 \\ -9 & 3 & 1 \\ 12 & -4 & 10 \end{pmatrix}$,

$\frac{1}{63}\begin{pmatrix} -4 & -1 & 14 \\ 20 & 5 & -7 \\ -11 & 13 & 7 \end{pmatrix}$, $\frac{1}{2142}\begin{pmatrix} 425 & -193 & -196 \\ 85 & 37 & -140 \\ -238 & 98 & 266 \end{pmatrix}$;

(ii) $\begin{pmatrix} 8 & 3 & -3 \\ 7 & 5 & 3 \\ 1 & 5 & 1 \end{pmatrix}$, $\begin{pmatrix} 2 & 1 & -3 \\ 5 & -5 & -1 \\ 1 & 1 & 3 \end{pmatrix}$, $\begin{pmatrix} 17 & 9 & 7 \\ 18 & 8 & -1 \\ 6 & 20 & 4 \end{pmatrix}$, $\begin{pmatrix} 21 & 6 & -8 \\ 37 & 8 & 6 \\ 11 & -3 & 0 \end{pmatrix}$,

$\begin{pmatrix} 5 & 6 & 1 \\ 2 & 0 & 3 \\ -3 & 1 & 2 \end{pmatrix}$, $\begin{pmatrix} 3 & 1 & 0 \\ 1 & 5 & 2 \\ 0 & 2 & -1 \end{pmatrix}$, $\begin{pmatrix} 21 & 37 & 11 \\ 6 & 8 & -3 \\ -8 & 6 & 0 \end{pmatrix}$, $-\frac{1}{91}\begin{pmatrix} -3 & -13 & 2 \\ -11 & 13 & -23 \\ 18 & -13 & -12 \end{pmatrix}$,

$-\frac{1}{26}\begin{pmatrix} -9 & 1 & 2 \\ 1 & -3 & -6 \\ 2 & -6 & 14 \end{pmatrix}$, $\frac{1}{2366}\begin{pmatrix} 18 & 24 & 100 \\ 66 & 88 & -422 \\ -199 & 129 & -54 \end{pmatrix}$;

(iii) $\begin{pmatrix} 4 & 8 & 2 \\ 8 & 8 & 3 \\ 1 & 3 & 4 \end{pmatrix}$, $\begin{pmatrix} -2 & 6 & 2 \\ 6 & -2 & -1 \\ 1 & -1 & 6 \end{pmatrix}$, $\begin{pmatrix} 10 & 40 & 12 \\ 24 & 24 & 5 \\ 4 & 16 & -3 \end{pmatrix}$, $\begin{pmatrix} 10 & 24 & 7 \\ 38 & 24 & 17 \\ 13 & 5 & -3 \end{pmatrix}$,

$\begin{pmatrix} 1 & 7 & 1 \\ 7 & 3 & 1 \\ 2 & 1 & 5 \end{pmatrix}$, $\begin{pmatrix} 3 & 1 & 0 \\ 1 & 5 & 2 \\ 0 & 2 & -1 \end{pmatrix}$, $\begin{pmatrix} 10 & 38 & 13 \\ 24 & 24 & 5 \\ 7 & 17 & -3 \end{pmatrix}$, $-\frac{1}{216}\begin{pmatrix} 14 & -33 & 1 \\ -34 & 3 & 13 \\ 4 & 6 & -46 \end{pmatrix}$,

$-\frac{1}{26}\begin{pmatrix} -9 & 1 & 2 \\ 1 & -3 & -6 \\ 2 & -6 & 14 \end{pmatrix}$, $\frac{1}{5616}\begin{pmatrix} -157 & 107 & 240 \\ 335 & -121 & 96 \\ -122 & 262 & -672 \end{pmatrix}$;

(iv) $\begin{pmatrix} \frac{1+\sqrt{3}}{2} & \frac{1+\sqrt{3}}{2} & 0 \\ -\frac{1+\sqrt{3}}{2} & \frac{1+\sqrt{3}}{2} & 0 \\ 0 & 0 & 2 \end{pmatrix}$, $\begin{pmatrix} \frac{1-\sqrt{3}}{2} & \frac{\sqrt{3}-1}{2} & 0 \\ \frac{1-\sqrt{3}}{2} & \frac{1-\sqrt{3}}{2} & 0 \\ 0 & 0 & 0 \end{pmatrix}$, $\begin{pmatrix} 0 & 1 & 0 \\ -1 & 0 & 0 \\ 0 & 0 & 1 \end{pmatrix}$,

$\begin{pmatrix} 0 & 1 & 0 \\ -1 & 0 & 0 \\ 0 & 0 & 1 \end{pmatrix}$, $\begin{pmatrix} 1/2 & -\sqrt{3}/2 & 0 \\ \sqrt{3}/2 & 1/2 & 0 \\ 0 & 0 & 1 \end{pmatrix}$, $\begin{pmatrix} \sqrt{3}/2 & -1/2 & 0 \\ 1/2 & \sqrt{3}/2 & 0 \\ 0 & 0 & 1 \end{pmatrix}$,

$\begin{pmatrix} 0 & -1 & 0 \\ 1 & 0 & 0 \\ 0 & 0 & 1 \end{pmatrix}$, $\begin{pmatrix} 1/2 & -\sqrt{3}/2 & 0 \\ \sqrt{3}/2 & 1/2 & 0 \\ 0 & 0 & 1 \end{pmatrix}$, $\begin{pmatrix} \sqrt{3}/2 & -1/2 & 0 \\ 1/2 & \sqrt{3}/2 & 0 \\ 0 & 0 & 1 \end{pmatrix}$,

$\begin{pmatrix} 0 & -1 & 0 \\ 1 & 0 & 0 \\ 0 & 0 & 1 \end{pmatrix}$;

2. (i) $\begin{pmatrix} 2 & 0 & 1 \\ 6 & 0 & 3 \\ 4 & 0 & 2 \end{pmatrix}$, 4; (ii) $\begin{pmatrix} 12 & 8 & 20 \\ 21 & 14 & 35 \\ 6 & 4 & 10 \end{pmatrix}$, 36;

(iii) $\begin{pmatrix} 1 & -1 & -1 \\ -2 & 2 & 2 \\ 3 & -3 & -3 \end{pmatrix}$, 6; (iv) $\begin{pmatrix} -2 & 4 & 2 \\ -1 & 2 & 1 \\ 0 & 0 & 0 \end{pmatrix}$, 0;

3. (i) $\begin{pmatrix} 0 & -i \\ i & 0 \end{pmatrix}$, Hermitean; (ii) $\begin{pmatrix} 1-i & 2+i & 5+2i \\ 2-3i & 1-2i & 7-3i \\ 4+i & 3-4i & 4+i \end{pmatrix}$, not Hermitean

(iii) $\begin{pmatrix} 0 & -i & 0 \\ i & 0 & -i \\ 0 & i & 0 \end{pmatrix}$, Hermitean; (iv) $\begin{pmatrix} 1 & 2-i & 1+3i \\ 2+i & 4 & 3i \\ 1-3i & -3i & 3 \end{pmatrix}$, not Hermitean;

4. (i) $\begin{pmatrix} 1/3 & 2/3 & -2/3 \\ 2/3 & 1/3 & 2/3 \\ 2/3 & -2/3 & -1/3 \end{pmatrix}$, (ii) $\begin{pmatrix} \sqrt{3}/2 & 1/2 & 0 \\ -1/2 & \sqrt{3}/2 & 0 \\ 0 & 0 & 1 \end{pmatrix}$; both are orthogonal matrices;

5. (i) $x = 0$, $y = 5$, $z = 1$; (ii) $x = 6/7$, $y = 10/7$, $z = -2/7$; (iii) $x = 2$, $y = 3$, $z = -4$; (iv) $x = 0$, $y = -2$, $z = 1$; (v) $x = -48/53$, $y = -59/53$, $z = 7/53$;

6. (i) 1: $x_1 = x_2$, $x_3 = 0$; $1 + \sqrt{2}$: $x_1 = -x_3/\sqrt{2}$, $x_2 = x_3/\sqrt{2}$, x_3; $1 - \sqrt{2}$: $x_1 = x_3/\sqrt{2}$, $x_2 = -x_3/\sqrt{2}$, x_3;

(ii) 1: $x_1 = -2x_3$, $x_2 = -2x_3$; 2: $x_1 = x_2 = -x_3$; 3: $x_1 = 4x_3$, $x_2 = x_3/2$, x_3;

(iii) 0: $x_1 = \surd 3x_3$, $x_2 = 0$, x_3; 2: $x_1 = \frac{1}{2}x_2$, x_2, $x_3 = (\surd 3/2)x_2$; -2: $x_1 = -\frac{1}{2}x_2$, x_2, $x_3 = -(\surd 3/2)x_2$;
(iv) 2: $x_1 = 0$, $x_2 = ix_3$; $\surd 2$: $x_1 = \surd 2x_3$, $x_2 = -ix_3$, x_3; $-\surd 2$: $x_1 = -\surd 2x_3$, $x_2 = -ix_3$, x_3.

CHAPTER 11

1. (i) $y = \sin^{-1}(cx)$, (ii) $y = c(x^2 + 1)$, (iii) $y = c(1 + x) - 1$, (iv) $\ln y = -(x^2/2y^2) + c$, (v) $(y - x) = c(y + x)^3$, (vi) $y \exp(x^2) - x^2 = c$, (vii) $x^6y^3 + x^4y^5 = c$, (viii) $y = \frac{1}{4}x^4 + c/x$, (ix) $y = (x + c)\exp(-x^2)$, (x) $y = -(5/\sin x)\exp(\cos x) + c/\sin x$, (xi) $y = \frac{1}{2}x^3 + cx^3 \exp(1/x^2)$;
2. (i) $8n_0$, (ii) $\frac{1}{8} \times 10^4$;
3. $kt = 1/(a - x) - 1/a$, $1/ak$;
4. $\lambda_{Ba} = 0.0578$ days^{-1}, $\lambda_{La} = 0.0693$ hours^{-1}; 314.7 units, 17 units, 11 units;
5. (i) $i = \exp(-Rt/L)(i_0 - E_0/R) + E_0/R$,

$$\text{(ii) } i = \frac{L\omega^2}{L^2\omega^2 + R^2}\left[\frac{R}{L\omega^2}\sin \omega t - \frac{1}{\omega}\cos \omega t\right] + \exp(-Rt/L)\left[i_0 + \frac{L\omega}{L^2\omega^2 + R^2}\right];$$

6. $$t = \frac{1}{5k_1}\ln\left[\frac{(x + 2)}{2(1 - x)}\right];$$

7. $$t = \frac{1}{2k_2\surd[(k_1a/k_2) + (k_1^2/4k_2^2)]} \times \left\{\ln\left|\frac{\surd[(k_1a/k_2) + (k_1^2/4k_2^2)] + (k_1/2k_2) + x}{\surd[(k_1a/k_2) + (k_1^2/4k_2^2)] - (k_1/2k_2) - x}\right| - \ln\frac{\surd[(k_1a/k_2) + (k_1^2/4k_2^2)] + (k_1/2k_2)}{\surd[(k_1a/k_2) + (k_1^2/4k_2^2)] - (k_1/2k_2)}\right\};$$

8. $$kt = \frac{1}{(b - a)(c - a)}\ln\left(\frac{a}{a - x}\right) + \frac{1}{(a - b)(c - b)}\ln\left(\frac{b}{b - x}\right) + \frac{1}{(a - c)(b - c)}\ln\left(\frac{c}{c - x}\right);$$

9. (i) $y = c_1 e^{-3x} + c_2 e^{2x}$, (ii) $c_1 e^{3x} + c_2 e^{-x}$,
(iii) $c_1 \cos 2x + c_2 \sin 2x$, (iv) $c_1 x e^{-2x} + c_2 e^{-2x}$,
(v) $e^{2x}(c_1 \cos 3x + c_2 \sin 3x)$, (vi) $e^{-x}(c_1 \cos 2x + c_2 \sin 2x)$;

10. $x = 0.04 \cos(\sqrt{3}t)$;

11. (i) $x = 0.04 e^{-t/2048} \cos(\sqrt{3}t)$, (ii) $x = -0.04 e^{-3t} + 0.08 e^{-t}$;

12. (i) $y = -0.2(\cos 3x + 3 \sin 3x)$, (ii) $y = \frac{1}{4}x(-3 \cos 2x + \sin 2x)$,
(iii) $y = -(4/50)\sin 2x - (3/50) \cos 2x$,
(iv) $(x^2/3) + (2/9)x - (25/27)$,
(v) $(x^5/15) - (x^4/9) + (13/27)x^3 - (13/27)x^2 - (x/3)$,
(vi) $(5/2)e^{3x}$, (vii) $\frac{1}{2}x^2 e^{-2x}$, (viii) $3 e^{-x}$;

13. (i) $y = c_1 e^{2x} + c_2 e^{-x} + (1/3)x e^{2x}$,
(ii) $e^{-x/5}(c_1 \cos 4x + c_2 \sin 4x) + 2x - 1$,
(iii) $c_1 e^{5x} + c_2 e^{-x} - (3/26)\cos x - (1/13)\sin x$,
(iv) $e^{-2x}(c_1 \cos 2x + c_2 \sin 2x) - \sin 3x - 3 \cos 3x$,
(v) $c_1 e^x + c_2 x e^x + \frac{1}{2} \cos x - \frac{1}{2} \sin x$;

14.
$$q = c_1 \exp\left\{\left[-\frac{R}{2L} + \frac{1}{2L}\sqrt{\left(R^2 - \frac{4qL}{C}\right)}\right]t\right\} + c_2 \exp\left\{\left[-\frac{R}{2L} - \frac{1}{2L}\sqrt{\left(R^2 - \frac{4qL}{C}\right)}\right]t\right\} + \frac{E_0 L\left[(q/CL) - \alpha^2\right]}{L^2\left[(q/CL) - \alpha^2\right]^2 + R^2\alpha^2} \sin \alpha t - \frac{E_0 R\alpha}{L^2\left[(q/CL) - \alpha^2\right]^2 + R^2\alpha^2} \cos \alpha t.$$

CHAPTER 12

1. $u(x,t) = \sum_{r=1}^{\infty} c_r \exp(-r^2\pi^2 kt/\ell^2)\sin(r\pi x/\ell)$;

2. $\psi(x,y) = \sum_{r=1}^{\infty} c_r \sin(r\pi x/a)\sinh\left[r\pi(b - y)/a\right]$;

3. $\frac{r^2}{R}\frac{d^2R(r)}{dr^2} + \frac{r}{R}\frac{dR(r)}{dr} = k^2$; $\frac{1}{\Theta(\theta)}\frac{d^2\Theta}{d\theta^2} = -k^2$;

4. (i) $\psi(x,y,z) = \frac{8}{a^{3/2}} \sin(n_x \pi x/a)\sin(n_y \pi y/a)\sin(n_z \pi z/a)$,
(ii) $\psi(x,y,z) = \frac{8}{\sqrt{(abc)}} \sin(n_x \pi x/a)\sin(n_y \pi y/b)\sin(n_z \pi z/c)$.

CHAPTER 13

1. (i) 1.414, -1.414; (ii) 0.311, (iii) 2.798 radians, (iv) - 2.427, (v) 0.708, (vi) 3.146;
2. (i) 0.8795, 0.8814, (ii) 0.4471, 0.4458, (iii) 2.5413, 2.5456, (iv) 1.8539, 1.8536, (v) 0.9068, 0.9097, (vi) 1.0970, 1.0948;
3. 0.8362, 0.8862, exact result 0.8862;
4. Numerical solutions:

(i)	y(1)	y(2)	y(3)	y(4)	y(5)
Euler method	0.5	-3.0	-9.5	-19.0	-31.5
predictor-corrector method	0.5	-3.0	-9.5	-19.0	-31.5

(ii)	y(0.1)	y(0.2)	y(0.3)	y(0.4)	y(0.5)
Euler method	0.090	0.163	0.222	0.267	0.303
predictor-corrector method	0.090	0.163	0.222	0.268	0.304

(iii)	y(1)	y(2)	y(3)
Euler method	1.927	33.453	247.554
predictor-corrector method	2.029	34.146	250.136

(iv)	y(1)	y(2)	y(3)	y(4)	y(5)
Euler method	0.655	0.214	-0.422	-0.669	-0.301
predictor-corrector method	0.678	0.248	-0.415	-0.699	-0.341

Analytical solutions:

(i) $y = x - (3x^2/2) + 1$, (ii) $y = x\,e^x$,

(iii) $y = 2(x^2 - x)e^x + 0.391$, (iv) $y = \frac{1}{2}(\cos x + \sin x)$;

5. (i) (a) $x = y = z = u = 1$, (b) $x = 14.42$, $y = -7.09$, $z = -2.45$, $u = 3.07$; (ii) $x = 1$, $y = 2$, $z = 3$, $w = 0$;
6. (i) 0, no inverse; (ii) 831, $\frac{1}{831}\begin{pmatrix} -98 & 44 & 47 & 56 \\ 155 & 100 & 409 & -326 \\ 84 & 81 & -159 & -48 \\ -4 & -83 & -32 & 121 \end{pmatrix}$

CHAPTER 14

1. (i) 15.59, 15.6, 0.0289, 0.17, 0.0538; (ii) 20.99, 21.0, 0.2344, 0.4842, 0.0625; (iii) 44.80, 45, 299.72, 17.31, 0.972;
2. (i) 30.85%, (ii) 6.68%, (iii) 0.621%;
3. $\bar{x} \pm 0.675\sigma$;
4. (i) $y = 1.0236x + 0.8818$, $\alpha_m^2 = 0.001247$, $\alpha_b^2 = 0.01091$;

   (ii) $y = 101.09x - 3.293$, $\alpha_m^2 = 0.8123$, $\alpha_b^2 = 31.2736$;
5. Regression of y on x gives $y = 5.0181x + 0.0460$; regression of x on y gives $y = 5.0276x - 0.0484$;
6. $y = 0.998 + 0.0495x + 0.9987x^2$;
7. $\chi^2(\phi = 8) = 5.04$, sample from normal distribution;

   $\chi^2(\phi = 18) = 38.79$, significant deviation from normality;
8. $u = 3.68$: very highly significant increase in purity, 81.64 ± 1.67; $t = 2.67$: significant increase in purity 95% confidence limits 81.64 ± 2.66.

Index